THE
M☉TIVATE
SERIES

Macmillan Texts for Industrial, Vocational and Technical Education

Essential Mathematics
for Technicians

LEEDS COLLEGE OF BUILDING

Advisors: *J.N. Karunau*   *D. Wood*

MACMILLAN

First published 1999 by
MACMILLAN EDUCATION LTD
London and Basingstoke,
Companies and representatives throughout the world

ISBN 0–333–67796–X

10	9	8	7	6	5	4	3	2	1
08	07	06	05	04	03	02	01	00	99

This book is printed on paper suitable for recycling and
made from fully managed and sustained forest sources.

Typeset by EXPO Holdings, Malaysia

Printed in Hong Kong

A catalogue record for this book is available from the
British Library.

Illustrations by Tek Art
Photographs by Alan Thomas

Cover illustration courtesy of Telegraph Colour Library/Chris Bell

Contents

Contents

Arithmetical operations

Introduction

Technical work is often numerical. The technician uses numbers and formulae as well as metal and wood. Throughout this book you will see the connections between mathematics and technology.

You use arithmetical operations in everyday life. In this chapter you see how arithmetical operations are used in technology.

1.1 Basic operations

Quantities

A **quantity** is an amount we can measure. We can measure a distance as 5 metres, a time as 3 seconds, a mass as 7 kilograms. These are quantities. There are electrical quantities of current, voltage and resistance, such as 9 amps, 2 volts, 12 ohms. The basic operations of arithmetic are applied either to numbers such as 5 and 7, or to quantities such as 5 kg and 7 kg.

$$5 + 7 = 12 \qquad 5\,\text{kg} + 7\,\text{kg} = 12\,\text{kg}$$

Note that the quantities are the same sort. We cannot add kilograms and seconds.

'5 kilograms + 7 seconds' is nonsense.

Mixed quantities

Quantities are sometimes combined. Examples are

Speed = distance divided by time.

60 m/s is the same as 120 metres in 2 seconds

Density = mass divided by volume.

2000 kg/m^3 is the same as 4000 kg in 2 m^3

Power consumption = power times time.

200 kW hr is the same as 100 kW for 2 hours

The four basic operations

Now we give examples of how arithmetic is applied to quantities. The four basic operations of arithmetic are addition, subtraction, multiplication and division.

Addition

The symbol for addition is +. The following all mean the same.

$$7 + 8$$

the sum of 7 and 8

7 added to 8

the total of 7 and 8

7 plus 8

In each case the result is 15.

EXAMPLE 1.1

Three electrical components with resistances 12 Ω, 10 Ω and 15 Ω are placed in series. (Ω stands for ohms) The total resistance is found by adding the single resistances. Find this total resistance.

Solution

We want the sum of the resistances. Add 12, 10 and 15, obtaining 37.

The total resistance is 37 Ω

SELF TEST 1.1

An empty fuel tank has a mass of 125 kg, and it can contain 257 kg of fuel. What is the mass of the tank when it is full?

382 kg

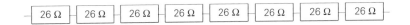

Figure 1.1

Subtraction

The symbol for subtraction is −. The following all mean the same.

> 12 − 3
> the difference between 12 and 3
> 12 minus 3
> 3 subtracted from 12
> 12 less 3

In each case the result is 9.

EXAMPLE 1.2

The water content of 57 kg of raw cotton is 8 kg. Find the mass of the dry cotton.

Solution
We want the difference between 57 and 8. Subtract 8 from 57, obtaining 49.

The dry mass is 49 kg

SELF TEST 1.2

A drill is 11 mm long. What is its length after 2 mm has worn away?

9 mm

Multiplication

The symbol for multiplication is ×. The following all mean the same.

> 5 × 8
> the product of 5 and 8
> 5 multiplied by 8
> 5 times 8

In each case the result is 40.

EXAMPLE 1.3

The *tex* of a textile yarn is the mass in grams of 1000 m. If a yarn has tex 270, find the mass of 6000 m.

Solution
The length of 6000 m consists of six lengths of 1000 m, each of which has a mass of 270 g. We want the product of 6 and 270. Multiply 6 × 270, obtaining 1620.

The mass is 1620 grams

SELF TEST 1.3

Eight electrical components, each with resistance of 26 Ω, are placed in series, as shown in Figure 1.1. What is the total resistance of the components?

208 Ω

Division

The symbol for division is ÷. The following all mean the same.

> 30 ÷ 6
> 30 divided by 6
> 6 divided into 30
> 30 over 6

In each case the result is 5. This is the **quotient**.

If one number does not divide exactly into another, there is a **remainder**. If 30 pens are shared between 7 people, each will receive 4 pens, and there will be 2 left over.

30 divided by 7 gives a quotient of 4 and a remainder of 2.

EXAMPLE 1.4

3000 m of a yarn has a mass of 1800 grams. Find the tex of the yarn. (Tex was defined in Example 1.3.)

Solution
The tex is the mass of 1000 m. Divide 1800 by 3, obtaining 600.

The tex is 600

SELF TEST 1.4

A tank contains 550 litres of petrol. How many 5 litre cans could be filled from it?

110 cans

EXAMPLE 1.5

A shelf is 600 mm long. Cubical boxes of side 70 mm are to be placed on it. How many boxes will go onto the shelf, and how much space will be left over?

Solution
Divide 600 by 70. The quotient is 8, and the remainder is 40.

8 boxes will go onto the shelf, and there will be 40 mm left over

SELF TEST 1.5

A barrel contains 50 litres of water. How many 8 litre cans can be filled from it, and how much will be left over?

6 cans, 2 litres

Formulae

A **formula** gives a general rule involving quantities. Use the formula by substituting numbers for the quantities.

EXAMPLE 1.6

The force in a wire is given by the formula

$$force = stress \times area.$$

Find the force if the stress is 450 N/mm^2 and the area is 4 mm^2. The unit of force is the newton (N).

Solution

Apply the formula, putting 450 for the stress and 4 for the area.

$$force = 450 \times 4 = 1800$$

The force is 1800 N

SELF TEST 1.6

The power of a machine is given by the formula

$$power = \frac{work\ done}{time\ taken}.$$

Find the power if 8000 J of work are done in 40 seconds. The unit of power is the watt (W). The unit of work is the joule (J).

200 W

1.2 Order of operations

Basic operations

There are four basic operations in arithmetic: addition, subtraction, multiplication and division.

If several numbers are added together, the order of adding does not matter.

$$3 + 8 + 12 = 11 + 12 = 23 \quad \text{(adding 3 and 8 first)}$$
$$3 + 8 + 12 = 3 + 20 = 23 \quad \text{(adding 8 and 12 first)}$$

Similarly, if several numbers are multiplied together, the order of multiplying does not matter.

But if a mathematical expression involves different operations then the order *does* matter. If the expression involves both addition and multiplication, the multiplication is done first.

$$7 + 2 \times 3 \text{ means 'multiply 2 by 3, then add 7'.}$$

The result is 13.

Similarly, division is done before subtraction.

$$12 - 4 \div 2 \text{ means 'divide 4 by 2, then subtract from 12'.}$$

The result is 10.

In general, division and multiplication are done before addition and subtraction.

When the expression involves addition and subtraction, they are done from left to right.

$$9 - 3 + 5 \text{ means 'subtract 3 from 9, then add 5'.}$$

The result is 11.

EXAMPLE 1.7

Certain fuses are sold in packets of 8. How many fuses are there in seven complete packets and three odd fuses?

Solution

The number of fuses is given by the expression

$$7 \times 8 + 3.$$

Multiply 7 by 8, obtaining 56. Now add 3, obtaining 59.

There are 59 fuses in total

SELF TEST 1.7

Three types of transistor are available, with prices given in Table 1.1.

Table 1.1

Type	Price
A	#23
B	#31
C	#48

Find the total cost of nine transistors: two of type A, four of type B and three of type C.

#314

EXAMPLE 1.8

Figure 1.2 shows a spindle. Lengths are in mm. Find the length of the middle section.

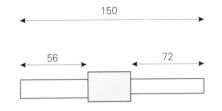

Figure 1.2

Solution

The total length is 150 mm. The outer sections are 56 mm and 72 mm. Subtract 56 and 72 from 150.

$$150 - 56 - 72$$

Evaluate this from left to right. Subtract 56 from 150, obtaining 94. Now subtract 72, obtaining 22.

The middle section has length 22 mm

SELF TEST 1.8

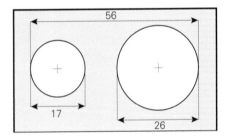

Figure 1.3

Figure 1.3 shows two holes drilled in a plate. Lengths are in mm. Find the shortest distance between the edges of the holes.

13 mm

Brackets

The order of operations tells you to multiply before adding. If you want to add first, use **brackets**. You do an operation in brackets before any other operation.

$(7 + 2) \times 3$ means 'add 7 and 2, then multiply by 3'.

The result is 27.

$(12 - 4) \div 2$ means 'subtract 4 from 12, then divide by 2'.

The result is 4.

$9 - (3 + 5)$ means 'add 3 and 5, then subtract from 9'.

The result is 1.

SELF TEST 1.9

Evaluate the following.
a) $3 + 4 \times 9$ b) $(3 + 4) \times 9$
c) $8 - 4 - 1$ d) $8 - (4 - 1)$

a) 39   b) 63   c) 3   d) 5

EXAMPLE 1.9

Figure 1.4 shows part of a circuit containing resistances of 5 Ω, 6 Ω and 8 Ω in series. If a current of 12 A flows through this part of the circuit, the potential difference across the resistances, V volts, is given by multiplying the current by the total resistance. Find the value of V.

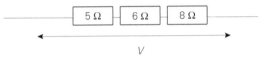

Figure 1.4

Solution

We add the resistances, 5, 6 and 8. We then multiply the result by 12. The addition is done first, hence it must be put in brackets. The expression is

$$12 \times (5 + 6 + 8).$$

The addition is in brackets. Add 5, 6 and 8, obtaining 19. Now multiply by 12, obtaining 228.

$$V = \textbf{228 volts}$$

SELF TEST 1.10

Two tanks contain 800 litres and 600 litres of liquid respectively. The total mass of the liquid is 1680 kg. What is the density of the liquid? (The density of a substance is its mass divided by its volume.)

1.2 kg/litre

Fractions

Suppose a fraction is given as one expression divided by another. Evaluate the expressions and then divide. Consider the following

$$\frac{5 + 3}{8 - 4}.$$

The top is 8, and the bottom is 4. hence the result is 8 ÷ 4, i.e. 2.

SELF TEST 1.11

Evaluate the following. Remember the rules about order and brackets.

a) $\dfrac{19 - 7}{1 + 3}$ b) $12 \div 3 + 1$ c) $12 \div (3 + 1)$

a) 3   b) 5   c) 3

EXAMPLE 1.10

20 kg of raw fibre is cleaned, and the processed fibre has a mass of 18 kg. The percentage cleaning efficiency is given by

$$CE\% = \frac{20 - 18}{20} \times 100\%.$$

Evaluate this expression.

Solution
Evaluate the top of the fraction first, obtaining 2. Now divide by 20, and multiply by 100. The result is 10.

The value of CE % is 10%

SELF TEST 1.12

The elastic recovery of a yarn is given by

$$\text{elastic recovery} = \frac{\text{extended length} - \text{recovered length}}{\text{total extension}}.$$

A yarn was stretched from 1.1 m to 1.6 m, i.e. a total extension of 0.5 m. It then recovered to 1.2 m. Find its elastic recovery.

0.8

EXAMPLE 1.11

Evaluate
a) $-4 \times -3 \times -2$ b) $(3 - 8) \times (1 - 7)$.

Solution
a) The product of -4 and -3 is $+12$. Multiply this by -2, obtaining -24.

$$-4 \times -3 \times -2 = -24$$

b) The subtractions are in brackets. Do these first, obtaining

$$(3 - 8) \times (1 - 7) = -5 \times -6$$

The product of -5 and -6 is $+30$.

$$(3 - 8) \times (1 - 7) = 30$$

SELF TEST 1.13

a) At the top of Kilimanjaro the temperature is $-15°$C. In Dar es Salaam the temperature is $31°$C. What is the difference between these temperatures?

46°C

b) Evaluate the following.

   i) $-6 \times 5 \div -10$

   ii) $(-4 - 8) \times (3 - 12)$

   iii) $-2 - (5 - 7)$

i) 3   ii) 108   iii) 0

1.3 Negative numbers

The thermometer in Figure 1.5 measures temperature in degrees Celsius. Any temperature below zero is a negative temperature. Suppose the temperature rises from $-8°$C to $15°$C. The rise in temperature is the difference between the two values.

$$15° - (-8°) = 15° + 8° = 23°$$

Hence subtracting a negative number is like adding a positive number.

Notice also that the product of -1 and -8 is $+8$. In general, when we multiply or divide one negative number by another the result is positive.

Minus times minus equals plus

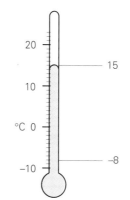

Figure 1.5

1.4 Factors

We can write 10 as 2×5. So 2 and 5 are **factors** of 10.

> Some numbers have no factors, apart from 1 and themselves. These numbers are **prime** numbers.

The prime numbers up to 20 are 2, 3, 5, 7, 11, 13, 17 and 19.

Eggs are often sold in cartons of 6. The number 6 can be factorised as $6 = 2 \times 3$. Hence the cartons are 2 eggs by 3 eggs. If eggs were sold in cartons of 7 (a prime number) the eggs could not be arranged in a neat rectangle.

Factorising numbers

To factorise a number, divide it by primes until a prime is left. You can find some factors as follows:

2   A number ending in 0, 2, 4, 6 or 8 is divisible by 2

3   Add the digits of the number. If the result is divisible by 3, then the original number is divisible by 3.

5   A number ending in 0 or 5 is divisible by 5.

EXAMPLE 1.12

Factorise 78.

Solution
The number ends in 8. Hence 2 is a factor.

$$78 = 2 \times 39$$

The digits of 39 add up to 12, which is divisible by 3. Divide 39 by 3.

$$39 \div 3 = 13$$

So

$$78 = 2 \times 3 \times 13.$$

13 is a prime number.

The factorisation is $2 \times 3 \times 13$

SELF TEST 1.14

Factorise
  a) 140
  b) 144.

a) $2 \times 2 \times 5 \times 7$
b) $2 \times 2 \times 2 \times 2 \times 3 \times 3$

HCF and LCM

Suppose we have a lawn which is 9 m by 15 m. It is to be covered by whole squares of turf. What is the length of the sides of these squares?

The side of the square must divide into 9. It must also divide into 15. So we want a number which divides into both 9 and 15. The highest such number is 3. Figure 1.6 shows the lawn.

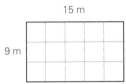

Figure 1.6

> In general, given two numbers, the highest number which divides into both of them is their **Highest Common Factor (HCF)**.

The HCF of 9 and 15 is 3.

Suppose we have two wheels, one of which turns round in 9 seconds, the other in 15 seconds. When will they both have made a complete number of turns?

The first wheel makes a complete turn after every multiple of 9 seconds. The second wheel makes a complete turn after every multiple of 15 seconds. So we want a number which is a multiple of both 9 and 15. The least such number is 45. Both wheels make complete turns after 45 seconds.

> In general, given two numbers, the least number which they both divide into is their **Least Common Multiple (LCM)**.

The LCM is 9 and 15 is 45.

Finding HCF and LCM

First factorise both the numbers. For the HCF, take the factors which occur in *both* the numbers. For the LCM, take the factors which occur in *either* of the numbers. If a factor occurs two or more times, then include it two or more times.

$$9 = 3 \times 3 \qquad 15 = 3 \times 5$$

The factor occurring in both numbers is 3. Hence the HCF is 3.

The factors needed to make either number are 3, 3, and 5. Hence the LCM is $3 \times 3 \times 5 = 45$. Note that the LCM includes two 3s.

The same method applies when we find the HCF or LCM of three or more numbers.

EXAMPLE 1.13

Find the HCF and LCM of 8, 12 and 20.

Solution

Factorise the three numbers.

$8 = 2 \times 2 \times 2 \qquad 12 = 2 \times 2 \times 3 \qquad 20 = 2 \times 2 \times 5$

The factors which occur in all three numbers are 2 and 2. The product of these is 4.

The HCF is 4

The factors which occur in at least one of the numbers are 2, 2, 2, 3 and 5. The product of these is 120.

The LCM is 120

SELF TEST 1.15

Find the HCF and LCM of
  a) 24 and 15
  b) 30, 12 and 18.

a) **3, 120**   b) **6, 180**

EXAMPLE 1.14

Lengths of pipe are either 6 m long or 8 m long. Find the shortest length which can be made up using either 6 m pipes or 8 m pipes.

Solution

The length must be divisible by 6 and by 8. Hence we want the LCM of 6 and 8. Factorise 6 and 8.

$6 = 2 \times 3 \qquad 8 = 2 \times 2 \times 2$

The LCM is $2 \times 2 \times 2 \times 3$, which is 24.

The shortest length is 24 m

SELF TEST 1.16

A machine has two components which need replacement, one after 18 days and the other after 15 days. After how long will they both need replacement on the same day?

90 days

EXAMPLE 1.15

Figure 1.7 shows a rectangular field, 60 m by 75 m. It is to be enclosed by sections of fencing. Find the greatest length of a section so that each side contains a whole number of sections.

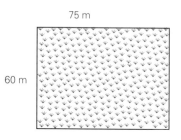

Figure 1.7

Solution

The length must divide exactly into 60 and into 75. Hence we want the HCF of 60 and 75. Factorise 60 and 75.

$60 = 2 \times 2 \times 3 \times 5 \qquad 75 = 3 \times 5 \times 5$

The HCF is 3×5, which is 15.

The greatest length of a section is 15 m

SELF TEST 1.17

A wall is 2400 mm by 3750 mm. Find the largest size of square tiles which could cover the wall.

side 150 mm

■ **CHECK YOUR UNDERSTANDING**

● The four basic operations are addition, subtraction, multiplication and division.
● Multiplication and division should be done before addition and subtraction.
● If the addition or subtraction should be done first, then put it in brackets.
● The product of two negative numbers is positive.
● A number which divides into another is a factor. A number which has no factors except 1 and itself is prime.
● The highest number which divides into two numbers is their HCF. The lowest number which they both divide into is their LCM.

REVISION EXERCISES AND QUESTIONS

1.1 Basic operations

1 Evaluate the following.
  a) $45 + 21$ b) $103 + 128$ c) $37 + 193$
  d) $76 - 41$ e) $194 - 113$ f) $173 - 89$
  g) 12×9 h) 100×22 i) 101×12
  j) $24 \div 8$ k) $600 \div 20$ l) $120 \div 15$

2 a) Find the sum of 12 and 33.
  b) Find the product of 8 and 12.
  c) Find the difference between 37 and 21.
  d) Find the quotient of 56 divided by 7.
  e) Find the quotient and remainder when 37 is divided by 8.

3 a) Find the total mass of concrete which consists of 50 kg sand, 100 kg gravel and 30 kg cement
  b) A job is divided into three parts, which take 18 hours, 12 hours and 15 hours respectively. Find the total time for the job.
  c) Find the total length of the spindle shown in Figure 1.8. Distances are in mm.

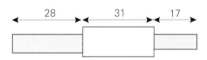

Figure 1.8

  d) A fence is made of sections which are 2.5 m long. How far will 16 of the sections stretch?
  e) What is the total mass of 65 screws, each of which has a mass of 3 grams?
  f) Two holes are drilled in a metal plate, as shown in Figure 1.9. Distances are in mm. Find the distance between the centres of the holes.

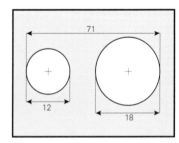

Figure 1.9

  g) A pharmacist weights out 75 μg of a medicine. How many 5 μg doses can be made from it?

4 The hardness of a metal is found by applying a force to it and measuring the area of the impression. The formula is
$$\text{hardness} = \frac{\text{load}}{\text{area}}.$$
A load of 100 N gave an impression of area 0.5 mm^2. Find the hardness.

5 The denier of a yarn is given by
$$\text{denier} = \frac{\text{mass in grams}}{\text{length in metres}} \times 9000.$$
Find the denier of a yarn if 1200 m has a mass of 2 g.

1.2 Order of operations

6 Evaluate the following.
  a) $2 + 7 \times 2$ b) $18 \times 5 - 2$ c) $32 \div 4 + 12$
  d) $9 + 6 \div 3$ e) $12 - 8 - 3$ f) $30 - 6 + 7$

7 What is the total cost of a radio at #58 and 20 batteries at #2 each?

8 Ten holes of diameter 10 mm are drilled in a steel plate. Their centres are 45 mm apart in a straight line. Find the distance between the left edge of the first hole and the right edge of the last hole. (Hint: draw a diagram to help.)

9 There are ten workers in a factory. Each receives #350, and an equal share of a bonus of #1250. How much does each worker receive?

10 Evaluate the following.
  a) $(2 + 7) \times 2$ b) $18 \times (5 - 2)$ c) $32 \div (4 + 12)$
  d) $(9 + 6) \div 3$ e) $12 - (8 - 3)$ f) $30 - (6 + 7)$

11 Find the total cost of eight sets of a cup and a saucer, if each cup costs #17 and each saucer costs #15.

12 Twelve bags of sand each have a mass 80 kg originally, but then each lost 5 kg through evaporation. Find the total mass after evaporation.

13 A sum of #320 is to be divided fairly between 6 boys and 4 girls. How much does each receive?

14 The percentage error in a measurement is given by
$$\text{percentage error} = \frac{\text{true value} - \text{measured value}}{\text{true value}} \times 100\%.$$
Find the percentage error when a mass of 50 kg is measured as 48 kg.

1.3 Negative numbers

15 Evaluate the following.
  a) -3×-6 b) $-8 \times -2 \times 7$
  c) $-3 \times -2 \times -6$ d) $-24 \div -8$
  e) $8 \div -2$ f) $-2 \times (4 - 7)$
  g) $(4 - 10) \times (6 - 8)$ h) $(2 - 10) \div -4$
  i) $(3 - 10) \times 2$

16 The temperature is $-4°C$. What is the temperature if
a) it rises by $9°C$? b) it falls by $9°C$?

1.4 Factors

17 Factorise the following.
a) 72 b) 150 c) 99 d) 1001

18 Find the HCF for the following pairs of numbers.
a) 24 and 16 b) 20 and 35
c) 15 and 60 d) 22 and 14

19 Find the LCM for the pairs of numbers in Question 18.

20 Find the HCF and the LCM of the following sets of numbers.
a) 24, 14, 30 b) 24, 30, 20

21 What is the least non-zero sum of money that can be made out of either #10 notes or #15 notes?

22 Two gear wheels are connected. One takes 12 seconds to rotate, the other takes 15 seconds to rotate. After how long will they both be at their original positions?

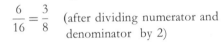

Fractions and decimals

Introduction

When you count people or cars, the result is a whole number. You cannot measure half a person, or 0.2 of a car. The number of people in a room, or the number of cars in a car park, must be a whole number, or **integer**.

But a reaction time could be $\frac{1}{2}$ of a second, or a parcel could have a mass 0.2 of a kilogram. Amounts like 1 kilogram, 1 metre, 1 second, 1 ampere and so on can be divided into smaller amounts.

There are many ways to represent numbers smaller than 1. There are fractions, decimals, percentages. The following all mean the same. They are all equal to 75 kg.

$\frac{1}{4}$ of 300 kg   0.25 of 300 kg   25% of 300 kg

In this chapter we show how to handle fractions and decimals.

2.1 Fractions

Take a cake, and cut it into 8 equal parts. Each part is $\frac{1}{8}$, or one-eighth, of the whole. In Figure 2.1 three of these parts are shaded. They are $\frac{3}{8}$, or three-eighths, of the whole.

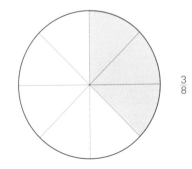

Figure 2.1

The top of a fraction is the **numerator**, and the bottom the **denominator**.

For the fraction $\frac{3}{8}$, the numerator is 3 and the denominator is 8.

$$\frac{3}{8} = \frac{\text{numerator}}{\text{denominator}}$$

If you multiply or divide both numerator and denominator of a fraction by the same number, you do not change the fraction. You can use this to simplify a fraction. This method is called **cancelling**.

In Figure 2.2, the cake of Figure 2.1 has been divided into 16 equal pieces. Now 6 of the pieces are shaded. This covers the same area as 3 out of 8 pieces.

$$\frac{6}{16} = \frac{3}{8} \quad \text{(after dividing numerator and denominator by 2)}$$

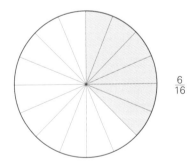

Figure 2.2

How to simplify a fraction by cancelling

Given a fraction, find the Highest Common Factor (HCF) of the numerator and denominator. Then divide both numerator and denominator by it. The HCF was defined in Section 1.4 on page 6.

Consider $\frac{30}{48}$. The HCF of 30 and 48 is 6. Divide both by 6.

Hence
$$\frac{30}{48} = \frac{5}{8}$$

EXAMPLE 2.1

A minute is a sixtieth of an hour. Express 25 minutes as a fraction of an hour.

Solution
We want 25 sixtieths, i.e. $\frac{25}{60}$. Divide numerator and denominator by 5, obtaining $\frac{5}{12}$.

25 minutes is $\frac{5}{12}$ of an hour

SELF TEST 2.1

Simplify the following fractions.

a) $\frac{8}{20}$ b) $\frac{15}{24}$ c) $\frac{35}{100}$

a) $\frac{2}{5}$ b) $\frac{5}{8}$ c) $\frac{7}{20}$

EXAMPLE 2.2

A tool kit contains spanners in sizes (inches) $\frac{1}{2}$, $\frac{3}{8}$, $\frac{1}{4}$, $\frac{3}{4}$, $\frac{7}{8}$, $\frac{5}{8}$, $\frac{3}{16}$, $\frac{7}{16}$, $\frac{9}{16}$. Arrange these in order of increasing size.

Solution
The largest denominator is 16. Alter the other fractions so that they all have a denominator of 16. For $\frac{1}{2}$, multiply numerator and denominator by 8, obtaining $\frac{8}{16}$. Change the other fractions similarly.

$$\frac{1}{2} = \frac{8}{16} \qquad \frac{3}{8} = \frac{6}{16} \qquad \frac{1}{4} = \frac{4}{16}$$
$$\frac{3}{4} = \frac{12}{16} \qquad \frac{7}{8} = \frac{14}{16} \qquad \frac{5}{8} = \frac{10}{16}$$
$$\frac{3}{16} \qquad\quad \frac{7}{16} \qquad\quad \frac{9}{16}$$

The smallest of these is $\frac{3}{16}$. The next is $\frac{4}{16}$, i.e. $\frac{1}{4}$. Continue up to the largest, which is $\frac{14}{16}$, i.e. $\frac{7}{8}$. In increasing order the sizes are
$$\frac{3}{16} \quad \frac{4}{16} \quad \frac{6}{16} \quad \frac{7}{16} \quad \frac{8}{16} \quad \frac{9}{16} \quad \frac{10}{16} \quad \frac{12}{16} \quad \frac{14}{16}.$$
Simplify these fractions to obtain the following.
$$\frac{3}{16} \quad \frac{1}{4} \quad \frac{3}{8} \quad \frac{7}{16} \quad \frac{1}{2} \quad \frac{9}{16} \quad \frac{5}{8} \quad \frac{3}{4} \quad \frac{7}{8}$$

SELF TEST 2.2

Arrange in increasing order:

$\frac{1}{3}$ $\frac{1}{4}$ $\frac{5}{6}$ $\frac{7}{12}$ $\frac{2}{3}$.

$\frac{1}{4}$ $\frac{1}{3}$ $\frac{7}{12}$ $\frac{2}{3}$ $\frac{5}{6}$

Improper fractions and mixed numbers

In all the fractions so far, the numerator has been less than the denominator. These are **proper** fractions. A fraction for which the numerator is greater than the denominator is an **improper** fraction.

$\dfrac{7}{8}$ is a proper fraction.

$\dfrac{13}{9}$ is an improper fraction.

A **mixed number** like $2\frac{2}{3}$ includes a whole number, 2, and a fraction, $\frac{2}{3}$. A mixed number can be converted to an improper fraction.

Multiply the whole number by the denominator of the fraction.

$$2\tfrac{2}{3} = 2 + \tfrac{2}{3}$$
$$= \frac{6}{3} + \frac{2}{3} = \frac{8}{3}$$

Figure 2.3 shows that they are equal. On the top of the picture there are two whole cakes and two thirds of a cake. In the bottom of the picture the whole cakes have been divided into 3 equal parts. In total there are eight thirds of a cake.

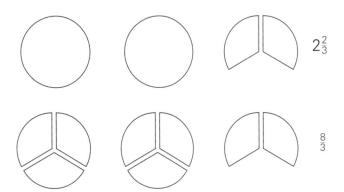

Figure 2.3

An improper fraction can be converted to a mixed number. Divide the numerator by the denominator to find how many 'whole ones' there are. The quotient gives the whole number, and the remainder gives the numerator of the fraction.

$\frac{21}{8}$, divide 21 by 8 to give 2 with remainder 5

$$\frac{21}{8} = 2\frac{5}{8}$$

EXAMPLE 2.3

a) Convert $5\frac{1}{4}$ to an improper fraction.

b) Convert $\frac{26}{11}$ to a mixed number.

Solution

a) Multiply 5 by 4, obtaining 20. Hence $5 = \frac{20}{4}$. Add this to $\frac{1}{4}$.

$$5\frac{1}{4} = \frac{21}{4}$$

b) Divide 26 by 11. The result is 2, with remainder 4.

$$\frac{26}{11} = \mathbf{2\frac{4}{11}}$$

SELF TEST 2.3

a) Convert $3\frac{5}{8}$ to an improper fraction.

$\frac{29}{8}$

b) Convert $\frac{32}{7}$ to a mixed number.

$4\frac{4}{7}$

Arithmetic of fractions

Multiplication and division

To multiply two fractions, multiply their numerators to get the final numerator, and multiply their denominators to get the final denominator.

$$\frac{7}{10} \times \frac{3}{8} = \frac{21}{80}$$

To divide one fraction by another, turn the second fraction upside down and then multiply the fractions.

$$\frac{4}{9} \div \frac{7}{10} = \frac{4}{9} \times \frac{10}{7}$$
$$= \frac{40}{63}$$

When we turn a fraction upside down, the result is the **reciprocal** of the fraction.

The reciprocal of $\frac{7}{10}$ is $\frac{10}{7}$.

When multiplying or dividing mixed numbers, express them as improper fractions.

$$2\frac{1}{3} \times \frac{1}{16} = \frac{7}{3} \times \frac{1}{16} = \frac{7}{48}$$

Sometimes multiplying is made easier by cancelling first.

$$\frac{5}{{}_3\cancel{9}} \times \frac{\cancel{3}^1}{4} = \frac{5}{12}$$

SELF TEST 2.4

Evaluate the following.

a) $\frac{5}{21} \times \frac{14}{25}$ b) $\frac{6}{31} \div \frac{5}{8}$ c) $1\frac{3}{4} \times 3\frac{1}{3}$

a) $\frac{2}{15}$ b) $\frac{48}{155}$ c) $5\frac{5}{6}$

EXAMPLE 2.4

A pharmacist weighs out $\frac{5}{8}$ of a gram of a medicine. This is divided into three equal parts. Find the mass of each part.

Solution

Each part is a third of the original amount. Hence multiply $\frac{5}{8}$ by $\frac{1}{3}$.

$$\frac{5}{8} \times \frac{1}{3} = \frac{5}{24}$$

Each part has a mass of $\frac{5}{24}$ g

SELF TEST 2.5

An inch is $\frac{1}{12}$ of a foot. Express $\frac{1}{20}$ of an inch as a fraction of a foot.

$\frac{1}{240}$ ft

EXAMPLE 2.5

How many lengths of $\frac{2}{3}$ m can be cut from a $5\frac{1}{3}$ m length of cloth?

Solution

First write $5\frac{1}{3}$ as an improper fraction. $5\frac{1}{3} = \frac{16}{3}$. Now divide this by $\frac{2}{3}$.

$$\frac{16}{3} \div \frac{2}{3} = \frac{16}{3} \times \frac{3}{2} = \frac{{}^8\cancel{16}}{{}_1\cancel{3}} \times \frac{\cancel{3}^1}{\cancel{2}_1} = \frac{8}{1} = 8$$

8 lengths of $\frac{2}{3}$ m can be cut

SELF TEST 2.6

A bottle contains $\frac{7}{10}$ of a litre. How many bottles can be filled from a 560 litre barrel?

800 bottles

Addition and subtraction

If two fractions have the same denominator, they can be added or subtracted by adding or subtracting the numerators.

$$\frac{2}{9} + \frac{5}{9} = \frac{7}{9} \qquad \frac{9}{11} - \frac{3}{11} = \frac{6}{11}$$

If two fractions do not have the same denominator, then make them the same first, as follows.

Find the Least Common Multiple (LCM) of the denominators. Both denominators divide into the LCM. Hence the LCM is also the **Least Common Denominator** (LCD). For the definition of LCM, see Section 1.4, page 6.

Suppose we want to add $\frac{3}{7}$ and $\frac{4}{9}$. The LCM of 7 and 9 is 63. This is the LCD. Multiply numerator and denominator of $\frac{3}{7}$ by 9, and multiply numerator and denominator of $\frac{4}{9}$ by 7.

$$\begin{aligned}
\frac{3}{7} + \frac{4}{9} &= \frac{27}{63} + \frac{28}{63} \\
&= \frac{55}{63}
\end{aligned}$$

EXAMPLE 2.6

Find the total length of the spindle shown in Figure 2.4. Lengths are in inches.

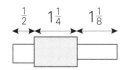

Figure 2.4

Solution

Add the lengths to find the total length. Add the whole numbers first, $1 + 1 = 2$. The denominators of the fractions are 2, 4 and 8. The LCD is 8.

$$\begin{aligned}
\frac{1}{2} + 1\frac{1}{4} + 1\frac{1}{8} &= 2 + \frac{4}{8} + \frac{2}{8} + \frac{1}{8} \\
&= 2\frac{7}{8}
\end{aligned}$$

The length is $2\frac{7}{8}$ inches

SELF TEST 2.7

Evaluate the following.

a) $\frac{6}{11} + \frac{2}{11}$ b) $\frac{3}{10} - \frac{1}{5}$ c) $\frac{4}{15} + \frac{5}{12}$

a) $\frac{8}{11}$ b) $\frac{1}{10}$ c) $\frac{41}{60}$

Order of operations

Fractions obey the same rules of order of operations as whole numbers. Do multiplication or division before addition or subtraction. If the addition or subtraction should be done first, use brackets.

EXAMPLE 2.7

Evaluate the following.

a) $\frac{1}{2} \times \frac{3}{8} + \frac{2}{3} \times \frac{2}{5}$ b) $\left(\frac{3}{14} + \frac{5}{12}\right) \div \frac{3}{4}$

Solution

a) Do the multiplications first.

$$\frac{1}{2} \times \frac{3}{8} = \frac{3}{16} \qquad \frac{2}{3} \times \frac{2}{5} = \frac{4}{15}$$

15 and 16 have no common factor. Hence the LCM of 15 and 16 is 240.

$$\frac{3}{16} + \frac{4}{15} = \frac{45}{240} + \frac{64}{240} = \frac{109}{240}$$

$$\frac{1}{2} \times \frac{3}{8} + \frac{2}{3} \times \frac{2}{5} = \frac{109}{240}$$

b) Do the addition in the brackets first. The LCM of 14 and 12 is 84.

$$\frac{3}{14} + \frac{5}{12} = \frac{18}{84} + \frac{35}{84} = \frac{53}{84}$$

Now divide by $\frac{3}{4}$, i.e. multiply by $\frac{4}{3}$.

$$\begin{aligned}
\frac{53}{84} \div \frac{3}{4} &= \frac{53}{84} \times \frac{4}{3} \\
&= \frac{53}{21} \times \frac{1}{3} \text{ (by cancelling)} \\
&= \frac{53}{63}
\end{aligned}$$

$$\left(\frac{3}{14} + \frac{5}{12}\right) \div \frac{3}{4} = \frac{53}{63}$$

SELF TEST 2.8

Ealuate the following.

a) $\frac{3}{4} \times \frac{2}{5} - \frac{1}{8} \times \frac{1}{15}$ b) $\left(\frac{3}{5} - \frac{1}{3}\right) \div \left(\frac{3}{4} + \frac{1}{8}\right)$

a) $\frac{7}{24}$ b) $\frac{32}{105}$

2.2 Decimals

In decimal fractions (decimals) the denominators are powers of 10, i.e. 10, 100, 1000 and so on.

$$2.73 = 2 + \frac{7}{10} + \frac{3}{100}$$

The point separating the whole number from the fraction is called the **decimal point**.

Decimal places

The digit after the decimal point is in the **first decimal place**. The digit after that is in the **second decimal place**, and so on. For 2.73, the digit 7 is in the first decimal place and 3 is in the second decimal place.

Some decimals finish after a certain number of decimal places. For example, $\frac{1}{4}$ is 0.25 exactly. These are **terminating** decimals. Some continue for ever. For example, $\frac{1}{3}$ is 0.333333 ..., where the 3s continue for ever. These are **recurring** decimals. To show that the 3s are recurring, put a dot on top.

$$\frac{1}{3} = 0.33333... = 0.\dot{3}$$

Suppose you have a decimal with a lot of decimal places. You might want to give only the first three decimal places. If the digit in the fourth decimal place is less than 5, round down. If it is 5 or more, round up.

1.2348 = 1.235, correct to three decimal places.
1.2343 = 1.234, correct to three decimal places.

EXAMPLE 2.8

Write out the first five decimal places of $0.\dot{3}\dot{7}$. Round it to three decimal places.

Solution
The dots mean that the 3s and 7s are repeated, as 0.373737 ... Take the first five digits.

0.37373

The digit in the fourth decimal place is 7, which is greater than 5. Hence round the 3 up to a 4.

$0.\dot{3}\dot{7} = 0.374$, **correct to three decimal places**

SELF TEST 2.9

Write out the first five decimal places of $0.2\dot{6}$. Round it to three decimal places.

0.26666   0.267

Significant figures

The first significant figure in a number is the first non-zero digit. The next digits, even if they are zero, are the next significant digits.

Table 2.1

	53.012	0.02548	439 300
First significant figure	5	2	4
Second significant figure	3	5	3
Third significant figure	0	4	9
Fourth significant figure	1	8	3

If a measurement is given to a certain number of significant figures, then the digits will be the same no matter what units are used.

0.05346 km = 53.46 m = 53 460 mm

All three numbers are given correct to four significant figures.

If the last significant figure is 0, leave it in to show the accuracy. To three significant figures, 1.298 is 1.30.

SELF TEST 2.10

Write the following correct to 3 significant figures.
a) 342 784   b) 0.17432
c) 1.2085   d) 0.003496

a) 343 000   b) 0.174   c) 1.21   d) 0.00350

Conversion

Convert between fractions and decimals as follows.

Fraction → decimal
Divide the numerator by the denominator.
$$\frac{3}{4} = 3 \div 4 = 0.75$$

Decimal → fraction
Write the denominator of the fraction as a power of 10.
Hence $$0.71 = \frac{71}{100}$$

EXAMPLE 2.9

We measure angles in **degrees**, °. Angles smaller than 1° are measured in minutes and seconds. A **minute**, ′, is a sixtieth of a degree. A **second**, ″, is a sixtieth of a minute. Express 12′ 54″ as a fraction of a degree and as a decimal.

Solution
The 12′ is 12 sixtieths of a degree, i.e. $\frac{12}{60}$.
Each second is a sixtieth of a sixtieth of a degree, i.e.

$$1'' = \frac{1}{60} \times \frac{1}{60}^\circ = \frac{1}{3600}^\circ$$

Hence 54″ is $\frac{54}{3600}^\circ$. Add the minutes and the seconds.

$$\frac{12}{60} + \frac{54}{3600} = \frac{720}{3600} + \frac{54}{3600} = \frac{774}{3600}$$

This fraction can be simplified to $\frac{43}{200}$.

$$12'54'' \text{ is } \frac{43}{200}^\circ$$

To convert to a decimal, divide 43 by 200, obtaining 0.215.

12′ 54″ is 0.215°

SELF TEST 2.11

a) Convert $\frac{13}{32}$ to a decimal.

b) Express $5°\ 30'\ 18''$ as a decimal.

a) **0.40625**   b) **5.505°**

EXAMPLE 2.10

Slip gauges are used to measure widths accurately. A set of slip gauges is shown in Figure 2.5.

Suppose you have a set of slip gauges with 47 components. Their widths, in mm, are given below. Show how to use the gauges to build up a width of 37.635 mm.

width in mm
1.005
2.01, 2.02, 2.03, 2.04, 2.05, 2.06, 2.07, 2.08, 2.09
2.10, 2.20, 2.30, 2.40, 2.50, 2.60, 2.70, 2.80, 2.90
1, 2, 3, 4, 5, 6, 7, 8, 9, 10, 11, 12,
13, 14, 15, 16, 17, 18, 19, 20, 21, 22, 23, 24
60, 80, 100.

Solution

Build up 37.635, starting with the least significant figure, 0.005.

Gauge: 1.005   Width remaining: 36.630
Gauge: 2.03   Width remaining: 34.60
Gauge: 2.60   Width remaining: 32.00
Gauge: 12   Width remaining: 20
Gauge: 20   Width remaining: 0

$$37.635 = 1.005 + 2.03 + 2.60 + 12 + 20$$

SELF TEST 2.12

Show how the slip gauges of Example 2.10 can be used for widths of

a) 42.715   b) 29.51.

a) **1.005 + 2.01 + 2.7 + 17 + 20**
b) **2.01 + 2.5 + 5 + 20**

Arithmetic of decimals

The arithmetic of decimals is similar to that of whole numbers.

Addition and subtraction

When you add or subtract decimal numbers, without using a calculator, make sure that the decimal points are above each other. Then the method is the same as for whole numbers. To add 4.29 and 2.36:

$$\begin{array}{r} 4.29 \\ +\ 2.36 \\ \hline 6.65 \end{array}$$

EXAMPLE 2.11

The mass of a bale of cotton is 63.34 kg. During drying, 7.86 kg of water is removed. Find the mass of the dry cotton.

Solution

Subtract 7.86 from 63.34. Make sure that the decimal points are in a line.

$$\begin{array}{r} 63.34 \\ -\ 7.86 \\ \hline 55.48 \end{array}$$

The dry weight is 55.48 kg

SELF TEST 2.13

Find, without a calculator:

a) $3.125 + 4.619$ b) $8.561 - 0.451.$

a) **7.744**   b) **8.11**

Figure 2.5 Slip gauges

EXAMPLE 2.12

Two holes are drilled in a metal plate, as shown in Figure 2.6. Distances are in mm. Find the least distance between the holes.

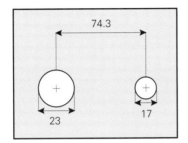

Figure 2.6

Solution

The distance between the centres of the holes is 74.3 mm. The holes have diameters 23 mm and 17 mm, hence their radii are 11.5 mm and 8.5 mm respectively. Subtract these from 74.3 mm.

$$74.3 - 11.5 - 8.5 = 54.3$$

The shortest distance is 54.3 mm

SELF TEST 2.14

Two holes are drilled in a metal plate, as shown in Figure 2.7. Distances are in mm. Find the distance between the centres of the holes.

71.2 mm

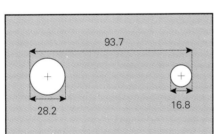

Figure 2.7

Multiplication

To multiply two decimals, change them to whole numbers by multiplying by 10. Keep multiplying by 10 until you have a whole number. Multiply the whole numbers, then divide by the powers of 10.

To find 1.34×2.7, change the numbers to 134 and 27, by multiplying by 100 and by 10 respectively. $134 \times 27 = 3618$. Now divide by 100 and by 10, obtaining 3.618.

$$1.34 \times 2.7 = \frac{134 \times 27}{100 \times 10} = \frac{3618}{1000} = 3.618$$

EXAMPLE 2.13

A current of 0.032 amps flows for 0.0054 seconds. Find the total charge which has passed. (Charge = current × time).

Solution

Multiply 0.032 and 0.0054 by 1000 and 10 000 respectively, converting to 32 and 54.

$$32 \times 54 = 1728$$

Now divide by 1000 and 10 000, obtaining 0.000 172 8.

0.000 172 8 coulombs have passed

SELF TEST 2.15

Multiply 0.185 and 0.0004.

0.000 074

Division

When you divide one decimal by another, you can convert it to a division of whole numbers. Multiply both decimals by 10 the same number of times.

$$2.47 \div 1.7 = 247 \div 170$$

Here we multiplied both terms by 100. You now have a division of whole numbers.

EXAMPLE 2.14

Liquid of mass 62.5 kg occupies 0.08 m³. Find its density. (Density = mass ÷ volume.)

Solution

We want $62.5 \div 0.08$. Multiply both these numbers by 100.

$$62.5 \div 0.08 = 6250 \div 8 = 781.25$$

The density is 781.25 kg/m³

SELF TEST 2.16

Divide 12.37 by 0.05.

247.4

CHECK YOUR UNDERSTANDING

● The top of a fraction is the numerator, and the bottom is the denominator. Fractions are not changed if both numerator and denominator are multiplied by the same number.

● A mixed number involves both a whole number and a fraction. In an improper fraction, the numerator is greater than the denominator.

● When multiplying fractions, multiply the numerators and multiply the denominators.

● When dividing one fraction by another, turn the second fraction upside down and then multiply.

● When adding or subtracting fractions, ensure that they have the same denominator. Then add the numerators.

● In decimal fractions, the denominators are powers of 10. The digit in the first decimal place has a denominator of 10, the digit in the second place has a denominator of 100, and so on.

● The digit after the decimal point is in the first decimal place. The next digit is in the second decimal place. When rounding a number correct to two decimal places, round up if the digit in the third decimal place is 5 or greater. Otherwise round down.

● The first non-zero digit of a number is the first significant figure. The next digit, even if it is zero, is the second significant figure, and so on.

● When adding or subtracting decimals, make sure that the decimal points are in a line.

● When multiplying decimals, convert to whole numbers by multiplying by powers of 10. Perform the multiplication, then divide by the powers of 10.

● When dividing decimals, convert both to whole numbers by multiplying both by the same power of 10.

REVISION EXERCISES AND QUESTIONS

2.1 Fractions

1 Simplify the following fractions.
   a) $\frac{5}{15}$
   b) $\frac{18}{24}$
   c) $\frac{28}{63}$

2 Convert the following improper fractions to mixed numbers.
   a) $\frac{23}{16}$
   b) $\frac{52}{15}$
   c) $\frac{47}{3}$

3 Convert the following mixed numbers to improper fractions.
   a) $3\frac{7}{8}$
   b) $2\frac{4}{7}$
   c) $5\frac{7}{12}$

4 Evaluate the following, simplifying your answers when possible.
   a) $\frac{5}{12} \times \frac{7}{9}$
   b) $\frac{3}{7} \times \frac{2}{3}$
   c) $1\frac{1}{4} \times 2\frac{1}{3}$
   d) $\frac{7}{16} \div \frac{2}{3}$
   e) $\frac{5}{11} \div \frac{15}{22}$
   f) $1\frac{4}{5} \div 3\frac{5}{8}$
   g) $\frac{7}{12} + \frac{1}{12}$
   h) $\frac{5}{7} + \frac{4}{7}$
   i) $3\frac{3}{4} + 4\frac{3}{4}$
   j) $\frac{4}{5} + \frac{2}{3}$
   k) $\frac{4}{9} + \frac{3}{8}$
   l) $\frac{5}{8} + \frac{3}{4}$
   m) $\frac{7}{15} - \frac{4}{15}$
   n) $\frac{5}{7} - \frac{3}{8}$
   o) $4\frac{1}{4} - 3\frac{2}{3}$

5 Express 12 minutes as a fraction of an hour.

6 How many minutes are there in $1\frac{3}{4}$ hours?

7 Express $3' \, 50''$ as a fraction of a degree.

8 A cake with a mass $\frac{3}{4}$ kg is divided into 5 equal parts. What is the mass of each part?

9 A man walks $\frac{3}{8}$ km in $\frac{1}{4}$ hour. What is his speed, in km/hr?

2.2 Decimals

10 Round the following to 2 decimal places.
   a) 4.078
   b) 4.343
   c) 11.298
   d) 0.0042

11 Round 6.95896 to
   a) 2 decimal places
   b) 3 decimal places
   c) 4 decimal places.

12 Write the following correct to 3 significant figures.
   a) 2.458
   b) 987 230
   c) 0.01798
   d) 50.492

13 Convert the following fractions to decimals.
   a) $\frac{73}{100}$
   b) $\frac{5}{8}$
   c) $\frac{13}{25}$
   d) $\frac{7}{16}$

14 Convert the following fractions to decimals, giving your answers correct to 2 decimal places.
   a) $\frac{5}{6}$
   b) $\frac{3}{7}$
   c) $\frac{8}{11}$
   d) $\frac{11}{30}$

15 Convert the following decimals to fractions.
   a) 0.7
   b) 0.231
   c) 0.05
   d) 0.104

16 Evaluate the following without using a calculator.
   a) $7.32 + 8.47$
   b) $93.1 + 27.4$
   c) $0.0465 + 0.0783$
   d) $12.8 - 7.3$
   e) $4.17 - 3.73$
   f) $0.004\,63 - 0.003\,89$
   g) 3.2×3.5
   h) 0.43×0.71
   i) 1.2×0.052
   j) $7.2 \div 0.4$
   k) $0.05 \div 20$
   l) $0.0045 \div 0.0005$

17 Figure 2.8 shows two holes drilled in a plate. Find the distance between the centres of the holes. Distances are in mm.

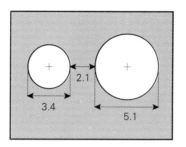

Figure 2.8

18 Find the length of the spindle shown in Figure 2.9. Distances are in mm.

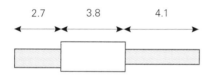

Figure 2.9

19 Figure 2.10 shows two balls in a tapering hole. Find the distance between the centres of the balls. Distances are in mm.

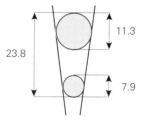

Figure 2.10

20 How many cans of 0.4 litres can be filled from a tank of 2040 litres?

21 A screw has a mass 2.8 grams. What is the total mass of 1200 similar screws?

22 A steel bar of length 4.2 m has a mass 14 kg. What is the mass per metre?

23 A drum contains 660 kg of chemical powder. How many 1.2 kg packets can be filled from it?

24 The speed of a flywheel is 1600 revolutions per minute. How many revolutions does it do in 4.1 minutes?

25 At 0°C, the resistance of an electrical component is 2.3 Ω. The resistance rises by 0.017 Ω for every rise of 1°C in temperature. Find the resistance at 25°C.

Percentages and ratios 3

Introduction

The materials used in technical work are often made up from other substances. Concrete, for example, consists of sand, aggregate and cement. If the amounts are varied, the type of concrete changes. The amount of cement in the concrete can be expressed in the following two ways.

As a percentage.
  The cement is 15% of the concrete.

As a ratio.
  The ratio of the cement to the other ingredients is 3:17.

3.1 Percentages

The words *percent* means "per hundred". Hence a percentage is a fraction with denominator of 100. For example

$$8\% = \tfrac{8}{100}$$

We use percentages because it is easier to use whole numbers rather than fractions. We often use percentages for proportion, interest, rate of increase and so on.

Finding the percentage

We can express the proportion of an ingredient as a percentage. A type of concrete, for example, might contain 10% cement.

  Divide the amount of the ingredient by the total amount, to find the proportion as a fraction. Then multiply by 100, to find the proportion as a percentage.

$$\text{percentage of cement} = \frac{\text{amount of cement}}{\text{total amount of concrete}} \times 100\%$$

SELF TEST 3.1

A bottle of 800 ml liquid contains 15 ml of alcohol. Find the percentage of alcohol in the bottle.

1.875%

Finding the amount

Suppose you are told that a material contains a certain percentage of an ingredient. To find the amount of the ingredient, divide the percentage by 100 and multiply by the total amount.

EXAMPLE 3.2

Mild steel has a carbon content of 0.25%. How much carbon is there in 500 kg of mild steel?

Solution
The percentage, 0.25%, corresponds to the fraction $\frac{0.25}{100}$. Multiply this by 500.

$$\frac{0.25}{100} \times 500 = 1.25$$

There is 1.25 kg of carbon

SELF TEST 3.2

A bottle of gin contains 40% alcohol by volume. If the bottle contains 750 ml, find the volume of alcohol.

> 300 ml

Percentage change

Often a percentage expresses the change of a quantity. The change might be an increase or a decrease. The result is expressed as a percentage of the *original* amount, not of the changed amount.

Suppose a quantity increases from 20 to 23. The increase is 3. The percentage increase is

$$\frac{3}{20} \times 100\% = 15\%$$

EXAMPLE 3.3

The resistance of a loop increased from 1000 Ω to 1050 Ω What was the percentage increase?

Solution
The increase was 1050 Ω–1000 Ω, i.e. 50 Ω. Divide 50 by 1000, then multiply by 100%.

$$\frac{50}{1000} \times 100\% = 5\%$$

The increase is 5%

SELF TEST 3.3

During a power surge, the voltage increased from 240 V to 270 V. What was the percentage increase?

> 12.5%

EXAMPLE 3.4

After cleaning, the mass of a delivery of wool decreased from 280 kg to 238 kg. Find the percentage decrease.

Solution
The actual decrease was 280 − 238, i.e. 42. Divide this by 280, and multiply by 100%.

$$\frac{42}{280} \times 100\% = 15\%$$

The percentage decrease was 15%

SELF TEST 3.4

After a new machine was installed, the time for a certain task decreased from 30 minutes to 27 minutes. Find the percentage decrease.

> 10%

Efficiency

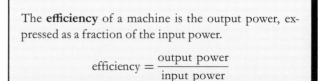

The **efficiency** of a machine is the output power, expressed as a fraction of the input power.

$$\text{efficiency} = \frac{\text{output power}}{\text{input power}}$$

Suppose the efficiency of a machine is 90%, i.e. $\frac{90}{100}$ or 0.9.

[1] If you are given the input power, multiply by 0.9 to find the output power.
[2] If you are given the output power, divide by 0.9 to find the input power.

EXAMPLE 3.5

A machine is 80% efficient. What input is needed for an output of 4000 W?

Solution
Using rule [2] above:

$$\text{input} = \frac{\text{output}}{\text{efficiency}}$$

The output is 80%, i.e. 0.8, of the input. To find the input, *divide* 4000 by 0.8.

$$\text{input} = 4000 \div 0.8 = 5000$$

An input of 5000 W is required

SELF TEST 3.5

a) A machine has an input power of 800 W, and an output power of 500 W. Find its percentage efficiency.

> 62.5%

b) A machine has an efficiency of 60%. Find the input power necessary for an output power of 900 W.

> 1500 W

c) A machine has an efficiency of 75%. What is the output power if the input power is 1500 W?

> 1125 W

Conversion

You can convert between fractions, decimals and percentages as follows.

Decimal → percentage
Move the decimal point two places to the right. $0.075 = 7.5\%$

Percentage → decimal
Move the decimal point two places to the left. $17\% = 0.17$

Percentage → fraction
The denominator of the fraction is 100. $8\% = \frac{8}{100} = \frac{2}{25}$

Fraction → percentage
Multiply the fraction by 100%. $\frac{5}{8} = \frac{5}{8} \times 100\% = 62.5\%$

EXAMPLE 3.6

The copper content of an alloy is 20%. Express this as a decimal and as a fraction.

Solution
Convert to a decimal by moving the decimal point two places to the left. We obtain 0.2.

The copper content is 0.2 of the alloy

Convert to a fraction by dividing by 100.

$$20\% = \frac{20}{100} = \frac{1}{5}$$

$\frac{1}{5}$ **of the alloy is copper**

SELF TEST 3.6

a) Convert $\frac{13}{32}$ to a percentage.

40.625%

b) Convert 18% to a fraction and to a decimal.

$\frac{9}{50}$, 0.18

3.2 Ratio

Ratios are used to compare two quantities. A sample of brass might contain copper and zinc in the ratio $9:2$. This means that for every 9 kg of copper there is 2 kg of zinc.

Ratios are similar to fractions. A ratio is unchanged if both terms are multiplied or divided by the same number. Use this fact to simplify a ratio. Divide both terms by their highest common factor.

The ratio $15:10$ is the same as the ratio $3:2$.

EXAMPLE 3.7

A sample of bronze contains 12 kg of copper and 3 kg of tin. Find the ratio of copper to tin, simplifying your answer.

Solution
The ratio of copper to tin is $12:3$. Both of these terms can be divided by 3.

The ratio of copper to tin is $4:1$

SELF TEST 3.7

A staircase rises 10 m for a horizontal distance of 12 m. Find the ratio of vertical to horizontal distance.

5:6

EXAMPLE 3.8

Simplify the ratio $\frac{1}{2}:\frac{1}{4}:\frac{3}{8}$.

Solution
The three denominators are 2, 4 and 8. These have LCM 8. Multiply each term by 8, obtaining 4, 2 and 3.

$$\frac{1}{2}:\frac{1}{4}:\frac{3}{8} = 4:2:3$$

SELF TEST 3.8

Simplify the ratio $2:\frac{1}{3}:\frac{2}{3}$.

6:1:2

EXAMPLE 3.9

Two workmen receive a bonus in the ratio $5:4$. If the first workman receives #120, find the amount received by the second workman.

Solution
The second workman receives $\frac{4}{5}$ as much as the first.
Multiply 120 by $\frac{4}{5}$, obtaining 96.

The second workman receives #96

SELF TEST 3.9

The ratio of men to women in a factory is $9:13$. If there are 270 men, find how many women there are.

390

Working with ratios

Suppose a substance contains two ingredients, in the ratio 5:7. Then there are 12 parts in total. The first ingredient makes up 5 parts, or $\frac{5}{12}$ of the total. The second ingredient makes up 7 parts, or $\frac{7}{12}$ of the total.

EXAMPLE 3.10

A cloth mixture contains cotton and polyester in the ratio 13:7. How much cotton is there in 300 kg of the cloth?

Solution
There are 13 + 7, i.e. 20, equal parts. Each part has a mass of 300 kg ÷ 20, i.e. 15 kg.
  Multiply this by 13 to find the mass of the cotton.

$$\text{mass of cotton} = \frac{300 \text{ kg}}{13 + 7} \times 13$$
$$= \frac{300}{20} \times 13 \text{ kg}$$
$$= 195 \text{ kg}$$

There is 195 kg of cotton

SELF TEST 3.10

The workforce of a factory is divided between men and women in the ratio 5:9. There are 700 workers in total. Find the number of women workers.

450

Three or more quantities

The method also works for ratios of three or more quantities.
  A type of concrete might contain sand, aggregate and cement in the ratio 2:5:1. There are 8 equal parts, hence the proportion of sand is $2 \times \frac{1}{8}$, i.e. $\frac{1}{4}$ of the total.

EXAMPLE 3.11

An alloy contains copper, zinc and tin in the ratio 10:2:3. Find the amount of zinc in 90 kg of the alloy.

Solution
There are 10 + 2 + 3, i.e. 15, parts. Each part has mass 90 kg ÷ 15, i.e. 6 kg.
  Multiply this by 2 to obtain the mass of zinc.

$$\text{mass of zinc} = \frac{90 \text{ kg}}{10 + 2 + 3} \times 2$$
$$= \frac{90}{15} \times 2 \text{ kg}$$
$$= 12 \text{ kg}$$

There is 12 kg of zinc

SELF TEST 3.11

A concrete contains sand, aggregate and cement in the ratio 5:3:1 by mass. Find the amount of aggregate in 330 kg of concrete.

110 kg

Comparing quantities

We can use ratios to compare different quantities. In this example the number of turns of wire on a transformer is compared with the voltages across the wires.

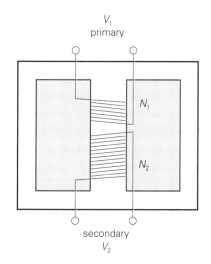

Figure 3.1 Transformer

Figure 3.1 shows a transformer. It contains two circuits, the primary circuit and the secondary circuit. The ratio between the voltages is equal to the ratio between the numbers of turns on the circuits.

primary voltage : secondary voltage =
number of turns on primary circuit :
                number of turns on secondary circuit
or
$$\frac{\text{primary voltage}}{\text{secondary voltage}} = \frac{\text{number of turns on primary circuit}}{\text{number of turns on secondary circuit}}$$
or
$$\frac{V_1}{V_2} = \frac{N_1}{N_2}$$

EXAMPLE 3.12

Refer to the formula above. If the primary and secondary number of turns are 100 and 25 respectively, what primary voltage will give a secondary voltage of 240 V?

Solution
The ratio $N_1 : N_2$ is 100 : 25, which is 4 : 1. If the primary voltage is V_1 volts, then we have that

$$V_1 : 240 = 4 : 1$$

or

$$\frac{V_1}{240} = \frac{4}{1}$$

Hence $V_1 = 240 \times 4 = 960$.

The primary voltage is 960 volts

SELF TEST 3.12

A transformer is designed to reduce 10 000 V to 250 V. If there are 400 turns on the primary circuit, find the number of turns on the secondary circuit.

10

Gear wheels

Gears are used in many machines. The ratio between their teeth gives the ratio of their speeds of rotation. In Figure 3.2, the gear wheels are meshed.

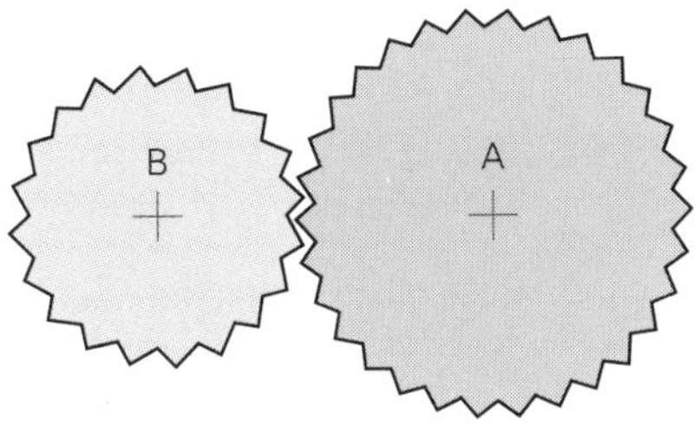

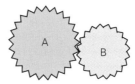

Figure 3.2

number of teeth of A : number of teeth of B
= speed of rotation of B : speed of rotation of A

or $\dfrac{\text{number of teeth of A}}{\text{number of teeth of B}} = \dfrac{\text{speed of rotation of B}}{\text{speed of rotation of A}}$

Note If A has more teeth than B, it rotates more *slowly*.

EXAMPLE 3.13

In Figure 3.3, the wheels A and B have 25 and 20 teeth respectively. If A rotates at 100 revolutions per second, find the speed of rotation of B.

Figure 3.3

Solution
The ratio of the teeth is 25 : 20, i.e. 5 : 4. A will rotate more slowly than B. So B will rotate more quickly than A. Using the formula above 5 : 4 = speed of rotation of B : 100.

$$\text{speed of rotation of B} = 100 \times \frac{5}{4} = 125$$

B rotates at 125 revolutions per second

SELF TEST 3.13

Gear wheels A and B are meshed. They have 60 and 50 teeth respectively.

a) If A rotates at 90 rpm (revolutions per minute), find the speed of B.

108 rpm

b) If B rotates at 300 rpm, find the speed of A.

250 rpm

■ **CHECK YOUR UNDERSTANDING**

● A percentage is a fraction in which the denominator is 100.
● If a quantity changes, its percentage change is the change expressed as a percentage of the original amount.
● Efficiency is the fraction of output over input. To find the output multiply the input by the efficiency. To find the input divide the output by the efficiency.
● To convert between decimals and percentages, move the decimal point by two places. To convert between fractions and percentages, multiply or divide by 100.
● A ratio compares the amounts of two or more quantities. The ratio is unchanged if all the amounts are multiplied or divided by the same number.
● A ratio can be used to give the amounts of ingredients in a material.

REVISION EXERCISES AND QUESTIONS

3.1 Percentages

1 Express 450 as a percentage of 1000.

2 Express 28 as a percentage of 50.

3 Find 15% of 800.

4 Find 23% of 25.

5 A cloth consists of 85% cotton, 15% polyester. Find the mass of cotton in 20 kg of the cloth.

6 An alloy contains 82% copper. Find the amount of copper in 50 kg of the alloy.

7 An amount of #1200 is increased by 12%. Find the new amount.

8 A worker has a monthly salary of #4800. Find his new salary after an 8% increase.

9 After drying, 300 kg of wool decreased in mass by 8%. Find the new mass.

10 When water is heated from 0°C to 40°C, the volume of dissolved oxygen decreases by 45%.

a) If 50 mm³ is dissolved at 0°C, how much is dissolved at 40°C?

b) If 22 mm³ is dissolved at 40°C, how much is dissolved at 0°C?

11 A spring of length 0.6 m is extended by 32%. Find the new length.

12 A bill is for #8500. A reduction of 8% is given for immediate payment. Find the reduced bill.

13 After washing, the length of a piece of cloth decreased by 8%. If it was 260 mm long before, find its length afterwards.

14 32 600 bricks are ordered for a building work. This includes 10% for wastage. How many bricks will be used?

15 A machine is 70% efficient. Find the output power if the input is 10 000 W. Find the input power needed for an output of 2100 W.

16 A firm makes #120 000 profit out of a turnover of #2 400 000. Find the profit as a percentage of turnover.

3.2 Ratios

17 A material contains 450 grams of cotton to 150 grams of polyester. Find the ratio of cotton to polyester.

18 A firm employs 250 men and 150 women. Find the ratio of men to women in the workforce.

19 A sheet of metal is 700 mm wide and 959 mm high. Find the ratio of width to height, in its simplest form.

20 An alloy contains mercury and silver in the ratio 2 : 7. How much silver would be mixed with 42 g of mercury?

21 Figure 3.4 shows a worm gear. Suppose you have a worm gear where the wheel turns once for every 10 turns of the shaft. Express this as a ratio between the numbers of turns. If the wheel turns 7 times, how many times does the shaft turn?

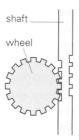

shaft
wheel

Figure 3.4

22 For a certain cotton fibre, the ratio of length to diameter is 2500 : 1. Find the diameter of a 35 mm long fibre.

23 Solder consists of tin and lead in the ratio 3 : 2. Find the mass of lead in 12 kg of solder.

24 A pastry recipe require butter and flour in the ratio 2 : 3. How much flour is needed for 400 g of pastry?

25 Concrete for a ramp consists of sand, gravel and cement in the ratio 2 : 5 : 1. How much of each is needed for 400 kg of concrete?

26 An area of land is divided between three brothers in the ratio 9 : 8 : 7. If the total area is 3600 m² find the shares.

27 A bonus of #5000 is to be shared between four workers in the ratio 4 : 5 : 5 : 6. What are the shares?

28 A car jack converts effort to load in the ratio 3 : 35. Find the effort needed to raise a car of mass 1050 kg.

29 Two gear wheels are meshed. Wheel A has 30 teeth and wheel B has 48 teeth.
a) Find the speed of B, if A rotates at 80 rpm.
b) Find the speed of A, if B rotates at 100 rpm.

30 Gear wheel A has 40 teeth. It rotates at 100 rpm. It is connected to wheel B. Find the number of teeth on B if
a) B rotates at 160 rpm.
b) B rotates at 80 rpm.

Indices

Introduction

The four basic operations are addition, subtraction, multiplication and division. In this chapter we discuss a fifth operation, taking powers. When a number is multiplied by itself many times, the result is a power.

Powers help us to represent very large and very small numbers. For example, electrical current consists of the flow of charged particles called electrons. We measure current in amperes. How many electrons per second make up one ampere? The answer is very large.

6 280 000 000 000 000 000 electrons per second = 1 ampere

We need a way to describe very large numbers, and very small numbers. We can use special units, or a notation known as **standard form** (see page 29).

4.1 Powers

Consider a square with side 7 m. Its area is 7×7 square metres. This can be written as 7^2 m^2. This is the **square** of 7, or 7 squared.

Similarly, we write $7 \times 7 \times 7$ as 7^3. This is the cube of 7, or 7 cubed.

In general, if n 7s are multiplied together, the result is written 7^n. It is the nth power of 7, or 7 to the n. The n is called the **index**.

If x is any number, the product of n xs is the nth power of x.

$$x^n = x \times x \times x \times \ldots \times x$$

If a fraction is raised to a power, both numerator and denominator are raised to the power. For example

$$\left(\frac{2}{5}\right)^3 = \frac{2^3}{5^3} = \frac{2 \times 2 \times 2}{5 \times 5 \times 5} = \frac{8}{125}$$

Order of operations

Remember from Chapter 1 that multiplication is done before addition. Similarly, taking powers is done before the other four operations.

2×3^2 means: 'square 3, then multiply by 2'.
The result is 18.

$$2 \times 3^2 = 2 \times 9 = 18$$

If you want to do the other operation first, then put it in brackets.

$(2 \times 3)^2$ means 'multiply 2 by 3, then square the result.'
The final result is 36.
$$(2 \times 3)^2 = (6)^2 = 36$$

EXAMPLE 4.1

Evaluate the following.
  a) $2 + 5^2$ b) $(2 + 5)^2$

Solution
  a) The square of 5 is 25. Add 2, obtaining 27.
  $$2 + 5^2 = 2 + 5 \times 5 = 2 + 25 = 27$$
  b) The sum of 2 and 5 is 7. Square this, obtaining 49.
  $$(2 + 5)^2 = 7^2 = 49$$
  a) $2 + 5^2 = 27$ b) $(2 + 5)^2 = 49$

SELF TEST 4.2

Evaluate the following.

    a) $8 \div 2^2$ b) $(8 \div 2)^2$

                                           a) 2   b) 16

Roots

Taking roots is the opposite to taking powers. The square of 12 is 144. The **square root** of 144 is 12. The symbol for a root is $\sqrt{}$.

$$12^2 = 12 \times 12 = 144. \text{ Hence } 12 = \sqrt{144}$$

So if a square has area 144 m^2, its side is 12 m.

Note   The square of -12 is also 144. $(-12)^2 = 144$.
    The square root is always the positive value. $\sqrt{144} = +12$.

    The **cube root** of 1000 is written $\sqrt[3]{1000}$.

$$10^3 = 10 \times 10 \times 10 = 1000$$
$$\text{Hence } 10 = \sqrt[3]{1000}$$

So if a cube has volume 1000 m^3, its side is 10 m.
    In general, the nth root of x is written $\sqrt[n]{x}$.

SELF TEST 4.3

Find

    a) $\sqrt{64}$ b) $\sqrt[3]{64}$ c) $\sqrt[3]{1\,000\,000}$.

                              a) 8   b) 4   c) 100

EXAMPLE 4.2

A cubical buiding has volume 512 m^3. Find its side.

Solution
Take the cube root of 512, obtaining 8. $(8 \times 8 \times 8 = 512)$

                        The side is 8 m

SELF TEST 4.4

A square field has area 625 m^2. Find its side.

                                      25 m

Arithmetic of powers

There are three laws for multiplying powers, dividing powers and taking powers of powers.

Multiplying

Consider $2^3 \times 2^4$. There are three 2s multiplied together and four 2s multiplied together. The result is seven 2s multiplied together.

$$2^3 \times 2^4 = (2 \times 2 \times 2) \times (2 \times 2 \times 2 \times 2) = 2^7 = 2^{3+4}$$

[1]

> When two powers are multiplied, the indices are added.

Dividing

Consider $3^7 \div 3^4$. Written as a fraction, there are seven 3s multiplied together in the numerator and four 3s multiplied together in the denominator. The four 3s in the denominator cancel, leaving three 3s multiplied together.

$$3^7 \div 3^4 = \frac{3 \times 3 \times 3 \times 3 \times 3 \times 3 \times 3}{3 \times 3 \times 3 \times 3} = 3 \times 3 \times 3 = 3^3$$
$$3^7 \div 3^4 = 3^{7-4} = 3^3$$

[2]

> When two powers are divided, the indices are subtracted.

Powers of powers

Consider $(4^2)^3$. This is (4×4) repeated three times. In total there are six 4s multiplied together

$$(4^2)^3 = (4 \times 4) \times (4 \times 4) \times (4 \times 4) = 4^6$$
$$(4^2)^3 = 4^{2 \times 3}$$

[3]

> When a power is raised to a power, the indices are multiplied.

EXAMPLE 4.3

Computer memory is measured in **bytes**. A **kilobyte** is 2^{10} bytes. A **gigabyte** is 2^{30} bytes. How many kilobytes are there in a gigabyte?

Solution
Divide 2^{30} by 2^{10}. Use rule [2] above, subtracting the indices.

$$2^{30} \div 2^{10} = 2^{30-10} = 2^{20}$$

There are 2^{20} kilobytes in a gigabyte

SELF TEST 4.5

The first BBC microcomputer had a memory of 16 kilobytes. How many bytes is this? Express your answer as a power of 2. [Hint: find 16 as a power of 2.]

2^{14} bytes

Zero, negative and fractional indices

We can extend powers to zero, negative and fractional indices. In all cases the three laws of powers still hold.

Power of zero

Consider $10^1 \div 10^1$, which is equal to 1. Use rule [2] above

$$1 = 10^1 \div 10^1 = 10^{1-1} = 10^0. \text{ Hence } 10^0 = 1.$$

[4]

> For any positive number a, $a^0 = 1$.

Negative powers

Consider $3^0 \div 3^2$. This is $1 \div 3^2$, i.e. $\frac{1}{9}$. Use rule [2] above

$$3^0 \div 3^2 = 3^{0-2} = 3^{-2}. \text{ Hence } 3^{-2} = \frac{1}{3^2}$$

[5]

> A negative power of a number is the reciprocal of the positive power.
> $$a^{-n} = \frac{1}{a^n}$$

Fractional powers

Consider $8^{\frac{1}{3}} \times 8^{\frac{1}{3}} \times 8^{\frac{1}{3}}$, i.e. $(8^{\frac{1}{3}})^3$. Use rule [1] above

$$8^{\frac{1}{3}} \times 8^{\frac{1}{3}} \times 8^{\frac{1}{3}} = 8^{\frac{1}{3}+\frac{1}{3}+\frac{1}{3}} = 8^1 = 8$$

Hence $8^{\frac{1}{3}}$ is the cube root of 8, $\sqrt[3]{8}$.

[6]

> The $\frac{1}{n}$th power of a number is its nth root.
> $$x^{\frac{1}{n}} = \sqrt[n]{x}$$

EXAMPLE 4.4

Evaluate the following.
  a) $49^{\frac{1}{2}}$ b) 6^{-2} c) 5^0

Solution
  a) $49^{\frac{1}{2}} = \sqrt{49}$. The square root of 49 is 7.
$$49^{\frac{1}{2}} = 7$$

  b) $6^{-2} = \frac{1}{6^2}$.
    Take the reciprocal of 6^2, i.e. the reciprocal of 36.
$$6^{-2} = \frac{1}{36}$$

  c) Any positive number to the power 0 is 1.
$$5^0 = 1$$

SELF TEST 4.6

Evaluate the following.
  a) $27^{\frac{1}{3}}$ b) 3^0 c) 2^{-4}

a) 3   b) 1   c) $\frac{1}{16}$

EXAMPLE 4.5

Evaluate the following.
  a) $5 + 4^{\frac{1}{2}}$ b) $(5 + 4)^{\frac{1}{2}}$
Solution
  a) Take the power first. The square root of 4 is 2. Add this to 5.
    $5 + 2 = 7$.
$$5 + 4^{\frac{1}{2}} = 7$$

  b) Add 5 and 4, obtaining 9. The square root of 9 is 3.
$$(5 + 4)^{\frac{1}{2}} = 3$$

SELF TEST 4.7

Evaluate
  a) $\frac{1}{2} + 2^{-1}$ b) $(\frac{1}{2} + 2)^{-1}$

a) 1 b) $\frac{2}{5}$

EXAMPLE 4.6

Simplify $2^5 \times 4^3$ by writing as a single power.
Solution
Note that 4 is 2^2. Hence
$$2^5 \times 4^3 = 2^5 \times (2^2)^3$$
Use rule [3] $= 2^5 \times 2^6$
Use rule [1] $= 2^{11}$

$$2^5 \times 4^3 = 2^{11}$$

SELF TEST 4.8

Simplify $3^4 \times 9^2 \div 27^2$ by writing as a power of 3.

3^2

EXAMPLE 4.7

Evaluate the following.

a) $8^{\frac{2}{3}}$ b) $\left(\frac{1}{4}\right)^{-\frac{1}{2}}$

Solution

a) Write $8^{\frac{2}{3}}$ as $(8^{\frac{1}{3}})^2$. The cube root of 8 is 2. Square 2, to obtain 4.

$$8^{\frac{2}{3}} = 4$$

b) Write $\frac{1}{4}$ as 4^{-1}.

$$\left(\frac{1}{4}\right)^{-\frac{1}{2}} = (4^{-1})^{-\frac{1}{2}}$$

Use rule [3] $= 4^{\frac{1}{2}}$

$= 2$

$$\left(\frac{1}{4}\right)^{-\frac{1}{2}} = 2$$

SELF TEST 4.9

Evaluate the following.
a) $16^{\frac{3}{4}}$ b) $\left(\frac{1}{2}\right)^{-3}$

a) 8   b) 8

4.2 Units

The most important system of units is the SI (Système Internationale). This is based on the metre, kilogram and second, and is sometimes known as the MKS system. Sometimes we use the Imperial system, which involves feet, pounds and seconds. There is a conversion table on page 240.

Table 4.1 SI Units

	Unit	Symbol of unit
Length	metre	(m)
Mass	kilogram	(kg)
Time	second	(s)

Larger or smaller units are obtained by adding prefixes to the basic units. A millimetre, for example, is a thousandth of a metre. A millisecond is a thousandth of a second. Notice that *milli* always means a thousandth. The prefixes are given in Table 4.2.

Table 4.2 Prefixes used in metric units

Name and symbol		Multiplying factor	
tera	T	1 000 000 000 000	
giga	G	1 000 000 000	billion
mega	M	1 000 000	million
kilo	k	1 000	thousand
milli	m	0.001	thousandth
micro	μ	0.000 001	millionth
nano	n	0.000 000 001	billionth
pico	p	0.000 000 000 001	
femto	f	0.000 000 000 000 001	

Note that the powers of 10 change in steps of 3. There is no single word in the SI system to describe a multiplying factor of 10 000 000 for example. We write 40 000 000 N as 40 MN.

There are other prefixes in use.

Table 4.3 Some more metric prefixes

hecti	h	100	hundred
deci	d	0.1	tenth
centi	c	0.01	hundredth

Note For most units, *kilo* means 1000. In Example 4.3 on page 26, we defined a kilobyte as 2^{10} bytes. (We would expect a kilobyte to be 1000 bytes). 2^{10} is actually 1024, which is little more than 1000. A kilobyte is a name used to mean about 1000 bytes (it is actually 1024 bytes).

EXAMPLE 4.8

Convert 70 kilowatts (kW) to watts (W).

Solution

Each kilowatt is 1000 watts. $70 \times 1000 = 70\,000$.

70 kW is 70 000 W

EXAMPLE 4.9

Convert 0.000 006 farads (F) to micro farads (μF).

Solution

Each μF is a millionth of a farad. Multiply by 1 000 000, i.e. move the decimal point six places to the right.

0.000 006 F is 6 μF

SELF TEST 4.10

Convert
a) 0.002 kilonewtons (kN) to newtons (N)
b) 52 000 000 joules (J) to megajoules (MJ).

a) 2 N   b) 52 MJ

EXAMPLE 4.10

The power of a machine has a maximum of 1.4 MW. How many kilowatts of power does it use when working at half its maximum?

Solution

Divide 1.4 by 2, obtaining 0.7 MW. Write this in terms of kW. 1 MW is equal to 1000 kW. Hence 0.7 MW is equal to 700 kW.

The machine uses 700 kW of power.

SELF TEST 4.11

A load of 1.8 MN is carried equally by three piers. How much does each pier carry? Give your answer in kilonewtons.

600 kN

EXAMPLE 4.11

A pill contains 450 μg of a medicine. How much is contained in four pills?

Solution

Multiply 450 by 4, obtaining 1800. 1000 μg is equal to 1 mg, hence 1800 μg is equal to 1.8 mg.

The pills contain 1.8 mg of the medicine

SELF TEST 4.12

Fifty electrical wires carry a total of 30 μA. If the current is shared equally, find how much each wire carries.

600 nA

EXAMPLE 4.12

Find the total of 1.3 km and 750 m.

Solution

Convert the m to km. 750 m is equal to 0.75 km. Add 0.75 to 1.3, obtaining 2.05.

The total is 2.05 km

SELF TEST 4.13

Find the total of 7.1 MN and 820 kN.

7.92 MN

EXAMPLE 4.13

A current of 1.4 mA is reduced by 600 μA. Find the new value of the current.

Solution

1.4 mA is equal to 1400 μA. Subtract 600 from 1400, obtaining 800.

The new value of the current is 800 μA

SELF TEST 4.14

Find the total of 400 μg, 350 μg and 520 μg.

1.27 mg

4.3 Standard form

At the beginning of the chapter we wrote down the number of electrons in a coulomb. It was

6 280 000 000 000 000 000

It is difficult to handle a number written like this. Instead we write it as 6.28, multiplied by 10 eighteen times, i.e. as 6.28×10^{18}. We say the number is written in standard form.

A number in standard form has only one digit before the decimal point. The size of the number is shown by powers of 10. For example

$$12\,000\,000 = 1.2 \times 10^7.$$

The number part, i.e. 1.2, is the **mantissa**, and the power of 10, i.e. 7, is the **exponent**.

Large numbers

To convert a large number to standard form, move the decimal point to the left. The number of times it is moved gives the power of 10.

$$1\,2\,0\,0\,0\,0\,0\,0$$

Here the decimal point moves 7 times, giving the result above, 1.2×10^7.

Small numbers

Standard form is also used for very small numbers. In this case the power of 10 is negative.

$$0.000\,000\,001\,2 = 1.2 \times 10^{-9}$$

To convert a small number to standard form, move the decimal point to the right. The number of times it moves gives the (negative) power of 10.

$$0.0\,0\,0\,0\,0\,0\,0\,1\,2$$

Here the decimal point moves 9 times, giving the result above, 1.2×10^{-9}.

Conversion

To convert a number in standard form back to ordinary notation, move the decimal point back as many times as the power of 10, inserting 0s where necessary.

$$3.72 \times 10^6 = 3\,720\,000$$
Hence $3.72 \times 10^6 = 3\,720\,000$

EXAMPLE 4.14

Convert to standard form.
   a) 25 000   b) 0.000 000 023
Solution
   a) Move the decimal point 4 places to the left.
   $$25\,000 = 2.5 \times 10^4$$
   b) Move the decimal point 8 places to the right.
   $$0.000\,000\,023 = 2.3 \times 10^{-8}$$

SELF TEST 4.15

Convert to standard form.
   a) 538 000   b) 0.000 000 24
   a) 5.38×10^5 b) 2.4×10^{-7}

EXAMPLE 4.15

Write out in full.
   a) 6.3×10^5 b) 2.7×10^{-4}
Solution
   a) Move the decimal point five places to the right, putting in 0s.
   $$6\,3\,0\,0\,0\,0.$$
   $$6.3 \times 10^5 = 630\,000$$
   b) Move the decimal point four places to the left, putting in 0s.
   $$.0\,0\,0\,2\,7$$
   $$2.7 \times 10^{-4} = 0.000\,27$$

SELF TEST 4.16

Write out in full.
   a) 3.9×10^4 b) 6.1×10^{-6}
   a) 39 000   b) 0.000 006 1

Adjusting to standard form

In standard form, there should be only one digit before the decimal point. After a calculation, you may need to adjust a number to put it in standard form.

EXAMPLE 4.16

Convert to standard form.
   a) 52.3×10^{12} b) 0.034×10^9
Solution
   a) There should be only one digit before the decimal point. Move the decimal point 1 place to the left, and increase the power of 10 by 1.
   $$52.3 \times 10^{12} = 5.23 \times 10^{13}$$
   b) Move the decimal point two places to the right, and decrease the power of 10 by 2.
   $$0.034 \times 10^9 = 3.4 \times 10^7$$

SELF TEST 4.17

Convert to standard form.
   a) 984×10^{12} b) 0.43×10^{23}
   a) 9.84×10^{14} b) 4.3×10^{22}

EXAMPLE 4.17

Convert to standard form.
   a) 27×10^{-5} b) 0.52×10^{-11}
Solution
   a) Be careful when the exponent is negative. Change 27 to 2.7. Add 1 to -5. The result is -4.
   $$27 \times 10^{-5} = 2.7 \times 10^{-4}$$
   b) Change 0.52 to 5.2. Then subtract 1 from -11, obtaining -12.
   $$0.52 \times 10^{-11} = 5.2 \times 10^{-12}$$

SELF TEST 4.18

Convert to standard form.
   a) 103×10^{-8} b) 0.17×10^{-6}
   a) 1.03×10^{-6} b) 1.7×10^{-7}

Standard form and units

Sometimes we need to convert units (as studied in section 4.2) using our knowledge of standard form. Multiplying or dividing by powers of 1000 is usually the solution. A *kilo* unit is 1000 units, i.e. 10^3 units. A *milli* unit is $\frac{1}{1000}$ units, i.e. 10^{-3} units.

EXAMPLE 4.18

   a) Write 3.2×10^5 N in terms of kN.
   b) Write 83.4 MN in terms of N, using standard form.
   c) Write 5.3 μs in terms of seconds, using standard form.

Solution

a) Each kN is 1000 N. Hence divide by 1000, i.e. by 10^3.

$$3.2 \times 10^5 \text{ N} = \frac{3.2 \times 10^5}{10^3} \text{ kN}$$
$$= 3.2 \times 10^2 \text{ kN}$$

3.2×10^5 N $= 3.2 \times 10^2$ kN $= 320$ kN

b) Each MN is 10^6 N. Hence multiply by 10^6.

$$83.4 \text{ MN} = 83.4 \times 10^6 \text{ N}$$

Now convert to standard form.

83.4 MN $= 8.34 \times 10^7$ N

c) A μs is 10^{-6} s. Hence

$5.3 \, \mu$s $= 5.3 \times 10^{-6}$ s

SELF TEST 4.19

Convert
a) 23.1 megawatts (MW) to watts, using standard form,
b) 2.31×10^{-8} watts to microwatts (μW).

a) 2.31×10^7 W   b) 2.31×10^{-2} μW

Arithmetic of numbers in standard form

Multiplication

To multiply numbers in standard form, multiply the mantissas (the number parts) and add the exponents (the powers of 10).

$$(2 \times 10^6) \times (3 \times 10^7) = 6 \times 10^{13}$$

Division

To divide numbers in standard form, divide the mantissas and subtract the exponents.

$$(8 \times 10^{16}) \div (4 \times 10^5) = 2 \times 10^{11}$$

EXAMPLE 4.19

Evaluate the following, leaving the answers in standard form.
a) $3.2 \times 10^7 \times 2 \times 10^5$ b) $(6.3 \times 10^8) \div (3 \times 10^5)$

Solution

a) Multiply 3.2 by 2, obtaining 6.4. Add 7 and 5, obtaining 12.

$$\mathbf{3.2 \times 10^7 \times 2 \times 10^5 = 6.4 \times 10^{12}}$$

b) Divide 6.3 by 3, obtaining 2.1. Subtract 5 from 8, obtaining 3.

$$\mathbf{(6.3 \times 10^8) \div (3 \times 10^5) = 2.1 \times 10^3}$$

SELF TEST 4.20

Evaluate the following, leaving your answers in standard form.
a) $2 \times 10^{19} \times 4.8 \times 10^8$ b) $(5.5 \times 10^8) \div (5 \times 10^3)$

a) 9.6×10^{27} b) 1.1×10^5

Adjustment to standard form

Suppose you have multiplied two numbers in standard form, and the mantissa is greater than 10. Reconvert to standard form, by moving the decimal point and adjusting (increasing) the exponent.

$$(4 \times 10^8) \times (3 \times 10^5) = 12 \times 10^{13} = 1.2 \times 10^{14}$$

Suppose you have divided two numbers in standard form, and the mantissa is less than 1. Reconvert to standard form, in the same way, but this time you will decrease the exponent.

$$(3 \times 10^8) \div (4 \times 10^{14}) = 0.75 \times 10^{-6} = 7.5 \times 10^{-7}$$

EXAMPLE 4.20

Evaluate the following, leaving the answers in standard form.
a) $5.7 \times 10^7 \times 2 \times 10^3$ b) $(1.2 \times 10^{15}) \div (2 \times 10^6)$

Solution

a) Multiply 5.7 by 2, obtaining 11.4. add 7 and 3, obtaining 10. 11.4 is greater than 10 so move the decimal point and increase the power of 10.

$$5.7 \times 10^7 \times 2 \times 10^3 = 11.4 \times 10^{10} = 1.14 \times 10^{11}$$
$$\mathbf{5.7 \times 10^7 \times 2 \times 10^3 = 1.14 \times 10^{11}}$$

b) Divide 1.2 by 2, obtaining 0.6. Subtract 6 from 15, obtaining 9. 0.6 is less than 1, so move the decimal point and decrease the power of 10.

$$(1.2 \times 10^{15}) \div (2 \times 10^6) = 0.6 \times 10^9 = 6.0 \times 10^8$$
$$\mathbf{(1.2 \times 10^{15}) \div (2 \times 10^6) = 6 \times 10^8}$$

SELF TEST 4.21

Evaluate the following, leaving your answers in standard form.
a) $7 \times 10^{12} \times 2 \times 10^6$ b) $(1.2 \times 10^{15}) \div (6 \times 10^5)$

a) 1.4×10^{19} b) 2×10^9

EXAMPLE 4.21

A power station has a capacity of 1.8×10^8 W. During an off-peak period it works at half capacity. Find its power during this period.

Solution

Divide 1.8×10^8 by 2, obtaining 0.9×10^8.

Put into standard form by moving the decimal point and decreasing the power of 10.

$$\text{The power is } 9 \times 10^7 \text{ W}$$

Note   This answer can also be written as 90 MW

SELF TEST 4.22

A machine uses 4.8×10^5 W of power. Find how much energy it uses in 400 seconds. (1 watt = 1 joule per second.)

$$\boxed{1.92 \times 10^8 \text{ J (192 MJ)}}$$

Negative exponents

Be careful when the exponents are negative.

EXAMPLE 4.22

Evaluate the following, leaving your answers in standard form.

a) $3.1 \times 10^{-8} \times 4 \times 10^{-7}$ b) $(5.5 \times 10^{-5}) \div (5 \times 10^{-11})$

Solution

a) Multiply the mantissas, obtaining 12.4. The sum of -8 and -7 is -15.

$$3.1 \times 10^{-8} \times 4 \times 10^{-7} = 12.4 \times 10^{-15}$$

Reduce to standard form, by changing 12.4 to 1.24. Add 1 to -15, obtaining -14.

$$\mathbf{3.1 \times 10^{-8} \times 4 \times 10^{-7} = 1.24 \times 10^{-14}}$$

b) Divide 5.5 by 5, obtaining 1.1. Subtract -11 from -5, $(-5-(-11))$, obtaining $+6$.

$$\mathbf{(5.5 \times 10^{-5}) \div (5 \times 10^{-11}) = 1.1 \times 10^6}$$

SELF TEST 4.23

Evaluate the following, leaving your answers in standard form.

a) $6.1 \times 10^8 \times 2 \times 10^{-16}$ b) $(4.2 \times 10^6) \div (2 \times 10^{-8})$

$$\boxed{\text{a) } 1.22 \times 10^{-7} \quad \text{b) } 2.1 \times 10^{14}}$$

Addition and subtraction

If two numbers in standard form have the same exponents, they can be added or subtracted by adding or subtracting the mantissas.

$$(3 \times 10^5) + (4 \times 10^5) = 7 \times 10^5$$

If the numbers have different exponents, then they cannot be added immediately. (We cannot immediately add metres and kilometres). Adjust the number with the lower exponent.

$$(3 \times 10^8) + (4 \times 10^7)$$
$$= (3 \times 10^8) + (0.4 \times 10^8) = 3.4 \times 10^8$$

EXAMPLE 4.23

A fully laden ship has a mass of 5.3×10^7 kg. Its cargo has a mass of 1.7×10^6 kg. Find the mass of the ship when the cargo has been unloaded.

Solution

Convert the second figure so that its power of 10 is 7. Then subtract the mass of the cargo from the laden mass of the ship.

$$5.3 \times 10^7 - 1.7 \times 10^6 = 5.3 \times 10^7 - 0.17 \times 10^7$$
$$= 5.13 \times 10^7$$

The unladen mass is 5.13×10^7 kg

SELF TEST 4.24

Evaluate the following.

a) $6.1 \times 10^5 + 3.2 \times 10^5$ b) $8.3 \times 10^8 + 5.2 \times 10^8$
c) $1.4 \times 10^7 - 1.3 \times 10^7$ d) $6.26 \times 10^8 + 4.1 \times 10^7$

$$\boxed{\text{a) } 9.3 \times 10^5 \quad \text{b) } 1.35 \times 10^9}$$
$$\boxed{\text{c) } 1 \times 10^6 \quad \text{d) } 6.67 \times 10^8}$$

SELF TEST 4.25

Two resistors are in series. Their resistances are $3.5 \times 10^3 \, \Omega$ and $4.2 \times 10^4 \, \Omega$. Find the total resistance.

$$\boxed{4.55 \times 10^4 \, \Omega \text{ (45.5 k}\Omega)}$$

Negative exponents

Be careful when the exponents are negative.

EXAMPLE 4.24

Evaluate $5.23 \times 10^{-8} + 7.1 \times 10^{-9}$.

Solution

Increase the exponent of the second number to -8.

$$5.23 \times 10^{-8} + 7.1 \times 10^{-9} = 5.23 \times 10^{-8} + 0.71 \times 10^{-8}$$
$$= 5.94 \times 10^{-8}$$

$$\mathbf{5.23 \times 10^{-8} + 7.1 \times 10^{-9} = 5.94 \times 10^{-8}}$$

SELF TEST 4.26

Evaluate $2.98 \times 10^{-6} + 8.3 \times 10^{-7}$.

$$\boxed{3.81 \times 10^{-6}}$$

Engineering notation

A number in **engineering notation** has the mantissa from 1 up to 1000, and the exponent a multiple of 3. The following are in engineering notation.

3.7×10^6 47.2×10^{15} 754×10^{18} 367.3×10^{-21}

Note that the SI units follow engineering notation. For example

$1\,\text{MN} = 10^6\,\text{N}$ $1\,\text{kN} = 10^3\,\text{N}$
$1\,\text{mN} = 10^{-3}\,\text{N}$ $1\,\mu\text{N} = 10^{-6}\,\text{N}$

To convert from standard form to engineering notation, lower the exponent until it is a multiple of 3, and adjust the mantissa accordingly.

$4.1 \times 10^{13} = 41 \times 10^{12}$ $8.23 \times 10^{23} = 823 \times 10^{21}$
$5.12 \times 10^{-14} = 51.2 \times 10^{-15}$ $6.201 \times 10^{-25} = 620.1 \times 10^{-27}$

EXAMPLE 4.25

An electrical component has a capacitance of 7×10^{-5} F. Express this in engineering notation.

Solution
Subtract 1 from -5, obtaining -6 (i.e. divide by 10). -6 is divisible by 3. Multiply 7 by 10.

The capacitance is 70×10^{-6} F (or 70 μF)

SELF TEST 4.27

Convert the following to engineering notation.
   a) 8.3×10^{17} b) 9.2×10^{16}
   c) 2.5×10^{-7} d) 5.21×10^{-14}

a) 830×10^{15} b) 92×10^{15}
c) 250×10^{-9} d) 52.1×10^{-15}

4.4 Logarithms

The fourth power of 10 is 10 000.

$$10^4 = 10\,000$$
10 to the power of 4 = 10 000

The **logarithm** function is the reverse of the power function.

$$\log 10\,000 = 4$$
Similarly $10^2 = 100$ so $\log 100 = 2$

If $10^x = a$, then $x = \log a$.
In words, the logarithm of a number is the power to which 10 must be raised in order to get that number.

The rules of logarithms are similar to the laws for powers.

[1] $\log ab = \log a + \log b$

[2] $\log \dfrac{a}{b} = \log a - \log b$

[3] $\log a^n = n \log a$

Note   Rule 1 reduces multiplication to addition.
         Rule 2 reduces division to subtraction.
         Rule 3 reduces powers to multiplication.

In Chapter 5 we explain the use of logarithms for calculation. Many people have calculators which perform all the calculations formerly done by using logarithms. But logarithms are also used for many other purposes.

EXAMPLE 4.26

Find log 1000 and log 0.000 000 1.
Solution
1000 is 10^3. Hence
$$\log 1000 = 3$$
0.000 000 1 is 10^{-7}. Hence
$$\log 0.000\,000\,1 = -7$$

SELF TEST 4.28

Find log 1 000 000 and log 0.001.

6, -3

EXAMPLE 4.27

Simplify log 50 + log 2.
Solution
Use rule [1] for logs.
$$\log 50 + \log 2 = \log(50 \times 2) = \log 100$$
$$100 = 10^2 \text{ so } \log 100 = 2$$
$$\log 50 + \log 2 = 2$$

SELF TEST 4.29

Simplify log 30 − log 300.

-1

Logarithms to other bases

Logarithms can be found to any positive base. Consider base 2 logarithms:

if $2^n = x$, then $\log_2 x = n$.

So for example, $2^3 = 8$. Hence $\log_2 8 = 3$.

EXAMPLE 4.28

Find

   a) $\log_3 81$ b) $\log_9 3$.

Solution

   a) We want n, such that $3^n = 81$. We know that $81 = 3^4$, hence $n = 4$.

$$\log_3 81 = 4$$

   b) We want n, such that $9^n = 3$. We know that 3 is $\sqrt{9}$, i.e. $9^{\frac{1}{2}}$. Hence $n = \frac{1}{2}$.

$$\log_9 3 = \frac{1}{2}$$

SELF TEST 4.30

Find

   a) $\log_2 16$ b) $\log_{49} 7$.

                             a) 4   b) $\frac{1}{2}$

■ **CHECK YOUR UNDERSTANDING**

● The number a to the nth power is written a^n. These powers obey the rules

$$a^n \times a^m = a^{n+m} \qquad a^n \div a^m = a^{n-m} \qquad (a^n)^m = a^{nm}.$$

● Zero, negative and fractional powers are given by

$$a^0 = 1 \qquad a^{-n} = \frac{1}{a^n} \qquad a^{\frac{1}{n}} = \sqrt[n]{a}$$

● The basic units are the metre for length, the kilogram for mass, and the second for time. Larger and smaller units are obtained by adding prefixes. For example,

   1 *kilo*metre = 1000 metres
   1 *micro*second = 0.000 001 seconds

● A number in standard form has one digit before the decimal point, and is multiplied by a power of 10.
● To multiply standard form numbers, multiply the number parts and add the powers of 10.
● To divide standard form numbers, divide the number parts and subtract the powers of 10.
● To add or subtract standard form numbers, first adjust so that they have the same power of 10.
● In engineering notation, the power of 10 is a multiple of 3 and the number part is between 1 and 1000.
● The logarithmic function is the inverse of taking powers.

   If $10^n = x$, then $\log x = n$

● Logs obey the following rules.

   $\log (n \times m) = \log n + \log m$
   $\log (n \div m) = \log n - \log m$
   $\log n^m = m \log n$

● Logs can be found to other bases. If $a^n = x$, then $\log_a x = n$.

REVISION EXERCISES AND QUESTIONS

4.1 Powers

1 Evaluate the following.

   a) 8^2 b) 2^6 c) $(7-2)^3$ d) $7 - 2^3$

2 Evaluate the following.

   a) $\sqrt{121}$ b) $\sqrt{\frac{1}{4}}$ c) $\sqrt[3]{27}$ d) $\sqrt[3]{\frac{1}{8}}$

3 Evaluate the following.

   a) $100^{\frac{1}{2}}$ b) 6^0 c) $16^{\frac{1}{4}}$ d) 6^{-2}

4 Simplify the following by writing as single powers of one number.

   a) $3^5 \times 3^8$ b) $7^{12} \div 7^4$ c) $(2^7)^5$

   d) $3^8 \times 9^4$ e) $8^5 \div 2^9$ f) $27^5 \div 9^4 \times 3^6$

4.2 Units

5 Convert the following.

   a) 0.02 MN to N   b) 30 000 F to kF
   c) 0.000 000 23 g to mg   d) 120 000 μm to mm

6 A power of 1 watt (W) is equal to 1 joule (J) per second, i.e. $1\,W = 1\,J/s$. Find the number of joules in 1 kW hour. Give your answer a) in standard form, b) in megajoules.

7 In the following, give the answer in the appropriate unit.

   a) Multiply 40 MN by 50
   b) Add 640 mg to 750 mg
   c) Divide 75 mm by 250
   d) Subtract 1.2 mA from 1.9 mA
   e) Add 2.2 mV to 900 μV
   f) Add 440 kP to 1.7 MP

4.3 Standard form

8 Convert the following to standard form.

   a) 63 000 000 000   b) 0.000 000 12
   c) 91×10^9 d) 0.42×10^{12}

9 Write in full

   a) 4.54×10^6 b) 1.02×10^{-4}.

10 Convert the following, writing your answers in full.

   a) 6×10^8 N to MN   b) 5.4×10^{-8} kg to mg
   c) 4.1×10^{-9} MΩ to mΩ d) 1.03×10^{13} μF to MF

11 Evaluate the following, leaving your answers in standard form.

   a) $2.3 \times 10^8 \times 3 \times 10^{12}$ b) $3.7 \times 10^5 \times 3 \times 10^6$
   c) $(4.8 \times 10^{12}) \div (4 \times 10^6)$ d) $(1.6 \times 10^3) \div (8 \times 10^9)$
   e) $3.4 \times 10^8 + 2.7 \times 10^8$ f) $1.9 \times 10^9 - 1.7 \times 10^9$
   g) $2.3 \times 10^{12} + 4.2 \times 10^{11}$ h) $8.3 \times 10^{21} - 1.4 \times 10^{20}$

12 Evaluate the following, leaving your answers in standard form.

a) $2.5 \times 10^{-4} \times 2 \times 10^{8}$ b) $3.3 \times 10^{-10} \times 3 \times 10^{-7}$

c) $(4.8 \times 10^{-6}) \div (4 \times 10^{9})$ d) $(6.6 \times 10^{-13}) \div (3 \times 10^{-5})$

e) $9.1 \times 10^{-6} + 1.2 \times 10^{-6}$ f) $3.4 \times 10^{-7} + 2.3 \times 10^{-6}$

13 Convert to engineering notation.

a) 5×10^{8} b) 5.8×10^{19} c) 2.3×10^{-13}

14 The modulus of elasticity of iron is approximately $200\,000\,000\,000\ \mathrm{N\,m}^{-2}$.

a) Write this modulus in standard form.

b) Express the modulus in mega newtons per m².

4.4 Logarithms

15 Find the following.

a) $\log \frac{1}{1000}$ b) $\log_2 32$ c) $\log_3 \frac{1}{9}$ d) $\log_{16} 2$

16 Simplify the following.

a) $\log 20 + \log 50$ b) $\log 25 + \log 40$

c) $2 \log 2 + \log 2.5$ d) $\log 8 - 3 \log 2$

17 Log 5 is approximately 0.7. Without using a calculator or tables, find the approximate values of the following.

a) $\log 25$ b) $\log 2$ c) $\log 500$

d) $\log \frac{1}{2}$ e) $\log \frac{1}{8}$

Techniques of calculation

Introduction

As a technician, you have to make many calculations. You should do them quickly and accurately. Some simple calculations are done in the head, or on paper. But this can be very slow for complicated calculations.

In this chapter we look at two aids for calculation. A calculator, and tables.

5.1 Use of calculators

Recently calculators have become cheaper and more powerful. With a calculator, your arithmetic can be much quicker, more accurate and more reliable. Learn how to use your calculator, and find out all the operations it can do. Practise using your calculator, so that you are confident that its results are correct. Use the questions throughout this book to practise on.

Figure 5.1 shows two sorts of calculator.

Figure 5.1(A) A basic calculator

Figure 5.1(B) A scientific calculator

An ordinary calculator (A) can perform the basic operations of +, −, × and ÷.

A scientific calculator (B) can evaluate more complicated expressions. It can evaluate functions like log, which we studied in Chapter 4, and sin, cos and tan, which we shall study later in this book.

There are many different calculators available. The instructions for your calculator may be slightly different from the instructions in this section. If the instructions here do not work for your calculator, then read the manual of your calculator to find how to use it.

Single operations

To work out $43 + 4$, press the buttons in the following order.

The answer 47 should appear. Don't forget to press = at the end.

Note AC sets the calculator back to zero. C cancels (or clears) the last numbers you entered.

SELF TEST 5.1

Use a calculator to evaluate the following.
 a) $56 + 23$ b) $71 - 18$ c) 4×24 d) $81 \div 27$

 a) 79 b) 53 c) 96 d) 3

Combined operations

Suppose an expression involves more than one operation, for example $3 \times 5 + 4 \times 7$. A scientific calculator can work it out in one go.

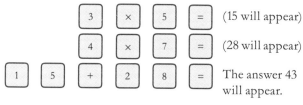

The answer 43 will appear.
An ordinary calculator may not be able to do this.
Work out the multiplications separately and then add.

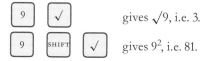

SELF TEST 5.2

Use a calculator to evaluate the following.
 a) $3.1 \times 1.7 + 2.6 \times 4.2$
 b) $0.42 \times 63 - 0.31 \times 49$
 c) $25 \div 0.25 + 39 \div 0.3$

 a) 16.19 b) 11.27 c) 230

Shift

On a scientific calculator, a single key may perform two operations. To apply the second operation press the key labelled 'shift', or 'second function'.

For example, there may be a key with $\sqrt{}$ on it, and x^2 above it, as shown in Figure 5.2. This key performs both square and square root.

gives $\sqrt{9}$, i.e. 3.

gives 9^2, i.e. 81.

Note Your calculator may have INV instead of SHIFT or 2ND FUNCTION

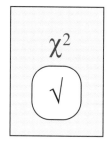

Figure 5.2 Calculator key with two functions

SELF TEST 5.3

Use a calculator to evaluate the following. (Round to four significant figures, if necessary.)
 a) $\sqrt{49}$ and 49^2 b) $\sqrt{0.25}$ and 0.25^2 c) $\log 3.12$ and $10^{3.12}$

 a) 7, 2401 b) 0.5, 0.0625 c) 0.494, 1318

Brackets

A scientific calculator can work out expressions using brackets. To work out $4 \times (3 + 7)$ press the following

The answer 40 will appear.

With an ordinary calculator, first work out the terms inside the brackets. Then multiply by 4.

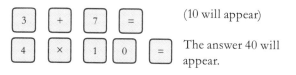

(10 will appear)

The answer 40 will appear.

SELF TEST 5.4

Use a calculator to evaluate the following. (Round to four significant figures, if necessary.)
 a) $(3.2 + 7.4) \times (6.2 - 1.5)$ b) $1.2374 \div (3.105 - 1.945)$

 a) 49.82 b) 1.067

Powers

A scientific calculator has a button to work out powers. It is labelled x^y or y^x or a^n
 To find 5^3, press the following

 The answer 125 will appear.

The button labelled $x^{\frac{1}{y}}$ will work out roots. To find $\sqrt[5]{32}$, press the following

 The answer 2 will appear.

Note You may have to use the shift button before you use the x^y or $x^{\frac{1}{y}}$ button.

SELF TEST 5.5

Use a calculator to evaluate 7.23^3 and $\sqrt[6]{12.7}$, correct to four significant figures.

377.9, 1.527

Fractions

On a scientific calculator, there may be a button labelled $a\frac{b}{c}$. Use this for fractions.

To enter $\frac{6}{7}$, for example, press

 6⌐7 appears.

Note Your calculator may show fractions in a different way.

You can also enter mixed numbers. To enter $3\frac{6}{7}$, for example

 3⌐6⌐7⌐ appears.

To convert a fraction to a decimal, press the $a\frac{b}{c}$ button after pressing the = button. For example, for $\frac{3}{4}$

 0.75 appears.

To convert back to a fraction, press $a\frac{b}{c}$ again.

The calculator can convert mixed numbers to improper fractions. On many calculators this is done by the shift and the fraction buttons. For example, for $2\frac{4}{5}$

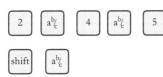 (enters the mixed number $2\frac{4}{5}$)

 The improper fraction $\frac{14}{5}$ (14⌐15) appears.

To convert an improper fraction to a mixed number, press =.

| 22 | $a\frac{b}{c}$ | 7 | (enters the improper fraction $\frac{22}{7}$) |

| = | The mixed number $3\frac{1}{7}$ appears. |

SELF TEST 5.6

a) Enter $3\frac{7}{8}$ and convert to an improper fraction.

b) Enter $\frac{45}{11}$ and convert to a mixed number.

a) $\frac{31}{8}$ b) $4\frac{1}{11}$

Arithmetic on fractions

The calculator can perform arithmetic on fractions. Use the same buttons as for arithmetic on ordinary numbers. To evaluate $\frac{4}{7} \times \frac{2}{3}$:

$\frac{8}{21}$ appears.

SELF TEST 5.7

Use a calculator to evaluate the following.

a) $\dfrac{8}{15} + \dfrac{4}{5} + \dfrac{5}{9}$ b) $\dfrac{5}{11} \times \dfrac{3}{10} + \dfrac{6}{11} \times \dfrac{7}{10}$

a) $1\frac{8}{9}$ b) $\frac{57}{110}$

Negative numbers

A scientific calculator has a button labelled $\pm$. This makes a positive number negative, (and also makes a negative number positive). To enter -8, for example, press

Use this button to enter negative powers. To find 5^{-3}, for example

The answer 0.008 appears.

Note The calculator may show $8.^{-03}$. This means 8×10^{-3} or 0.008.

SELF TEST 5.8

Use a calculator to evaluate

a) -7.87×-4.12 b) 2^{-4}.

a) 32.4244   b) 0.0625

π button

π is a number (approximately 3.142) which is used in many calculations. We shall look at π again in chapter 15. The value of π is stored on a scientific calculator. To evaluate π × 7, for example

The answer 21.99 (corr to 4 significant figures) appears.

SELF TEST 5.9

Evaluate $\pi 4^2$, correct to 4 significant figures.

> 50.27

Memory

All scientific calculators and some ordinary calculators have a memory. Some scientific calculators have several memories. You can store a number in the memory. This is very useful when doing a long calculation, or when using the same number several times. The following give examples of these uses.

Often the Min button puts a number into the memory. The MR button recalls the number from memory.

EXAMPLE 5.1

Work out the following expression, without writing down anything except the final answer.

$$\frac{3.27 + 4.19}{1.26 - 0.45}$$

Solution
First work out the bottom line. Store the result in the memory. Then work out the top line, and divide by the memory. The sequence is

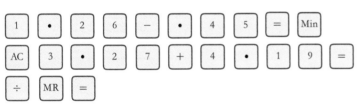

The answer 9.2098765 will appear. Give this number correct to three significant figures.

The expression is 9.21 (corr to 3 s.f.)

Note You could work out the expression by using brackets, instead of the memory.

EXAMPLE 5.2

Evaluate the following expression, correct to 4 significant figures.

$$1.236\,74 + 4 \times 1.236\,74^2 + 5 \times 1.236\,74^3$$

Solution
The number 1.236 74 appears three times. Put it in the memory. Then work out the expression, using the memory three times.

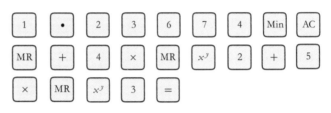

The answer 16.81297217 will appear.

The expression is 16.81 (corr to 4 s.f.)

SELF TEST 5.10

a) Use the memory of your calculator to evaluate:
   $2.3651 - 3 \times 2.3651^2 + 2 \times 2.3651^3$.
b) Use the memory of your calculator or brackets to evaluate: $\dfrac{5.392 + 4.187}{1.462 + 4.195}$

Give your answers correct to 4 significant figures.

> a) 12.04   b) 1.693

Standard form

A scientific calculator has a button labelled EXP. Use this for numbers in standard form. To enter 5×10^8, for example, press

   5.^{08} will appear.

(we met this notation on page 38.)

For a negative power of 10, press ± after the power. To enter 5×10^{-8}, for example

5 EXP 8 ±   5.$^{-08}$ will appear.

Ordinary arithmetic can now be done on numbers in standard form.

To evaluate $5 \times 10^{12} \times 6 \times 10^{13}$ press the following

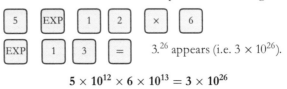

3.^{26} appears (i.e. 3×10^{26}).

$$5 \times 10^{12} \times 6 \times 10^{13} = 3 \times 10^{26}$$

SELF TEST 5.11

Use a calculator to evaluate $3.1 \times 10^9 + 4.3 \times 10^{10}$.

$$4.61 \times 10^{10}$$

Other facilities

Your calculator may be able to perform many other functions, for example to round numbers to 3 decimal places, to work in engineering notation and so on. Read the manual to find what is available.

In later chapters we will cover the use of other buttons.

5.2 Calculation with tables

You can use **tables** to calculate. For example, there is a table to find the square root of any number. If you have a calculator, you can use it to find square roots and so on. But there are many functions which do not appear on a calculator, and for which you have to use tables. If you do advanced statistical work, then you have to use tables.

Books of tables are available separately. Tables may be '3-figure' or '4-figure'. The following description is for '4-figure' tables. Look in a book of tables and find the square root tables. On each page, the first two significant figures are in the column on the left. The third significant figure appears in the columns across the page. The fourth significant figure appears in the 'mean differences' on the right. The next example shows how to use square root tables.

Square roots

EXAMPLE 5.3

Use tables to find the square root of 5.378.

Solution
Find the square root tables. Find 5.3 in the left hand column. Go across the row to the column headed with 7. You should find 2.317. Under the 8 column in the 'differences' find 2. This is added to the final digit of 2.317, obtaining 2.319.

The square root of 5.378 is 2.319

SELF TEST 5.12

Use tables to find the square roots of these numbers.
  a) 3.917   b) 75.35

$$a)\ 1.979 \quad b)\ 8.681$$

Note   Tables are less accurate than a calculator. They may be wrong in the fourth significant figure. Using a calculator, the square root of 75.35 is 8.680, correct to four significant figures, not 8.681.

Values less than 1 and over 100

There are square root tables for values between 1 and 10, and for values between 10 and 100.

If the number is less than 1, multiply by 100 until it is greater than 1. You can now use the tables.

If the number is greater than 100, divide by 100 until it is less than 100. You can now use the tables.

EXAMPLE 5.4

Find the square roots of
  a) 0.053 78 and b) 5 378 000.

Solution
a) Multiply by 100, obtaining 5.378. This now lies between 1 and 100.

$$0.05378 = 5.378 \div 100$$
$$\sqrt{0.05378} = \sqrt{5.378} \div \sqrt{100}$$
$$= 2.319 \div 10$$

The square root of 0.05378 is 0.2319

b) Divide by 100 three times, obtaining 5.378. This is dividing by 1 000 000.

$$5\,378\,000 = 5.378 \times 1\,000\,000$$
$$\sqrt{5\,378\,000} = \sqrt{5.378} \times \sqrt{1\,000\,000}$$
$$= 2.319 \times 1000$$

The square root of 5 378 000 is 2319

SELF TEST 5.13

Use tables to find the square roots of
  a) 391.7 and b) 0.7535.

$$a)\ 19.79 \quad b)\ 0.8681$$

Decreasing functions

With some functions the answers decrease rather than increase as the numbers get larger. For these functions, *subtract* the differences.

EXAMPLE 5.5

Use reciprocal tables to find the reciprocal of 4.378, i.e. $\frac{1}{4.378}$.

Solution

Find the 4.3 row. Go across to the 7 column, and find 0.2288. Under the 8 column find 4. *Subtract* this from the final digit of 0.2288, obtaining 0.2284.

The reciprocal of 4.378 is 0.2284

SELF TEST 5.14

Find the reciprocal of 9.217.

0.1085

EXAMPLE 5.6

Find the reciprocal of 0.4378.

Solution

The tables cover numbers between 1 and 10. Multiply 0.4378 by 10, to get a number in this range.

$$0.4378 = 4.378 \div 10$$

$$\frac{1}{0.4378} = \frac{1}{4.378 \div 10}$$

$$= \frac{1}{4.378} \times 10$$

$$= 0.2284 \times 10$$

The reciprocal of 0.4378 is 2.284

SELF TEST 5.15

Find the reciprocal of 92.17.

0.01085

Logarithms

If you do not have a calculator, you can use logarithms to multiply and divide. Without a calculator, addition and subtraction are much easier than multiplication and division. As we saw in chapter 4 the laws of logarithms reduce multiplication to addition and division to subtraction. Hence logarithms are used for calculation. The three laws of logarithms are as follows.

[1] $\log ab = \log a + \log b$

[2] $\log \frac{a}{b} = \log a - \log b$

[3] $\log a^n = n \log a$

EXAMPLE 5.7

Find log 2.476.

Solution

In the logarithm tables, find the row 24, go across to the 7 column and find 3927.

Under 6 in the differences section find 11, add this on, giving 3938.

so   log 2.476 = 0.3938

log 2.476 = 0.3938

A book of tables will contain logarithms. It will also contain antilogarithms (antilogs), which are the inverse of logarithms.

log 5.3 = 0.7243   so   antilog 0.7243 = 5.3

If $10^x = a$ then $\log a = x$ and antilog $x = a$.

Multiplication and division using logs

Using rule [1], $\log ab = \log a + \log b$. So to find ab, look up in tables the logs of a and b. Add these logs. Then use antilogs to find ab. By using rule [2] a similar procedure applies for division but this time we subtract the logs. The next example shows a systematic way to set out the calculation.

EXAMPLE 5.8

Use logs to find 4.293×2.093.

Solution

Look up the logs of these numbers. Add the logs, then use the antilog table. The procedure is set out below. Follow the stages ①, ②, ③, ④.

	number	log	
①	4.293	0.6328	②
	2.093	0.3207 +	
④ (antilogging)	8.984	0.9535	(adding) ③

4.293 × 2.093 = 8.984

Note The fourth significant figure is not correct. Using a calculator, the product is 8.985. Log tables are not as accurate as a calculator.

SELF TEST 5.16

Use logs to find
a) 2.735×3.184 and b) $8.677 \div 4.073$.
Set out your calculations in the same way as example 5.8.

a) 8.710   b) 2.130

Numbers less than 1 or greater than 10

So far we have only looked at logs for numbers between 1 and 10. We can find the logs of numbers less than 1 or greater than 10 by adding or subtracting integers, as follows.

$$\log 127 = \log (100 \times 1.27) = \log 100 + \log 1.27$$

We know that $\log 100 = 2$ ($10^2 = 100$). Using tables we find that $\log 1.27 = 0.1038$. Hence

$$\log 127 = \log 100 + \log 1.27$$
$$= 2 + 0.1038$$
$$= 2.1038$$

Similarly,

$$\log 0.00127 = \log (1.27 \times 10^{-3}) = 0.1038 + (-3)$$

Usually we show the negative value with a bar. So we write the value of log 0.00127 as

$$\bar{3}.1038$$

To go in the other direction, suppose the end of a calculation is

$$\log x = 5.847$$

This means $\log x = 5 + 0.847$

The antilog of 0.847 is 7.031. The 5 corresponds to $\log 10^5$, i.e. log 100 000. Hence, using rule [1]

$$x = 100\,000 \times 7.031$$
$$= 703\,100$$

Suppose $\log y = \bar{2}.1958$.

The antilog of 0.1958 is 1.570. The $\bar{2}$ corresponds to $\log 10^{-2}$.

$$\log y = \bar{2} + 0.1958$$

Hence

$$y = 10^{-2} \times 1.570$$
$$= 0.0157$$

Suppose $\log a = -3.2761$.

then
$$\log a = (-4 + 4) - 3.2761$$
$$= -4 + (4 - 3.2761)$$
$$= -4 + 0.7239$$
$$= \bar{4}.7239$$

Note This is *not* the same as $\log a = \bar{3}.2761$
which means $\log a = -3 + 0.2761$.

Solution

a) Note that $12.32 = 10 \times 1.232$, and hence log $12.32 = 1 + 0.0906$.
Similarly log $54.41 = 1.7357$. Add these logs, to obtain 2.8263.
The antilog of 0.8263 is 6.704. Multiply this by 10^2, i.e. by 100. The calculation is as set out below.

	number	log
	12.32	1.0906
	54.41	1.7357 +
(antilogging)	670.4	2.8263 (adding)

$$12.32 \times 54.41 = 670.4$$

b) Note that $0.000\,983\,4 = 10^{-4} \times 9.834$, and hence
$$\log 0.000\,983\,4 = -4 + \log 9.834$$
$$= \bar{4}.9928.$$

Proceed as in part a), except subtract the logs instead of adding. Be careful when subtracting the negative numbers. When subtracting $\bar{3}$ from $\bar{4}$, the result is $\bar{1}$.

$$\bar{4} - \bar{3} = -4 - (-3) = -4 + 3 = -1 = \bar{1}$$

The antilog of 0.4045 is 2.538. Multiply by 10^{-1}, i.e. divide by 10.

	number	log
	0.0009834	$\bar{4}$.9928
	0.003875	$\bar{3}$.5883 −
(antilogging)	0.2538	$\bar{1}$.4045 (subtracting)

$$0.000\,983\,4 \div 0.003\,875 = 0.2538$$

c) Using rule [3] find the log of 214.6, and multiply by 3.

	number	log
	214.6	2.3316
		× 3
(antilogging)	9881000	6.9948 (multiplying by 3)

$$214.6^3 = 9\,881\,000$$

EXAMPLE 5.9

Use logs to evaluate the following.
  a) 12.32×54.41
  b) $0.000\,983\,4 \div 0.003\,875$
  c) 214.6^3

SELF TEST 5.17

Evaluate the following using logs.
  a) 307.5×17.29 b) $6.782 \div 0.002\,345$ c) 17.34^4.

a) 5316   b) 2892   c) 90 360

5.3 Evaluating expressions

In this chapter we have covered calculation, with a calculator or with logarithms. This section provides practice in evaluating expressions which may involve more than one operation. Be sure of the following:

- Evaluate expressions inside brackets before those outside
- Multiply or divide before adding or subtracting
- When multiplying or dividing two negative numbers, the result is positive

EXAMPLE 5.10

Two resistors of resistance 8.17 Ω and 10.32 Ω are connected in parallel. The total resistance R Ω is given by the expression below. Evaluate the expression. Give your answer to three significant figures.

$$R = \frac{1}{\frac{1}{8.17} + \frac{1}{10.32}}$$

Solution
The denominator of this fraction is

$$\frac{1}{8.17} + \frac{1}{10.32} = 0.2193$$

Hence
$$\frac{1}{\frac{1}{8.17} + \frac{1}{10.32}} = \frac{1}{0.2193}$$

Divide 0.2193 into 1, obtaining 4.5599...

The total resistance is 4.56 Ω corr to 3 s.f.

SELF TEST 5.18

Two capacitors of capacitance 27.35 μF and 39.36 μF are connected in series. The total capacitance C is given by the expression below. Evaluate the expression. Give your answer to 3 significant figures.

$$C = \frac{1}{\frac{1}{27.35} + \frac{1}{39.36}}$$

16.1 μF

EXAMPLE 5.11

Evaluate $10^{-\frac{4.5}{100}}$.

Solution
First evaluate $-\frac{4.5}{100}$, obtaining -0.045. From antilog tables or from the 10^x button on a calculator, find that $10^{-0.045} = 0.9016$.

$$10^{-\frac{4.5}{100}} = 0.9016$$

SELF TEST 5.19

Evaluate $10^{-(2.7-1.2)}$ correct to 3 significant figures.

0.0316

EXAMPLE 5.12

Evaluate $\sqrt{(0.13^2 - 0.11^2)}$ correct to 3 significant figures.
Solution
First evaluate the expression inside the $\sqrt{}$ sign.
$$0.13^2 - 0.11^2 = 0.0169 - 0.0121 = 0.0048$$
Now take the square root of 0.0048, obtaining 0.06928. . . .
$$\sqrt{(0.13^2 - 0.11^2)} = 0.0693 \text{ corr to 3 s.f.}$$

SELF TEST 5.20

Evaluate the following, giving your answers correct to 3 significant figures.
a) $\log(12.98 + 11.43^2)$ b) $\sqrt{(3.12 - 1.045^2)}$

a) 2.16 b) 1.42

EXAMPLE 5.13

Evaluate the expression $2\pi\sqrt{\left(\frac{1.673}{9.81}\right)}$ correct to 3 significant figures.

Solution
Do the division inside the brackets. Then take the square root, then multiply by 2π. With a calculator, you can evaluate the expression without writing anything down except the final answer.

$$2\pi\sqrt{\left(\frac{1.673}{9.81}\right)} = 2\pi\sqrt{0.1705...} = 2\pi 0.413... = 2.594...$$

The expression is 2.59 corr to 3 s.f.

SELF TEST 5.21

Evaluate the expression $\sqrt{\left(\frac{\pi 1.87^2 + \pi 0.95^2}{1 - 0.563^2}\right)}$ correct to 3 significant figures.

4.50

■ CHECK YOUR UNDERSTANDING

● An ordinary calculator can apply the four basic operations. A scientific calculator can evaluate many other operations and many functions. It can evaluate combined expressions, including expressions with brackets.

● Use of logs converts multiplication to addition, and division to subtraction. The tables give logs of numbers between 1 and 10. For larger or smaller numbers, add or subtract 1 for each power of 10.

REVISION EXERCISES AND QUESTIONS

Use either a calculator or tables to answer these questions. Give your answers correct to four significant figures. The solutions at the back of the book were found using a calculator. If you use tables your answers may be slightly different.

1   a) $4.295 + 2.674$ b) $9.285 - 6.662$ c) $86.45 - 6.399$
    d) 2.894×3.783 e) 8.562×6.377 f) 67.24×875.2
    g) 0.0563×4.972 h) $67.34 \div 4.093$ i) $0.3956 \div 93.98$
    j) $4.35^{1.5}$ k) $10.56^{1.9}$ l) 0.975^{12}
    m) 1.529^{-4} n) $988.3^{0.231}$ o) $0.1453^{-5.5}$

2 Evaluate the expressions below, leaving your answers as fractions.

    a) $\frac{1}{4} + \frac{2}{5}$ b) $\frac{7}{12} \times \frac{5}{21}$ c) $\frac{12}{13} \times \frac{3}{7}$
    d) $1\frac{3}{4} + 2\frac{3}{8}$ e) $4\frac{3}{5} - 2\frac{3}{10}$ f) $7\frac{1}{8} - 2\frac{5}{8}$
    g) $5\frac{3}{7} \times 2\frac{7}{10}$ h) $2\frac{7}{8} \div \frac{2}{3}$ i) $4\frac{6}{7} \div 6\frac{4}{9}$

3 Evaluate the following.

    a) $(3.45 + 2.17) \times (6.93 - 1.64)$
    b) $(0.463 - 0.184) \div (4.12 + 6.12)$

    c) $5^{2.13+7.19}$ d) $10^{8.12\times0.527}$ e) $0.764^{-4.23}$
    f) $10^{-3.25-2.74}$ g) $1.2371 + 1.2371^2 + 1.2371^3$
    h) $5 \times 7.372 + 8 \times 7.372^2 + 9 \times 7.372^3$
    i) $(5.746 - 5.709) \div 5.709$
    j) $\dfrac{8.562 + 9.026}{2.84 + 8.12}$ k) $\dfrac{56.8 - 12.6}{0.32 + 0.57}$ l) $\dfrac{12.63 \times 42.09}{54.90 \times 12.93}$

4 Evaluate the following.

    a) $\sqrt{2.456}$ b) $\sqrt{(75.34 + 28.43)}$
    c) $\sqrt[3]{(0.275 - 0.119)}$ d) $\sqrt{(2.96^2 + 3.48^2)}$
    e) $(\sqrt{7.481} + \sqrt{4.039})^3$ f) $\sqrt{(\sqrt{73.3} - \sqrt{21.7})}$
    g) $\log(3.284 - 1.229)$ h) $\log(65.34 \times 28.91)$
    i) $\pi(17.8 + 18.3)$ j) $\pi(32.6^2 - 27.9^2)$
    k) $\sqrt{(\pi\, 4.234^2 - 51.95)}$
    l) $\dfrac{\sqrt{1.674} + \sqrt{4.129}}{\sqrt{0.184} + \sqrt{0.751}}$ m) $\dfrac{1.256^2 + \pi 0.945^2}{36.81 - 21.84}$
    n) $5.32\sqrt{\left(\dfrac{32.1}{12.7}\right)}$ o) $\log\left(\dfrac{3.462}{1.007}\right)$
    p) $\log\left(\dfrac{1.273}{5.39 + 3.28}\right)$ q) $\sqrt{\left(\dfrac{\log 2763}{\log 29.5}\right)}$

5 Evaluate the following, leaving your answers in standard form.

    a) $7.35 \times 10^8 \times 6.12 \times 10^9$
    b) $1.253 \times 10^{12} \times 2.301 \times 10^7$
    c) $4.61 \times 10^{12} \div 5.62 \times 10^3$
    d) $6.025 \times 10^{18} \div 7.54 \times 10^6$
    e) $6.35 \times 10^{-4} \times 5.43 \times 10^{19}$
    f) $7.09 \times 10^{-23} \times 1.26 \times 10^{-8}$
    g) $3.27 \times 10^9 + 6.51 \times 10^{10}$
    h) $3.4 \times 10^{12} + 9.46 \times 10^{13}$
    i) $9.45 \times 10^{-41} \times 5.55 \times 10^{12}$
    j) $1.034 \times 10^{-12} + 2.664 \times 10^{-13}$

Accuracy and error 6

Introduction

When you count the number of people in a room, you obtain a whole number. Your answer is accurate. But when you measure the weight of a parcel, the result may not be a whole number. Your answer cannot be absolutely accurate.

You must be aware of the accuracy of your measurements. There are two sources of inaccuracy.

● Mistakes. You might make a mistake in your calculation. If you check your answer carefully, you will get rid of this inaccuracy.
● Measurement. You cannot measure length, time, mass and so on exactly. Your measurement is always inaccurate.

The first source of error can be avoided. The second cannot be avoided. When you measure a quantity, you must know how accurate your result is.

6.1 Error

Suppose the true mass of an object is 17.35 kg. Your balance might be inaccurate, and give the mass as 17.34 kg. The **error** is the difference between the true value and the measurement, 0.01 kg.

If the true value is a and the measurement is x, then the error is the difference between x and a. The error is always given as a positive value.

A way of writing the positive error is $x \sim a$.

Do not give an error to several significant figures. Give it correct to one or two significant figures.

When we give a measurement, we show its accuracy by the $\pm$ sign. This shows how far the true value is from the measurement.

If the measurement is given as 7.4 ± 0.1, then the true value could lie 0.1 on either side of 7.4. Hence the true value could be anywhere between 7.3 and 7.5.

EXAMPLE 6.1

The diameter of a shaft is given as 21.2 ± 0.2 mm. Find the range within which the diameter lies.

Solution
Add and subtract the error from the value, obtaining 21.4 and 21.0.

The diameter lies between 21.0 mm and 21.4 mm

SELF TEST 6.1

The bandwidth of a radio station is 12.4 ± 0.6 MH. Find the limits of the band.

11.8–13.0 MH

EXAMPLE 6.2

The diameter of a shaft is given as $3.40 \, ^{+0.04}_{+0.02}$ mm.
Find the limits of the diameter.

Solution
Here both limits are greater than 3.40. Add 0.02, obtaining 3.42. Add 0.04, obtaining 3.44.

The diameter lies between 3.42 mm and 3.44 mm

SELF TEST 6.2

The diameter of a ball-bearing is given as $9.0 \, ^{+0.5}_{+0.1}$ mm.
Find the limits between which the diameter lies.

9.1–9.5 mm

Relative errors

The importance of an error depends on the size of the true value. Obviously, an error of 0.01 kg is more important when measuring a piston of mass 0.43 kg than when measuring a car of mass 950 kg!

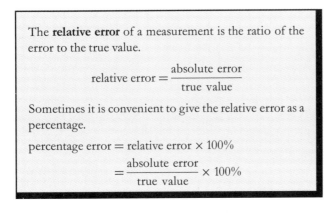

The **relative error** of a measurement is the ratio of the error to the true value.

$$\text{relative error} = \frac{\text{absolute error}}{\text{true value}}$$

Sometimes it is convenient to give the relative error as a percentage.

$$\text{percentage error} = \text{relative error} \times 100\%$$
$$= \frac{\text{absolute error}}{\text{true value}} \times 100\%$$

EXAMPLE 6.3

A distance of 9.6 m is measured as 9.3 m. Find the relative error and the percentage error.

Solution
The error is 0.3 m. Divide this by 9.6, obtaining 0.03125. Round this to 0.03 (one s.f.).

The relative error is 0.03

Multiply the relative error by 100, obtaining 3.

The percentage error is 3%

SELF TEST 6.3

A mass is given as 45 ± 3 kg. Find the relative error and the percentage error.

0.07, 7%

EXAMPLE 6.4

An electrical component is stated to have a resistance of 450 Ω ± 10%. Find the limits of the resistance.

Solution
10% of 450 is 45. Add and subtract this from 450, obtaining 495 and 405.

The resistance lies between 405 Ω and 495 Ω

SELF TEST 6.4

The percentage error in timing a race of 10.32 seconds is $\frac{1}{2}$%. Find the relative error and the absolute error.

0.005, 0.05 s

Decimal places

Suppose a measurement is given as 3.17, correct to 2 decimal places. The digits in the first two decimal places are correct. The digit in the third decimal place is unknown.

The greatest possible value is 3.175, otherwise the result would be rounded up to 3.18.

The least possible value is 3.165, otherwise the result would be rounded down to 3.16.

The value lies between 3.165 and 3.175. There could be an error of 0.005 on either side of 3.17.

The measurement is 3.17 ± 0.005

In general, when you give a value correct to a certain number of decimal places, the maximum error is 5 in the next decimal place.

EXAMPLE 6.5

A mass is given as 22.4 kg, correct to one decimal place. Find the maximum error and the maximum relative error.

Solution
The maximum error is 5 in the second decimal place, i.e. 0.05.

The maximum error is 0.05 kg

Divide the error by 22.4, obtaining 0.0022....

The maximum relative error is 0.002

SELF TEST 6.5

A length is given as 1.46 m, correct to two decimal places. Find the maximum error and the maximum percentage error.

0.005 m, 0.3%

Significant figures

If a number is given correct to three significant figures, then the error is found in a similar way. Suppose a reading is given as 3.17, correct to three significant figures. The reading lies between 3.165 and 3.175. The maximum error is 0.005.

In general, if a value is given correct to a certain number of significant figures, the maximum error is 5 in the next significant figure.

SELF TEST 6.6

A value is given as 0.03626, correct to four significant figures. Find the maximum possible error.

0.000 005

Appropriate accuracy

Suppose you have a metal rod of length 1 m, and you cut it into three equal lengths. Each length would be $\frac{1}{3}$ m. A calculator gives this as

$$\tfrac{1}{3} = 0.333\,333\,333\,3.$$

This answer is far too accurate. Round it to two decimal places.

$$\text{length} = 0.33 \text{ m}$$

In general, do not give an answer to too many decimal places or too many significant figures. The numbers you give should be correct.

SELF TEST 6.7

A loaf of about 2 kg is shared equally between 7 people. How much does each person get?

0.3 kg

6.2 Arithmetic of errors

When inaccurate measurements are combined, the errors increase. The rules are as follows.

- If measurements A and B are added, the errors are added.

error in $(A + B) = $ (error in A) + (error in B)

- If measurements A and B are subtracted, the errors are added.

error in $(A - B) = $ (error in A) + (error in B)

- If measurements A and B are multiplied, the maximum error is the maximum possible value of $A \times B$ minus the value of $A \times B$.

maximum value of $(A \times B)$
= (maximum value of A) × (maximum value of B)

maximum error in $(A \times B)$
= maximum value of $(A \times B) - (A \times B)$

- If measurements A and B are divided, the maximum error is the maximum possible value of $A \div B$ minus the value of $A \div B$.

maximum value of $(A \div B)$
= (maximum value of A) ÷ (*minimum* value of B)

maximum error in $(A \div B)$
= maximum value of $(A \div B) - (A \div B)$

Notes

1 Do not subtract errors, always think of the worst possible case.
2 When finding the maximum value of $A \div B$, use the *minimum* value of B.

EXAMPLE 6.6

The area of a building site is 500 ± 5 m^2. The area of a house to be built on it is 50 ± 1 m^2. What is the area remaining?

Solution

Subtract 50 from 500, obtaining 450. Even though you subtracted the areas, you *add* the errors. Add 5 and 1, obtaining 6.

The area remaining is 450 ± 6 m^2

SELF TEST 6.8

A lorry of mass 3200 kg carries a load of 1250 kg. The errors in the masses are 20 kg and 70 kg respectively. Find the total mass, giving the error.

4450 kg, $\pm$ 90 kg

EXAMPLE 6.7

The current through a circuit is measured as 5.5 ± 0.1 amps, and the resistance is measured as 8.42 ± 0.04 Ω. The potential difference along the circuit is calculated by multiplying the current by the resistance ($V = IR$). Find the maximum error in the calculation.

Solution

Multiply 5.5 and 8.42, obtaining 46.31.

The current could be as high as 5.6, and the resistance could be as high as 8.46. The product of these is 47.376. Subtract 46.31 to obtain the maximum possible error.

$$47.376 - 46.31 = 1.066$$

The maximum error in the potential difference is 1.1 V (corr to 2 s.f.)

SELF TEST 6.9

A car travels at 80 km/hr, for a time of 2.2 hours. The maximum error in the speed is 5 km/hr, and the maximum error in the time is 0.1 hours. Find the greatest possible distance travelled.

195.5 km

EXAMPLE 6.8

A distance of 23 km is travelled in 40 minutes. The distance has a possible error of 0.5 km, and the time has a possible error of 2 minutes. Find the speed of the journey, giving the error.

Solution
Divide 23 km by 40 minutes, obtaining 0.575 km per minute. The greatest possible speed is reached with the greatest possible distance and the *least* possible time. Hence divide 23.5 by 38, obtaining 0.618...

The difference between 0.618 ... and 0.575 is 0.0434...

The speed is 0.575 km per minute, with a maximum error of 0.043 km per min (corr to 2 s.f.)

SELF TEST 6.10

A potential difference of 4.6 ± 0.1 volts is across a component with resistance $1.2 \pm 0.1\ \Omega$. Find the current that flows through the component, and the maximum error.

3.83 A, 0.44 A

EXAMPLE 6.9

A rod has diameter 3.4 mm, and a hole has diameter 3.6 mm. Both figures are given correct to 1 decimal place. Find the greatest possible clearance when the rod is passed through the hole.

Solution
The clearance is the difference between the diameters. Each diameter is given correct to 1 decimal place, hence the error is 0.05 mm. Add these errors, obtaining 0.1 mm.

$$\text{Clearance} = (3.6 - 3.4) \pm 0.1\ \text{mm} = 0.2 \pm 0.1\ \text{mm}$$

The greatest possible clearance is 0.3 mm

SELF TEST 6.11

Three resistors are in series. Their values are $1.25\ \Omega$, $0.83\ \Omega$ and $1.52\ \Omega$. All values are given correct to 2 decimal places. Find the greatest and least values of the total resistance.

3.615 Ω, 3.585 Ω

Combining measurements

Suppose that *approximately* 100 kg of sand is added to *exactly* 5 kg of cement. The mass of the mixture is *approximately* 105 kg. When combining measurements, the accuracy is that of the *least* accurate measurement.

Suppose we add 4.5 and 2.364, where these numbers are given correct to one decimal place and three decimal places respectively. The answer should be given correct to one decimal place.

$$4.5 + 2.364 = 6.864$$
$$= 6.9\ (1\ \text{decimal place})$$

Suppose we are multiplying 2.7 and 0.017 453, where these numbers are given correct to 2 significant figures and 5 significant figures respectively. The answer should be given correct to 2 significant figures.

$$2.7 \times 0.017\,453 = 0.047\,1231$$
$$= 0.047\ (2\ \text{significant figures})$$

Note A whole number is accurate. Suppose we have 8 screws, weighing 0.55 g each, correct to two significant figures. The figure of 8 is accurate (assuming that we have counted correctly!). The total weight, 8×0.55 g, should be given correct to two significant figures.

EXAMPLE 6.10

A steel rod has length 1.247 m, correct to 3 decimal places. A length of 0.61 m, correct to 2 decimal places, is cut off. Find the length remaining.

Solution
Subtract 0.61 from 1.247, obtaining 0.637. The accuracy should be the same as the least accurate measurement, 2 decimal places.

The length remaining is 0.64 m (corr to 2 d.p.)

SELF TEST 6.12

Two measurements are $a = 324.6$, correct to 1 decimal place, and $b = 0.576$, correct to 3 decimal places. Find $a + b$.

325.2 (1 d.p.)

EXAMPLE 6.11

An electrical component has resistance $320\ \Omega$, correct to 2 significant figures. A current of 2.387 amps, correct to 4 significant figures, passes through it. Find the potential difference across the component.

Solution

$$\text{Potential difference} = \text{current} \times \text{resistance}$$

Multiply 320 by 2.387, obtaining 763.84. The less accurate of the original quantities was given correct to 2 significant figures. Hence round 763.84 to 2 significant figures.

The potential difference is 760 V (corr to 2 s.f.)

Two measurements are $x = 0.003\,524$, correct to four significant figures, and $y = 2.3$, correct to two significant figures. Find $x \times y$.

0.0081 (2 s.f.)

6.3 Approximation

It is easy to make mistakes when doing a calculation. A mistake is very dangerous if the answer is 10 times too large or 10 times too small. Suppose you have to multiply 2.856 and 7.155. Which of the following is correct?

2.043 468   20.434 68   204.3468

A mental approximation will confirm the right value. Round each number to one significant figure. Round 2.856 to 3, and round 7.155 to 7.

$$3 \times 7 = 21$$

21 is close to 20.434 68. If you got either of the other answers, then you probably entered the numbers wrongly on your calculator.

EXAMPLE 6.12

A journey of 125 km takes 1.84 hours. Find the average speed, making a check by approximation.

Solution

$$\text{Speed} = \text{distance} \div \text{time}$$

Divide 125 by 1.84, obtaining 67.93 ..., or 67.9 correct to 3 significant figures.

125 is approximately 120, and 1.84 is approximately 2.

$$120 \div 2 = 60$$

This is close to 67.9. The check confirms the answer.

The average speed is 67.9 km/hr (corr to 3 s.f.)

SELF TEST 6.14

Evaluate the following, making checks of your answers by approximation.
 a) $31.57 + 56.23$
 b) $5.28 \times 124\,820$
 c) $0.047\,23 \div 28.3$

a) 87.8 (check: 30 + 60 = 90)
b) 659 049.6 (check: 5 × 100 000 = 500 000)
c) 0.001 669 (check: 0.05 ÷ 30 = 0.0017)

EXAMPLE 6.13

Evaluate the following, correct to two decimal places. Make a check by approximation.

$$\frac{5.976 + 8.254}{0.127 + 0.307}$$

By tables or a calculator, you find that the expression is 32.79. When each number is rounded to one significant figure, it becomes

$$\frac{6+8}{0.1+0.3} = \frac{14}{0.4} = \frac{140}{4} = 35$$

35 is close to 32.79. This checks the answer.

The expression is 32.79

SELF TEST 6.15

Evaluate the following, correct to four significant figures. Check your answer by approximation.

$$\frac{32.2 + 98.7}{6.73 - 2.06}$$

28.03 (check: 130 ÷ 5 = 26)

■ **CHECK YOUR UNDERSTANDING**

● The difference between a measurement and the true value is the error in the measurement. The error divided by the true value is the relative error. The relative error expressed as a percentage is the percentage error.
● Suppose a measurement is given correct to a certain number of decimal places or significant figures. The maximum error is 5 in the next decimal place or significant figure.
● Do not write a measurement more accurately than is sensible.
● When you add or subtract measurements, add the errors. When you multiply or divide measurements, find the error by finding the greatest possible value.
● When combining measurements, the accuracy of the answer is that of the least accurate measurement.
● You can check calculations by rounding each number to one significant figure.

| REVISION EXERCISES AND QUESTIONS |

6.1 Error

1   A value of 4.382 is measured as 4.386. Find the error, the relative error and the percentage error.

2   A value of 0.000 34 is measured as 0.000 37. Find the error, the relative error and the percentage error.

3   Find the ranges within which the following lie.

   a) 5.6 ± 0.3 b) 987 ± 2 c) $0.000\ 23 \pm 0.000\ 01$
   d) $23.9 \pm 5\%$ e) $0.0173 \pm \frac{1}{2}\%$ f) $12\ 000 \pm 10\%$

4   Find the limits of the following measurements.

   a) $0.60\ ^{+0.06}_{+0.03}$ b) $12.7\ ^{+0.5}_{-0.2}$ c) $150\ ^{+50\%}_{-10\%}$

5   The relative error in a measurement of 12.3 mm was 0.05. Find the limits of the measurement.

6   The percentage error in measuring a time of 63 seconds was 10%. Find the limits of the time.

7   An approximation for π is $\frac{22}{7}$. A very accurate value, given by a calculator is 3.141 592 654. What is the percentage error in using $\frac{22}{7}$ as the value?

8   An electrical component has resistance $2500 \pm 5\%$ Ω. Find the limits of the resistance.

9   The voltage of a capacitor is given as $35\ ^{+150\%}_{-20\%}$ V. Find the limits of the voltage.

10   An electrical appliance works for voltages between 220 V and 240 V. Express this using the $\pm$ symbol.

11   A time is given as 2.434 seconds, correct to three decimal places. Find the maximum error and the maximum relative error.

12   A speed is given as 360 m s^{-1}, correct to two significant figures. Find the maximum error and the maximum percentage error.

6.2 Arithmetic of errors

13   Three lengths are given as 23.4 mm, 12.7 mm, 17.9 mm, each being given correct to 1 decimal place. Find the sum of the lengths. What is the maximum error in your result?

14   Two masses are 45.67 kg and 12.83 kg, both figures being given correct to 2 decimal places. Find the difference of the masses. What is the maximum error in your result?

15   Two measurements are 5.98 and 6.13, both being given correct to 3 significant figures. Find the product of the measurements. What is the maximum error in your result?

16   Two measurements a and b are given as 0.562 and 1.56 respectively, both being given correct to 3 significant figures.
Find $\frac{a}{b}$. What is the maximum error in your answer?

17   A batch of concrete is made up of 120 kg sand, 320 kg gravel, 70 kg cement and 1.2 kg colouring. Find the total mass.

18   Three resistors are placed in series. Their values are 125 Ω, 326 Ω and 2.12 Ω. What is the total resistance?

19   The pipe of Figure 6.1 has internal diameter 42.8 mm, a wall thickness of 4.34 mm, and it is surrounded by *about* 10 mm of insulation. What is the total diameter?

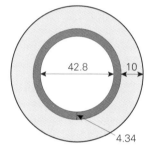

Figure 6.1   **An insulated pipe**

6.3 Approximation

20   Evaluate the following. Check your results by approximation.

   a) $43.64 + 51.23$ b) $0.006\ 64 - 0.001\ 94$
   c) 234×96.3 d) $594 \div 28.7$
   e) $5.28 \times (2.32 + 2.84)$ f) $0.07 \times 23 + 0.23 \times 68$
   g) $\dfrac{165 + 207}{2.3 + 3.8}$ h) $\dfrac{9.67 \times 6.28}{93 \times 22}$
   i) $\dfrac{0.782 \times 0.103}{12.4 + 29.4}$ j) $\sqrt{(2.48 + 8.24)}$
   k) $\sqrt{(7.35^2 + 3.56^2)}$ l) $(4.396 + 1.693)^2$

21   Find the total mass of a barrel of mass 23.7 kg containing 98.4 kg of water. Check your answer by approximation.

22   Find the mass of 0.0746 m^3 of liquid which has a density of 822 kg m^{-3}. Check your answer by approximation. (density = mass $\div$ volume)

23   The temperature for a chemical process is 722°C. If the furnace is now at 187°C, what rise in temperature is needed? Check your answer by approximation.

24   A square has side 58.3 m. What is its area? Check your answer by approximation.

Arithmetic in other bases

Introduction

Human beings have ten fingers and thumbs. That is probably the reason why we count in base 10. We use the **denary** system.

For some purposes we need to count in another base. There is a very old system of counting in base 60, and we still measure time in this system. Nowadays, computer arithmetic is often done in base 2 (**binary**). This is because numbers are stored in components which can be either on or off, (1 or 0). Computer programmers use **hexadecimal** or base 16, because information on a computer is often stored in packets of 16 components.

7.1 Time and angles, base 60

We measure time in hours, minutes and seconds. The sum of 40 minutes and 50 minutes is 1 hour 30 minutes.

$$40 \, \text{min} + 50 \, \text{min} = 90 \, \text{min} = 1 \, \text{hr} + 30 \, \text{min}$$

Notice that we carry over 60 minutes into 1 hour. Similarly, we carry over 60 seconds into 1 minute. We are using base 60.

Fractions of degrees

The base 60 system is also used for angles. Sometimes we measure fractions of a degree in **minutes** and **seconds**. There are 60 minutes in a degree, and 60 seconds in a minute. The symbols for minutes and seconds are $'$ and $''$ respectively.

$5° \, 12' \, 37''$ means
5 degrees, 12 minutes and 37 seconds.

Each minute is $\frac{1}{60}$ of a degree, and each second is $\frac{1}{3600}$ of a degree. Hence the angle above is

$$5 + \frac{12}{60} + \frac{37}{3600} = 5.2103°$$

Table 7.1 Conversion table of simple fractions of a degree

Fraction	Minutes
$\frac{1}{2}°$	$30'$
$\frac{1}{3}°$	$20'$
$\frac{2}{3}°$	$40'$
$\frac{1}{4}°$	$15'$
$\frac{3}{4}°$	$45'$
$\frac{1}{10}°$	$6'$
$\frac{1}{20}°$	$3'$
$\frac{1}{6}°$	$10'$
$\frac{1}{5}°$	$12'$

SELF TEST 7.1

a) Convert 5.75° to degrees, minutes and seconds.
b) Convert 15° 50′ to degrees. Give your answer as a fraction.

a) 5° 45′   b) $15\frac{5}{6}°$

Example 7.1 gives the conversion for more complicated numbers.

EXAMPLE 7.1

Convert 86° 23′ 41″ to a decimal, giving your answer correct to 3 decimal places.

Solution
Each minute is $\frac{1}{60}°$, and each second is $\frac{1}{3600}°$. Hence

$$86°23'41'' = (86 + \frac{23}{60} + \frac{41}{3600})°$$
$$= 86\frac{1421}{3600}°$$
$$= 86.395°$$

86° 23′ 41″ is equal to 86.395° (to 3 d.p.)

51

SELF TEST 7.2

Convert 26° 12′ 51″ to a decimal, giving your answer correct to 3 decimal places.

26.214°

Conversion to minutes and seconds

Consider 32.354°.

To convert to degrees, minutes and seconds, multiply the fractional part by 60.

$$0.354 \times 60 = 21.24$$

The whole number part of the product gives the minutes, i.e. 21′.

Multiply the fractional part of the product by 60.

$$0.24 \times 60 = 14.4$$

The whole number part of this product gives the seconds, i.e. 14″

32.354° equals 32° 21′ 14″

Example 7.2 shows the method.

EXAMPLE 7.2

Convert 63.453° to degrees, minutes and seconds. Give your answer correct to the nearest second.

Solution
Multiply 0.453 by 60, obtaining 27.18. This gives 27 minutes.
Multiply 0.18 by 60, obtaining 10.8. Round up to 11.

63.453° is 63° 27′ 11″

SELF TEST 7.3

Convert 12.824° to degrees, minutes and seconds, giving your answer correct to the nearest second.

12° 49′ 26″

Arithmetic in minutes and seconds

When you add minutes and seconds, remember that the carry-over occurs at 60, not at 10.

EXAMPLE 7.3

Evaluate the following.
a) 12° 48′ + 13° 25′   b) 45° 12′ 52″ + 21° 36′ 43″

Solution
a) Add 48 and 25, obtaining 73.

This is 60 + 13, i.e. 1′ 13′.

Add 1, 12 and 13, obtaining 26.

$$\begin{array}{r} 1 \\ 12°\ 48' \\ +\ 13°\ 25' \\ \hline 26°\ 13' \end{array}$$

12° 48′ + 13° 25′ = 26° 13′

b) The sum of 52 and 43 is 95. This gives 1′ and 35″.

Hence carry over 1′ to the minutes.

The sum of 1, 12 and 36 is 49.

The sum of 45 and 21 is 66.

$$\begin{array}{r} 1 \\ 45°\ 12'\ 52'' \\ +\ 21°\ 36'\ 43'' \\ \hline 66°\ 49'\ 35'' \end{array}$$

45° 12′ 52″ + 21° 36′ 43″ = 66° 49′ 35″

SELF TEST 7.4

Evaluate the following.
a) 41° 33′ + 47° 51′   b) 36° 42′ 39″ + 31° 30′ 25″

a) 89° 24′   b) 68° 13′ 4″

When you subtract minutes and seconds, you may need to 'borrow' from the next column. When you borrow 1°, you borrow 60′.

EXAMPLE 7.4

Evaluate the following.
a) 38° 25′ − 12° 47′   b) 72° 15′ 47″ − 21° 42′ 51″

Solution
a) 47 is greater than 25. We need to borrow 1°, i.e. 60′

For the minutes, 60 + 25 − 47 = 38

$$\begin{array}{r} 7\ \ 60 \\ 3\!\!\!/8°\ 25' \\ -\ 12°\ 47' \\ \hline 25°\ 38' \end{array}$$

For the degrees, subtract 12 from 37, obtaining 25.

38° 25′ − 12° 47′ = 25° 38′

b) 51 is greater than 43. We need to borrow 1′, i.e. 60″

For the seconds, 60 + 47 − 51 = 56

There are now 14′. This is less than 42.

We need to borrow 1°, i.e. 60′.

For the minutes, 60 + 14 − 42 = 32

$$\begin{array}{r} 60 \\ 1\ \ 4\ \ 60 \\ 7\!\!\!/2°\ 1\!\!\!/5'\ 47'' \\ -\ 21°\ 42'\ 51'' \\ \hline 50°\ 32'\ 56'' \end{array}$$

There are now 71°. Subtract 21, obtaining 50.

72° 15′ 47″ − 21° 42′ 51″ = 50° 32′ 56″

Evaluate the following.
   a) $29° 44' - 10° 51'$ b) $82° 27' 52'' - 39° 55' 29''$

a) 18° 53'   b) 42° 32' 23''

Note A scientific calculator may have a button which converts decimals to minutes and seconds. Often it is labelled

To enter $12° 40' 23''$ press

| 1 | 2 | ° ' " | 4 | 0 | ° ' " | 2 | 3 | ° ' " |

The display shows 12.6730...
This is $12° 40' 23''$ as a decimal.
To convert from degrees to degrees, minutes and seconds, press

| SHIFT | ° ' " |

To convert back again press | ° ' " |

Angle gauges

With a set of angle gauges you can set out angles very accurately. The sides of each gauge are at a fixed angle. By combining the gauges, you can add or subtract angles. In Figure 7.1, gauges of $9°$ and $3°$ are used to make $9° + 3°$, i.e. $12°$. In Figure 7.2, they are used to make $9° - 3°$, i.e. $6°$.

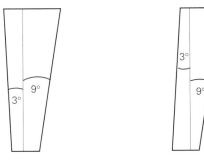

Figure 7.1
Adding angles

Figure 7.2
Subtracting angles

Table 7.2 Angles found in a set of angle gauges

Degrees	1	3	9	27	41	90
Minutes	1	3	9	27		
Seconds	3	9	27			

Show how these gauges can be used to build up angles of
   a) $17° 21'$ b) $30° 54' 33''$.

Solution
a)   For the minutes: $21 = 27 - 9 + 3$
     For the degrees: $17 = 27 - 9 - 1$
     Use these gauges $27°, -9°, -1°, +27', -9', +3'$
b)   For the seconds: $33 = 27 + 9 - 3$
     For the minutes: $54 = 60 - 9 + 3$
                        (the $1°$ gauge is a $60'$ gauge)
     For the degrees: $30 = 27 + 3$
Use these gauges $27°, +3°, +1°, -9', +3', +27'', +9'', -3''$

Show how the angle gauges can make up angles of
   a) $42° 7'$ b) $10° 23' 21''$.

a) $41° + 1° + 9' - 3' + 1'$
b) $9° + 1° + 27' - 3' - 1' + 27'' - 9'' + 3''$

7.2 Binary, base 2

In ordinary denary notation, there are ten symbols, $0, 1, 2$ up to 9. Larger numbers require several digits. The extra digits represent powers of 10.

$$583 = 5 \text{ hundreds} + 8 \text{ tens} + 3 \text{ units}$$
$$= 5 \times 10^2 + 8 \times 10 + 3$$

When 1 is added to 9, the result is 'carried over' to obtain 10.

$$\begin{array}{r} 9 \\ + 1 \\ \hline 10 \end{array}$$

Binary notation contains only two digits, 0 and 1. The digits represent powers of 2.

$$\text{binary } 1101 = 1 \times 2^3 + 1 \times 2^2 + 0 \times 2^1 + 1 \times 2^0$$
$$= 8 + 4 + 0 + 1 \text{ denary}$$
$$= 13 \text{ denary}$$

The 'carry over' occurs when 1 is added to 1.

$$\begin{array}{r} 1 \\ + 1 \\ \hline 10 \end{array}$$

Hence the number two is written 10. Three is written 11, four is 100 and so on.

Table 7.3 gives the conversion for the first twelve numbers.

Table 7.3 The first twelve numbers in denary and binary notation

Denary	1	2	3	4	5	6
Binary	11	10	11	100	101	110
Denary	7	8	9	10	11	12
Binary	111	1000	1001	1010	1011	1100

Converting denary to binary

EXAMPLE 7.6

Convert 37 to binary.

Solution
To convert from denary to binary, divide repeatedly by 2, until 0 is left.

37 ÷ 2 gives   18   remainder 1.
18 ÷ 2 gives   9   remainder 0.
9 ÷ 2 gives   4   remainder 1.
4 ÷ 2 gives   2   remainder 0.
2 ÷ 2 gives   1   remainder 0.
1 ÷ 2 gives   0   remainder 1.

The remainders are either 0 or 1. These remainders give the number in binary. The final remainder gives the left-most digit.

In binary, 37 is 100101

SELF TEST 7.7

Convert 59 to binary.

111011

Converting binary to denary

To convert from binary to denary, convert each digit to the appropriate power of 2. 1 is 2^0, 10 is 2^1, 100 is 2^2, 1000 is 2^3 and so on. Then add these numbers.

EXAMPLE 7.7

Convert 11101010 in binary to denary.

Solution
Put the digits in a row. Under each digit put the appropriate power of 2.

$$1 \quad 1 \quad 1 \quad 0 \quad 1 \quad 0 \quad 1 \quad 0$$
$$2^7 \quad 2^6 \quad 2^5 \quad 2^4 \quad 2^3 \quad 2^2 \quad 2^1 \quad 2^0$$

Add the numbers which are under the 1s.

$$2^7 + 2^6 + 2^5 + 2^3 + 2^1 = 128 + 64 + 32 + 8 + 2$$
$$= 234$$

The denary value is 234

SELF TEST 7.8

Convert 1001101101 to denary.

621

Arithmetic in binary

Adding

When you add numbers in binary, the 'carry' occurs at two. Hence when you add 1 + 1, carry 1 into the next column.

EXAMPLE 7.8

Add 100101 and 110111 in binary.

Solution
Set out the sum as shown below. The 'carry' digits are in the top row.

```
        1  1  1
    1  0  0  1  0  1
+      1  1  0  1  1  1
   ─────────────────────
   1  0  1  1  1  0  0
```

100101 + 110111 = 1011100

SELF TEST 7.9

Evaluate 111011 + 101111 in binary.

1101010

Multiplying

When multiplying one binary number by another, write out a copy of the first binary number, for each 1 in the second binary number. Then add the results.

EXAMPLE 7.9

Multiply 11011 by 1011 in binary.

Solution
Write out 11011 three times, once for each 1 in 1011. Then add the results.

```
2^7 2^6 2^5 2^4 2^3 2^2 2^1 2^0
            1  1  0  1  1    (For the right-most 1 in 1011, ×2^0)
         1  1  0  1  1       (For the next 1 in 1011, ×2^1)
   1  1  0  1  1             (For the left-most 1 in 1011, ×2^3)
   ─────────────────────
   1  0  0  1  0  1  0  0  1  (Adding)
   1  1  1 10  1  1  1
```

11011 × 1011 = 100101001

SELF TEST 7.10

Evaluate 10111 × 1101 in binary.

100101011

Note You can also do binary arithmetic by converting to denary, doing the calculation, then converting back to binary.

7.3 Hexadecimal, base 16

In hexadecimal, or **hex** for short, numbers are written in base 16. As 16 is greater than 10, we need new symbols for numbers from 10 to 15. We use the letters A to F.

Table 7.4 The first sixteen numbers in denary and hexadecimal notation

Denary	1	2	3	4	5	6	7	8
Hexadecimal	1	2	3	4	5	6	7	8
Denary	9	10	11	12	13	14	15	16
Hexadecimal	9	A	B	C	D	E	F	10

In hex, sixteen itself is written 10. Seventeen is written 11, and so on. The digits represent powers of 16.

$$\begin{aligned} \text{hex } 2C7 &= 2 \times 16^2 + 12 \times 16^1 + 7 \times 16^0 \\ &= 512 + 192 + 7 \text{ denary} \\ &= 711 \text{ denary} \end{aligned}$$

Converting denary to hexadecimal

The method is similar to that in binary. To convert from denary to hexadecimal, divide repeatedly by 16, until 0 is left. The remainders are numbers less than 16. Write down these remainders. The final remainder gives the left-most digit.

EXAMPLE 7.10

Convert 1016 to hexadecimal.

Solution
1016 ÷ 16 gives   63   remainder 8.
63   ÷ 16 gives   3   remainder 15 (i.e.F).
3   ÷ 16 gives   0   remainder 3.
Hence the number is 3F8.

In hexadecimal, the number is 3F8

SELF TEST 7.11

Convert 1453 to hex.

5AD

Converting hexadecimal to denary

Again, the method is similar to that in binary. To convert from hexadecimal to denary, convert to the appropriate power of 16. 1 is 16^0, 10 is 16^1, 100 is 16^2, 1000 is 16^3 and so on. Then add these numbers multiplied by the appropriate digit.

EXAMPLE 7.11

Convert BA5E to denary.
Solution

$$\begin{array}{cccc} B & A & 5 & E \\ 16^3 & 16^2 & 16^1 & 16^0 \end{array}$$

$$\begin{aligned} \text{hex BA5E} &= 11 \times 16^3 + 10 \times 16^2 + 5 \times 16 + 14 \\ &= 45056 + 2560 + 80 + 14 \text{ denary} \\ &= 47\,710 \text{ denary} \end{aligned}$$

The number is 47 710

SELF TEST 7.12

Convert 4EF9 to denary.

20 217

Converting binary and hexadecimal

Because $16 = 2^4$, it is easy to convert between binary and hexadecimal. Each group of four binary digits corresponds to a single hexadecimal digit.

The correspondence is in Table 7.5.

Table 7.5 Binary, hexadecimal and denary conversions

Binary	Hexadecimal	Denary
0000	0	0
0001	1	1
0010	2	2
0011	3	3
0100	4	4
0101	5	5
0110	6	6
0111	7	7
1000	8	8
1001	9	9
1010	A	10
1011	B	11
1100	C	12
1101	D	13
1110	E	14
1111	F	15

EXAMPLE 7.12

Convert the following.
a) 111001110010011011 to hex   b) D32A to binary

Solution

a) Write out the number in groups of four digits.

11 1001 1100 1001 1011

These correspond to 3, 9, C, 9 and B respectively.

The hex number is 39C9B

b) D, 3, 2 and A correspond to 1101, 0011, 0010 and 1010 respectively. Write out the full binary number

The binary number is 1101001100101010

SELF TEST 7.13

a) Convert 100101110 to hex
b) Convert FAB to binary

a) 12E,   b) 111110101011

Note   Some scientific calculators can work in binary and hex. If you have a calculator like this, then conversion is easy.

Binary coded decimal

Ordinary arithmetic uses the denary system (base 10). In **binary coded decimal** form (**bcd**), each denary digit is converted to four binary digits. These are joined together to form a string of 0s and 1 s.

EXAMPLE 7.13

Convert 37 to binary coded decimal.

Solution

In binary, 3 is 0011 and 7 is 0111. Put these together

The bcd form is 00110111

Note   The number 37 was converted to true binary in Example 7.6. Note that the two forms are different.

SELF TEST 7.14

Convert 59 to bcd.

01011001

EXAMPLE 7.14

Convert the bcd number 010001010010 to denary form.

Solution

Split the number into groups of four, as

0100 0101 0010

These correspond to the digits 4, 5 and 2 respectively.

The denary form is 452

SELF TEST 7.15

Convert 100100110101 in bcd to decimal.

935

■ CHECK YOUR UNDERSTANDING

● There are 60 minutes (′) in a degree. There are 60 seconds (″) in a minute. When doing arithmetic on angles expressed in minutes and seconds, the carry over happens at 60.
● In binary, the only digits are 0 and 1. The carry over happens at 2.
● In hexadecimal, there are digits from 1 to 15. 10 up to 15 are written as A, B, C, D, E and F. The carry over happens at 16.
● When converting between binary and hexadecimal, each group of four binary digits corresponds to one hexadecimal digit.
● In binary coded decimal (bcd) form, each group of four binary digits corresponds to one denary digit.

REVISION EXERCISES AND QUESTIONS

7.1 Time and angles, base 60

1 Convert the following to degrees, minutes and seconds.
   a) 8.25°   b) 28.2°   c) 17.8°
   d) 60.38°   e) 27.351°   f) 83.905°

2 Convert the following to decimals.
   a) 7° 30′   b) 61° 12′   c) 29° 40′
   d) 12° 21′   e) 20° 31′ 12″ f) 82° 0′ 36″

3 Evaluate the following, leaving your answers in degrees, minutes and seconds.
   a) 31° 25′ + 21° 45′   b) 40° 29′ + 17° 33′
   c) 12° 33′ 27″ + 29° 12′ 40″ d) 53° 40′ 29″ + 7° 19′ 38″
   e) 37° 12′ − 11° 52′   f) 49° 5′ − 31° 28′
   g) 54° 23′ 20″ − 27° 12′ 30″ h) 52° 18′ 25″ − 25° 20′ 39″

4 Show how the angle gauges of Table 7.2 can be used to make the following angles.
   a) 12° 8′   b) 30° 58′
   c) 30° 42′ 12″ d) 98° 19′ 48″

7.2 Binary, base 2

5 Convert the following denary numbers to binary.
   a) 27   b) 58   c) 93

6 Convert the following binary numbers to denary.

    a) 10010011   b) 111011   c) 100010

7 Evaluate the following binary expressions, leaving your answers in binary.

    a) $11101 + 10001$ b) $101010 + 110011$

    c) 1111×111 d) 1100×1001

7.3 Hexadecimal, base 16

8 Convert the following denary numbers to hex.

    a) 78   b) 2766   c) 47806

9 Convert the following hex numbers to denary.

    a) 41A   b) 3E9   c) 29A

10 Convert the following.

    a) 100010110 from binary to hex

    b) A3F from hex to binary

11 Convert the following.

    a) 45 to bcd

    b) 0100100100110101 in bcd to denary

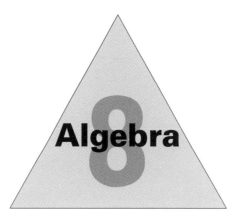

Algebra

Introduction

Suppose that you have a cooker with temperatures in °Celsius, but a recipe book with temperatures in °Fahrenheit. At the front of the book there may be a table converting Fahrenheit to Celsius, like that of Table 8.1.

Table 8.1 Conversion table for Fahrenheit and Celsius

° Fahrenheit	° Celsius
200	93
212	100
250	121
300	150
350	180
390	200
400	205
425	220
450	230
500	260

A table cannot give all the possible values. To find the exact conversion for °Fahrenheit to °Celsius, for all possible values, we need to have a rule or **formula**. The rule is:

Subtract 32, divide by 9, multiply by 5.

There is an algebraic formula for this rule.

$$C = (F - 32) \times \frac{5}{9}$$

Algebraic formulae provide short, accurate statements of rules. The rule works for all temperatures, not only those for cooking. It works for the temperature of melting iron, 1535°C, and for the liquefying point of nitrogen, −196°C.

8.1 Formulae

Science and technology contain many algebraic formulae. A formula is a general rule, true for all values. For example

$$\text{speed} = \text{distance} \div \text{time}$$

This formula, in words, gives the general rule for calculating speed. We can shorten it by giving letters for distance and time.

$$\text{speed} = d \div t$$

The letters in the formula are **variables**, which can stand for any number. In the formula above, the variables are d and t, which stand for any distance and any time.

A number multiplying a variable is called the **coefficient** of the variable. We do not need to use a × sign.

$$3 \times x + 7 = 3x + 7$$

In this formula, x is a variable, and 3 is its coefficient.

The variable letters in a formula stand for ordinary numbers. Hence the letters follow the same rules as numbers. Multiplication and division are done before addition and subtraction.

$3x + 7$ means 'multiply 3 and x and then add 7'

If the addition or subtraction should be done first, then use brackets.

$3(x + 7)$ means 'add x and 7, then multiply by 3'

When letters are multiplied, we do not need to use the × sign.

$$a \times b = ab$$

The rules governing positive and negative numbers apply to letters.

$$-a \times b = -ab \quad \text{(minus times plus is minus)}$$
$$-a \times -b = ab \quad \text{(minus times minus is plus)}$$

58

Notes

1 When multiplying numbers, we always use the × sign.

$$3 \times 7 \neq 37 \ (\neq \text{ means 'does not equal'})$$

2 The order of multiplication does not matter.

$$ab = ba$$

However, when multiplying numbers and letters, we usually put the number first. Write $3xy$, rather than $x3y$ or $xy3$.

8.2 Simplification of algebraic expressions

Often you can simplify an expression. Then when you substitute values, it will be easier, quicker, and more reliable.

EXAMPLE 8.1

Simplify the expression $5x \times 3y$.

Solution

Multiply 5 and 3, obtaining 15. This is the coefficient of $x \times y$, i.e. of xy.

$$5x \times 3y = 15xy$$

SELF TEST 8.1

Simplify the expression $7a \times 3b$.

21ab

Like terms

The expression $3x$ is the same as $x + x + x$. Similarly, simplifying $3x + 5x$ gives $8x$. The $3x$ and the $5x$ are **like terms**.

$$3x + 5x = 8x$$

But $3x$ and $5y$ are unlike terms. We cannot simplify $3x + 5y$, because x and y are unlike.

EXAMPLE 8.2

Simplify $5x + 7y - x + 8y$.

Solution

Combine the x terms, as $4x$. Combine the y terms, as $15y$. The x and y terms cannot be combined.

$$5x + 7y - x + 8y = 4x + 15y$$

SELF TEST 8.2

Simplify the following.

$$2x - 4y - x + 10y$$

x + 6y

Powers

A variable multiplied by itself is the square of the variable.

$$x \times x = xx = x^2$$

Similarly

$$yyy = y^3$$

Variables obey the same rules as numbers.

[1] $a^n \times a^m = a^{n+m}$ i.e. when multiplying, add the indices

[2] $a^n \div a^m = a^{n-m}$ (where $a \neq 0$) i.e. when dividing, subtract the indices

[3] $(a^n)^m = a^{nm}$ i.e. when taking a power of a power, multiply the indices

EXAMPLE 8.3

Simplify $8y^7 \div 2y^3$.

Solution

We can rewrite the expression like this.

$$\frac{8y^7}{2y^3}$$

Divide 8 by 2, obtaining 4. To divide y^7 by y^3, subtract the powers (rule [2]), obtaining y^4.

$$8y^7 \div 2y^3 = 4y^4$$

SELF TEST 8.3

Simplify $12z^7 \times 3z^2$.

$36z^9$

Zero, negative and fractional powers

Powers obey the following rules ($a > 0$ throughout).

[4] $a^0 = 1$ i.e. any number to the power 0 is 1

[5] $a^{-n} = \dfrac{1}{a^n}$ i.e. a negative power is the reciprocal of the positive power

[6] $a^{\frac{1}{n}} = \sqrt[n]{a}$ i.e. a fractional power is a root

Powers of variables obey the same rules as powers of numbers.

EXAMPLE 8.4

Simplify, by writing as single powers.
 a) $\sqrt{x^5}$ b) $k^{-5} \div k^{-2}$

Solution

a) The $\sqrt{}$ corresponds to a power of $\frac{1}{2}$.
$$\sqrt{x^5} = (x^5)^{\frac{1}{2}} = x^{2\frac{1}{2}}$$
$$\boldsymbol{\sqrt{x^5} = x^{2\frac{1}{2}}}$$

b) Subtract the powers
$$k^{-5} \div k^{-2} = k^{-5-(-2)} = k^{-5+2} = k^{-3}$$
$$\boldsymbol{k^{-5} \div k^{-2} = k^{-3}}$$

SELF TEST 8.4

Simplify by writing as single powers.
 a) $\frac{1}{\sqrt[3]{x}}$ b) $\sqrt{(x^{\frac{1}{4}} \div x^{\frac{1}{2}})}$

a) $x^{-\frac{1}{3}}$ b) $x^{-\frac{1}{8}}$

8.3 Substitution

Technical books and manuals have many formulae. The formula $V = IR$ gives the voltage when a current of I flows through a resistance of R.

Suppose you have a current of 5 amps, and a resistance of 7 ohms. Putting these values in
$$V = 5 \times 7 = 35 \text{ volts}$$
You **substitute** the numbers for the letters.

Substitution is the process of replacing an algebraic letter by a numerical value. This gives a special case of the general formula.

The formula at the beginning of the chapter converts from Fahrenheit to Celsius. It is true for all temperatures. If we substitute a number for F, then we find the corresponding value of C. For example, put $F = 50$.
$$C = (50 - 32) \times \frac{5}{9}$$
$$= 18 \times \frac{5}{9}$$
$$= 10$$
Hence $50°$F is equivalent to $10°$C.

EXAMPLE 8.5

Find the value of the formula $7x - 4$ when $x = 3$.

Solution
Substitute 3 for x.
$$7x - 4 = 7 \times 3 - 4$$
$$= 21 - 4$$
$$= 17$$

The value is 17

SELF TEST 8.5

Find the value of $8x + 2$ when $x = \frac{1}{2}$.

6

EXAMPLE 8.6

Find the value of $8x + 2y^2$ when $x = 5$ and $y = 3$.

Solution
Substitute 5 for x and 3 for y.
$$8x + 2y^2 = 8 \times 5 + 2 \times 3^2$$
$$= 40 + 2 \times 9$$
$$= 40 + 18$$
$$= 58$$

The value is 58

SELF TEST 8.6

Find the value of $3x^2 - 5y$ when $x = 2$ and $y = 4$.

−8

Subscripts

A **subscript** is a number or letter written below another letter, such as the 0 and n in I_0 and u_n. This is useful to describe quantities at different times. For example

I_0 the original value of the current, i.e. the value at $t = 0$
I_1 the current after 1 second.

EXAMPLE 8.7

After a rise in temperature of t, the length of a rod is given by
$$l = l_0 (1 + at)$$
If $l_0 = 1.7$ m and $a = 0.003$, find the length after a rise of $40°$C.

Solution

Substitute 1.7 for l_0, 0.003 for a and 40 for t.

$$l = l_0 (1 + at)$$
$$= 1.7(1 + 0.003 \times 40)$$
$$= 1.7(1 + 0.12)$$
$$= 1.7 \times 1.12$$
$$= 1.904$$

The length is 1.904 m

SELF TEST 8.7

The resistance, R Ω, of a wire at $t°C$ is given by

$$R = R_0 (1 + at).$$

If $R_0 = 23$ and $a = 0.015$, find the resistance at 20°C.

$$29.9 \ \Omega$$

EXAMPLE 8.8

The volume of a sphere is given by $V = \frac{4}{3}\pi r^3$, where r is the radius. Find the volume of a sphere of radius 63 mm. Put $\pi = 3.142$, or use the π button on your calculator.

Solution

Put $r = 63$ into the formula.

$$V = \frac{4}{3}\pi \times 63^3$$
$$= \frac{4}{3}\pi \times 250\,047$$
$$= 1\,047\,394\,....$$

The volume is 1 047 000 mm³

SELF TEST 8.8

The volume of a cone is $\frac{1}{3}\pi r^2 h$, where r is the base radius and h is the height. (See Figure 8.1). Find the volume of a cone with height 1.7 m and base radius 2.3 m.

$$9.417 \ \text{m}^3$$

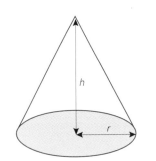

Figure 8.1   Volume of a cone $= \frac{1}{3}\pi r^2 h$

Substituting a formula into a formula

Sometimes we substitute a formula into another formula.

EXAMPLE 8.9

The power of an electrical circuit is given by $P = IV$. Use the formula $V = IR$ to express P in terms of I and R.

Solution

Replace V by IR in the first formula.

$$P = IV = I(IR) = IIR = I^2R$$

The formula is $P = I^2R$

SELF TEST 8.9

Find an expression for P in terms of V and R.

$$P = \frac{V^2}{R}$$

8.4 Construction of formulae

We construct a formula by converting a statement in words into an algebraic expression. At the beginning of this chapter we constructed the formula for converting from Fahrenheit temperature to Celsius. Here are some other examples.

Area of rectangle equals base times height

$$A = b \times h$$

Current in circuit equals voltage divided by resistance

$$I = V \div R$$

When you are given a statement in words, find the words which represent variables. Replace these by letters. Then find the operations performed on the variables. Replace these by $+$, $-$, $\times$ or $\div$. There are many ways the operations can be expressed in words.

   'sum' or 'add' is replaced by $+$
   'difference' or 'subtract' is replaced by $-$
   'product', 'times' or 'of' is replaced by $\times$
   'quotient' or 'divide' is replaced by $\div$

EXAMPLE 8.10

The potential difference, V, across a resistor is the product of the current, I, and the resistance, R. Write this as a formula.

Solution

Write V as I times R.

$$V = I \times R = IR$$
$$V = IR$$

SELF TEST 8.10

The stiffness, k, of a wire is its tension, T, divided by its extension e. Express this as a formula.

$$k = \frac{T}{e}$$

EXAMPLE 8.11

The area of a triangle is equal to half its base times its height. Write this as a formula.

Solution

The variables are the base and the height. Let these be b and h. The area is half the product of b and h. So multiply $\frac{1}{2}$, b and h.

$$\text{Area} = \frac{1}{2} \times b \times h$$

The area is $\frac{1}{2}bh$

SELF TEST 8.11

The area of an ellipse is a quarter of π times the product of the two diameters d_1 and d_2. (See Figure 8.2). Express this as a formula.

Area of ellipse $= \frac{1}{4}\pi d_1 d_2$

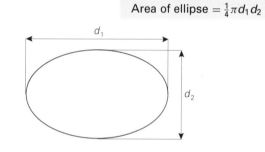

Figure 8.2 Ellipse

EXAMPLE 8.12

A pyramid has a square base. Its volume is a third of the base area times the height. Find a formula for the volume.

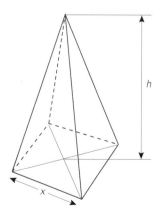

Figure 8.3 Pyramid

Solution

Let the side of the base be x, and the height h. The base area is $x \times x$, i.e. x^2. Multiply this by $\frac{1}{3}$ and by h

$$\text{Volume} = \frac{1}{3} \times x^2 \times h$$

The volume is $\frac{1}{3}x^2 h$

SELF TEST 8.12

The surface area of a sphere is found by squaring the radius, then multiplying by 4 and by π. Write this as a formula.

Surface area $= 4\pi r^2$

8.5 Expansion and factorisation

You do not always get a mathematical expression in the most useful form. Sometimes you need to change the expression before you use it.

Suppose you have an expression involving brackets. Removing the brackets is **expansion**. Putting an expression into brackets is **factorisation**.

Expansion

The expansion of brackets is the same for algebraic expressions as for numerical expressions.

$$x(a + b) = xa + xb$$

EXAMPLE 8.13

Expand and simplify $3(x + y) + 7(x - y)$.

Solution

Expand by the rule above.

$$3x + 3y + 7x - 7y$$

Simplify by collecting like terms.

$$10x - 4y$$
$$3(x + y) + 7(x - y) = 10x - 4y$$

SELF TEST 8.13

Expand and simplify $2(p - q) + 5(2p + 3q)$.

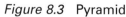

$12p + 13q$

Pairs of brackets

When two pairs of brackets are multiplied together, all the terms in the first pair must multiply all the terms in the second pair.

$$(x + y)(a + b) = x(a+b) + y(a + b)$$
$$= xa + xb + ya + yb$$

EXAMPLE 8.14

Expand and simplify $(2x + 3y)(x - y)$.

Solution

Multiply both terms in the first brackets by both terms in the second brackets.

$$(2x + 3y)(x - y) = 2x(x - y) + 3y(x - y)$$
$$= 2x \times x - 2x \times y + 3y \times x - 3y \times y$$
$$= 2x^2 - 2xy + 3yx - 3y^2$$

Collect like terms. Since $xy = yx$, $-2xy + 3yx = xy$.

$$(2x + 3y)(x - y) = 2x^2 + xy - 3y^2$$

SELF TEST 8.14

Expand and simplify $(3a + 4b)(2a - 5b)$.

$$6a^2 - 7ab - 20b^2$$

EXAMPLE 8.15

Expand and simplify $(2x - 5)^2$.

Solution

The expression inside the brackets is squared, i.e. multiplied by itself.

$$(2x - 5)^2 = (2x - 5)(2x - 5)$$
$$= 4x^2 - 10x - 10x + 25$$
$$= 4x^2 - 20x + 25$$

$$(2x - 5)^2 = 4x^2 - 20x + 25$$

Note Do not forget the middle term. $(2x - 5)^2 \neq 4x^2 + 25$.

SELF TEST 8.15

Expand and simplify $(3a + 2b)^2$.

$$9a^2 + 12ab + 4b^2$$

Factorisation

Factorisation is the opposite operation to expansion. If an expression is factorised, then there are fewer multiplications involved.

$$xa + xb = x(a + b)$$

Note There are two multiplications on the left hand side, but only one on the right.

EXAMPLE 8.16

Factorise $6ab - 9ac$.

Solution

The numbers 6 and 9 have a common factor of 3. The terms ab and ac have a common factor of a. Hence we can factorise by $3a$.

$$6ab - 9ac = 3a(2b - 3c)$$

SELF TEST 8.16

Factorise $6xy + 14xz$.

$$2x(3y + 7z)$$

EXAMPLE 8.17

The volume of a sphere of radius r is $\frac{4}{3}\pi r^3$. A hollow rubber ball has inner radius r and outer radius R, as shown in Figure 8.4. Find an expression for the volume of rubber, and factorise it.

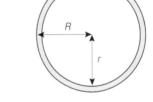

Figure 8.4 Hollow rubber ball

Solution

The volume of rubber is the difference between the total volume and the volume of the hollow inside.

$$\text{Volume of rubber} = \tfrac{4}{3}\pi R^3 - \tfrac{4}{3}\pi r^3$$

A factor of $\frac{4}{3}\pi$ can be taken out.

$$\textbf{Volume of rubber} = \tfrac{4}{3}\pi(R^3 - r^3)$$

Note In the factorised form, we only have to multiply by $\frac{4}{3}\pi$ once. It is easier to evaluate the formula in the factorised form.

SELF TEST 8.17

A square sheet of metal has side a m. Each m^2 of the sheet has mass ρ kg. A square of side b m is cut out. (See Figure 8.5). Find the mass of the remainder, factorising your answer.

$$\rho(a^2 - b^2)$$

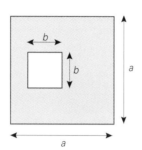

Figure 8.5 Metal sheet

 CHECK YOUR UNDERSTANDING

● In an algebraic formula, letters stand for numbers. The rules for numbers apply also to letters.
● Like terms involve the same letter or letters. Like terms can be combined.
● When the variables of a formula are substituted by numbers, the value of the formula is found.
● To make a formula, identify the variables and the operations. Replace the variables by letters, and the operations by $+, -, \times$ etc.
● Eliminating the brackets in a formula is expansion. Putting a formula into brackets is factorising.

REVISION EXERCISES AND QUESTIONS

8.1 Formulae

1   Simplify the following.
   a) $5x + 7x$ b) $8y - 2y$ c) $2\frac{1}{2}z + 3z$
   d) $7x + 5y - 3x + 4y$ e) $3a - 4b + 8a - 7b$
   f) $x^2 + 3x - 4x$ g) $5y^2 + 3y^2 + 7y + 4\frac{1}{2}y$
   h) $4xy + 7yx$ i) $2abc + 3acb + 4bac$
   j) $3ab + 4ab + a + 3b$ k) $6xy + 7x - 3y - 2x + 5yx$
   l) $2xy + 5yz + 2yx - zy$ m) $2.1x^2 + 7.3x^3 - x^2$
   n) $3x \times 5x$ o) $\frac{1}{2}y \times 4y$ p) $7a \times 4b$
   q) $6 \times 4n$ r) $-x \times 4y$ s) $-2a \times -4b$

   t) $-8z \times -3z$ u) $-p \times -3q \times 2r$
   v) $-x \times -y \times -z$ w) $-2x \times -3x$
   x) $-y \times -y \times -y \times -y$ y) $9a \div 3$
   z) $7b \div b$
   aa) $4ab \div a$ bb) $6pq \div 2q$
   cc) $4x^2 \div x$ dd) $8a^2b \div 4a$
   ee) $6x^2y^2 \div 2xy$ ff) $12m^2n^2 \div 4m^2n$
   gg) $2ab \div -b$ hh) $-7xy^2 \div -x$

8.2. Simplification of algebraic expressions

2   Simplify the following by writing as single powers.
   a) $x^5 \times x^6$ b) $a^4 \times a^5 \times a^7$ c) $p^{18} \times p^{12}$
   d) $y^{10} \div y^5$ e) $z^{12} \div z$ f) $q^5 \times q^6 \div q^3$
   g) $(x^3)^4$ h) $(y^5)^3$ i) $a^2 \times (a^2)^4$
   j) $(x^2 \times x^3)^4$ k) $(q^9 \div q^7)^2$ l) $(x^5 \times x^2)^3 \div x^3$

3   Write the following as single powers.
   a) $\sqrt{p}$ b) $(\frac{1}{x})^3$ c) $\frac{1}{\sqrt{y}}$
   d) $\sqrt{a^3}$ e) $\sqrt{x^{-7}}$ f) $(\sqrt{x})^3$
   g) $\sqrt[3]{y^2}$ h) $(x^2)^{\frac{1}{3}}$ i) $1/(\sqrt[4]{x})$
   j) $\sqrt{x} \times \sqrt[3]{x}$ k) $y^{-3} \div y$ l) $b^{-6} \times b^{-8}$
   m) $\sqrt{(x^4 \times x^5)}$ n) $x \div \sqrt[4]{x}$ o) $(y^{-3})^{-5}$

8.3. Substitution

4   Find the value of $7x - 5$ when x is a) 3, b) $\frac{3}{8}$, c) -7.

5   Find the value of $2y^2 - 3y$ when y is a) 3, b) $\frac{2}{3}$, c) -3.

6   Let $y = \sqrt{(x + 3)}$. Find y when x is a) 6, b) 2, c) $-2\frac{3}{4}$.

7   The third side of a triangle is given by $h = \sqrt{(a^2 + b^2)}$. Find h when $a = 5$ m and $b = 12$ m.

8   The kinetic energy, in Joules, of a moving body is given by $\frac{1}{2}mv^2$, where m is its mass and v is its speed. Find the kinetic energy of a ball of mass 2.3 kg moving at 27 m s^{-1}.

9   The potential energy, in Joules, of m kg raised a height h m is mgh, where g is approximately 9.81 m s^{-2}. Find the potential energy of 7.5 kg raised by 4.8 m.

10 The period, in seconds, of a pendulum of length l m is given by $2\pi\sqrt{(\frac{l}{g})}$ s, where g is approximately 9.81 m s^{-2}. Find the period of a pendulum of length 1.74 m.

11 A belt passes over a pulley at v m s^{-1}. The tensions on either side are F_1 N and F_2 N. The power, in watts, is equal to $v(F_1 - F_2)$ W. Find the power if $v = 26$, $F_1 = 960$ and $F_2 = 345$.

12 The surface area of a cylinder of radius r m and height h m is $2\pi r(r + h)$ m^2. Find the area of a cylinder with radius 0.256 m and height 1.533 m.

8.4 Construction of formulae

13 The rectangle shown in Figure 8.6 has length l m and width w m. Find an formula for its perimeter. (The total distance round it).

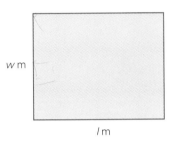

w m

l m

Figure 8.6 Rectangle

14 A pilot flew for 2 hours at v_1 km/hr, then for $2\frac{1}{2}$ hours at v_2 km/hr. Find the total distance travelled. Find the average speed.

15 The density of a chemical is d kg m^{-3}.

   a) Find the mass of 1.5 m^3 of the chemical, in terms of d.
   b) Find the volume of 850 kg of the chemical, in terms of d.

16 An alloy consists of copper and zinc in the ratio 3:2, by volume. Find the total mass of 0.5 m^3 of the alloy, if the densities of copper and zinc are d_1 kg m^{-3} and d_2 kg m^{-3} respectively.

17 A workman is paid #32 per hour. How much does he get for h hours?

18 The basic rate for a workman is #m per hour. Overtime is #2 per hour greater. How much does he receive for a week in which he worked 38 hours ordinary time and 6 hours overtime?

19 The gravitational force between two particles is the product of their masses, divided by the square of the distance between them, multiplied by the universal constant of gravity, G. Find the force between objects of masses m_1 and m_2 at a distance d apart.

8.5 Expansion and factorisation

20 Expand the following.

   a) $5(a + b)$ b) $7(x - y)$ c) $3(p + 2q)$
   d) $4(2x + 3y)$ e) $a(b + c)$ f) $2x(3y + z)$
   g) $x(3x + 7)$ h) $r(2r - t)$ i) $-(a + 7)$
   j) $-(x - y)$ k) $-3(n - 3m)$ l) $-2x(6 - x)$

21 Expand the following and simplify as far as possible.

   a) $2(x + y) + 3(x + 4y)$ b) $7(3a + 2b) + 8(2a + 3b)$
   c) $2(p + 3q) - 3(4p + q)$ d) $3(n + m) - 4(n - 2m)$
   e) $5(x + 7) - 3(x - 2)$ f) $7(2v - 3u) + 4(v - u)$
   g) $x(x + 5) + 2x(x - 3)$ h) $2a(a + 5b) + 3a(8a - 4b)$
   i) $x(2x + 3y) + y(3x + 9y)$ j) $2a(a + b) - 3b(a - b)$

22 Expand the following and simplify as far as possible.

   a) $(x + 7)(x + 3)$ b) $(x + 8)(x + 2)$
   c) $(y - 5)(y + 2)$ d) $(y - 4)(y - 8)$
   e) $(p + 9)(p - 1)$ f) $(2x + 1)(x + 5)$
   g) $(3y - 2)(y + 8)$ h) $(2x - 3)(3x - 2)$
   i) $(a + 3)(b + 4)$ j) $(x + 3)(y - 7)$
   k) $(2m + 3)(4n + 9)$ l) $(2k - 3)(7j - 1)$

23 Expand the following and simplify as far as possible.

   a) $(p + q)^2$ b) $(m - n)^2$ c) $(2a + b)^2$
   d) $(3r + 2t)^2$ e) $(5x - 3y)^2$ f) $(1 - 7x)^2$
   g) $(p - q)(p + q)$ h) $(2x + 3y)(2x - 3y)$
   i) $(4x + 2y)(2x - y)$ j) $(\frac{1}{2} + x)(\frac{1}{2} - x)$

24 Factorise the following.

   a) $3x + 6y$ b) $4a + 8$ c) $5z + 5$
   d) $7a - 21b$ e) $x^2 + 4x$ f) $3y - 6y^2$
   g) $ax + bx$ h) $x^2 + xy$ i) $4a^2 + 6ab$
   j) $15xy^2 + 10x^2y$ k) $a^3 + a^2 + a$
   l) $ab + ac + a^2$ m) $x^3y + x^2y^2 + xy^3$

Coordinates and graphs

Introduction

Technical books often contain graphs, which show how two quantities are related. It is often easier to understand quantities from a picture than from a formula or from a table of data.

Figure 9.1 shows the calibration graph of a measuring instrument. It shows the error for each measurement. It is useful, for at least two reasons.

● For each measurement, we can find the error, and hence find the true measurement.
● The general shape of the graph tells us that, as the measurement increases, the error also increases.

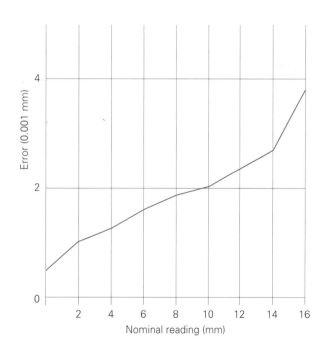

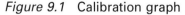

Figure 9.1 Calibration graph

9.1 Plotting graphs

On graph paper, positions are given in terms of two perpendicular lines. These are the **axes**. Usually the horizontal axis is the **x-axis**, and the vertical axis is the **y-axis**. The axes cross at the **origin**. See Figure 9.2.

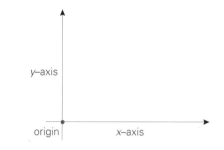

Figure 9.2

Along both axes, put in 1, 2, 3 and so on. See Figure 9.3. At the origin both x and y are 0. At the point labelled A, the x value is 4 and the y value is 3. The **x coordinate** is 4 and the **y coordinate** is 3. We say that A is at (4, 3). Notice that the x coordinate is given first. Sometimes we describe the point as A(4, 3).

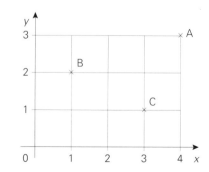

Figure 9.3

EXAMPLE 9.1

Give the coordinates of the point B of Figure 9.3.

Solution

The x coordinate is 1, and the y coordinate is 2.

B is at (1, 2)

SELF TEST 9.1

Give the coordinates of the point C of Figure 9.3.

(3, 1)

Fractional coordinates

Coordinates can be fractions. Make sure you read the divisions between integers correctly.

In Figure 9.4, there are 10 divisions between integers. Hence each division is 0.1. The x coordinate of point A is 1.3.

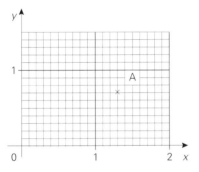

Figure 9.4

In Figure 9.5, there are 5 divisions between integers. Hence each division is 0.2. The x coordinate of point A is 2.8.

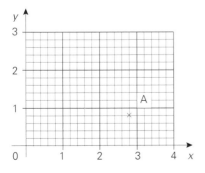

Figure 9.5

EXAMPLE 9.2

Find the coordinates of the point A in Figure 9.6.

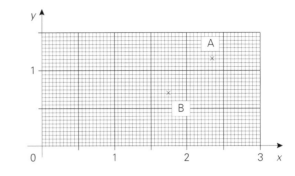

Figure 9.6

Solution

There are 20 divisions between integers. Hence each division is 0.05. The x coordinate is $2 + 7 \times 0.05$, i.e. 2.35. Similarly the y coordinate is 1.15.

The point A is at (2.35, 1.15)

SELF TEST 9.2

Give the coordinates of the point B in Figure 9.6.

(1.75, 0.7)

EXAMPLE 9.3

On Figure 9.7, place the point C(0.65, 1.3).

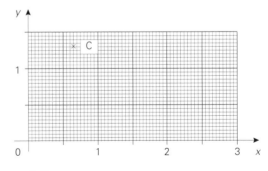

Figure 9.7

Solution

On the x-axis, go 13 divisions to the right of 0. On the y-axis, go 6 divisions above 1. The point with these coordinates is labelled C.

SELF TEST 9.3

Copy Figure 9.7 on graph paper. Mark the point D (2.7, 0.85).

EXAMPLE 9.4

Give the coordinates of the point A on Figure 9.8.

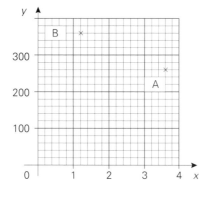

Figure 9.8

Solution

The x-axis is labelled with integers. But the y-axis goes up in steps of 100. There are 5 divisions between each 100, hence each division is 20.

A is at (3.6, 260)

SELF TEST 9.4

Give the coordinates of the point B on Figure 9.8.

(1.2, 360)

Negative coordinates

At the origin both coordinates are 0. To the left of the origin the x coordinate is negative, and below the origin the y coordinate is negative. On Figure 9.9, the point labelled A is at (−2, −1).

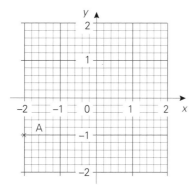

Figure 9.9

EXAMPLE 9.5

Find the coordinates of the point A of Figure 9.10.

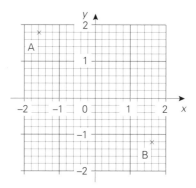

Figure 9.10

Solution

There are 5 divisions between integers, hence each is 0.2. The point is 3 units to the left of −1, and 4 units above 1.

A is at (−1.6, 1.8)

SELF TEST 9.5

Find the coordinates of the point B of Figure 9.10.

(1.6, −1.2)

9.2 Reading from graphs

Graphs show the relationship between two quantities. If you are given the value of one quantity, you can find the value of the other quantity.

EXAMPLE 9.6

The graph of Figure 9.11 shows the relationship between temperature and hardness for a certain material. Find
   a) the hardness at 600°C
   b) the temperature for a hardness of 1100 VPN.

Solution

a) From 600 on the horizontal axis, go up to the curve. Go across to the vertical axis, and read off the hardness.

   The hardness is approximately 1270 VPN

b) From 1100 on the vertical axis, go across to the curve. Go down to the horizontal axis, and read off the temperature.

   The temperature is 700°C

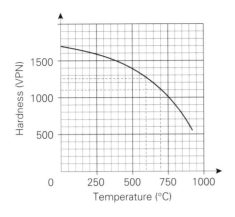

Figure 9.11 Graph of hardness and temperature

SELF TEST 9.6

From the graph of Figure 9.11, find the hardness at 500°C and the temperature for a hardness of 1500 VPN.

1400 VPN, 375°C

9.3 Constructing graphs

Technicians often need to construct a graph, in order to read information from it. The graph is constructed either from experimental data, or from a formula.

Construction from data

Suppose you are given pairs of values of two variables. Plot them on a graph, then join up with a line.

EXAMPLE 9.7

A micrometer is tested on standard gauges. Table 9.1 gives the error of the reading shown by the micrometer. Construct a graph (called a calibration chart) to show the data.

Table 9.1 Error generated by a micrometer

Gauge (mm)	2.5	5.2	7.8	10.9	13.0	15.6	18.1
Error (0.001 mm)	1	2	3	3	4	4	5

Solution
Number the *x*-axis with values between 0 and 20. Number the *y*-axis with values from 0 to 6. Label the axes, making sure to include the units. Plot the points, and join them up. The result is shown in Figure 9.12.

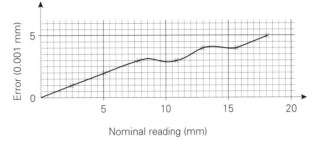

Figure 9.12 Calibration chart for a micrometer

SELF TEST 9.7

The hardness of a certain steel was measured at different temperatures. The results are in Table 9.2. Construct a graph to show the data.

Table 9.2 Relationship of temperature and hardness of steel

Temperature (°C)	0	100	200	300	400	500
Hardness (VPN)	850	830	790	740	610	500

Conversion graphs

You can make a graph to convert between two variables, such as Fahrenheit temperature and Celsius temperature.

EXAMPLE 9.8

At a certain time the exchange rate between the # and the US dollar is #17.5 for each US$. Construct a graph to convert between # and US$.

Solution
Set up axes as shown in Figure 9.13. Let the US$ axis run

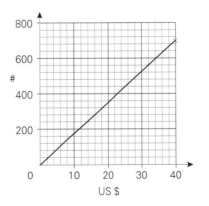

Figure 9.13 Graph of exchange rate between # and US$

between 0 and 40, and the # axis between 0 and 800. The graph goes through the origin (#0 is equal to US $0!). Also US$40 is equivalent to #700, so plot (40, 700) on the graph. Join this point with the origin as shown.

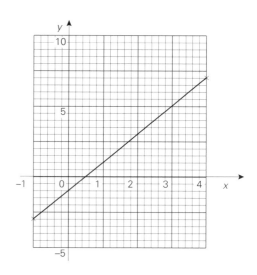

Figure 9.14   Graph of y = 2x − 1

SELF TEST 9.8

Freezing temperature is 0° in Celsius and 32° in Fahrenheit. Boiling temperature is 100° in Celsius and 212° in Fahrenheit. Construct a graph to convert temperatures from Celsius to Fahrenheit.

9.4 Linear graphs

We have drawn graphs from experimental data or from a conversion rate. We can also draw a graph from a theoretical formula. The graph gives a picture of how the formula behaves.

Suppose the formula gives y as a function of x. Construct a table, showing values of x and the corresponding values of y. Plot points on graph paper, and join the points up.

There are many different shapes of graph. Certain shapes occur frequently, and in time you will be able to recognise them. In this section we look at straight line graphs.

A **linear graph** is a straight line. It comes from an equation $y = mx + c$, where m and c are constant (fixed numbers).

On a linear graph, the slope (or **gradient**) is constant. A change of 1 in x causes a fixed change of m in y. These are examples of quantities which might have a linear graph.

● Temperature and resistance. The electrical resistance, $R\ \Omega$, of a wire at $T°C$ might be given by
$$R = aT + c$$

● Speed and time. When something is thrown downwards, its speed $v\ \text{ms}^{-1}$ after t seconds might be given by
$$v = gt + c$$

EXAMPLE 9.9

Plot the graph of $y = 2x - 1$, taking x values between −1 and 4.
Solution
For $x = -1$, $y = 2 \times -1 - 1 = -3$.
For $x = 4$, $y = 2 \times 4 - 1 = 7$.

Draw axes on graph paper, marking the x-axis between −1 and 4, and the y-axis between −5 and 10. Plot (−1, −3) and (4, 7). Join up with a straight line, as shown in Figure 9.14.

SELF TEST 9.9

Plot the graph of $y = 3x + 2$, for values of x between −2 and 3.
Find a point on your line and check that it obeys the equation $y = 3x + 2$.

Finding the equation of a straight line graph

If you have plotted two points on a straight line graph, you can join them up with a ruler.

The equation of a straight line is of the form $y = mx + c$. The gradient (or slope) is given by m

where $m = \dfrac{Y_2 - Y_1}{X_2 - X_1}$ [1]

$= \dfrac{\text{difference in } y\text{-values}}{\text{difference in } x\text{-values}}$ (See Figure 9.15)

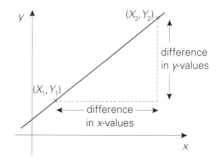

Figure 9.15   Straight line graph

Suppose you know the coordinates of one point on the line. Equation [1] could be written:

$$y - y\text{-value} = m \times (x - x\text{-value})$$

or $\qquad y - y\text{-value} = mx - m \times x\text{-value}$

rearranging $\qquad y = mx - m \times x\text{-value} + y\text{-value}$

Compare with $y = mx + c$. $\quad c = - m \times x\text{-value} + y\text{-value}$

This gives the value of c.

Alternatively in $y = mx + c$, if $x = 0, y = c$.

Hence c is the **y-intercept**, the point where the line crosses the y-axis.

> If we know the gradient, m and the y-intercept, c, of a straight line, we can write down the equation of the line.
>
> $$y = mx + c$$

EXAMPLE 9.10

Find the equation of the line which goes through $(1, 7)$ and $(3, 11)$.

Solution
The difference in y-values is $11 - 7$, i.e. 4. The difference in x-values is $3 - 1$, i.e. 2.

$$m = \frac{\text{difference in } y\text{-values}}{\text{difference in } x\text{-values}} = \frac{4}{2} = 2$$

Write down the equation, using the point $(1, 7)$.

$$y = mx + c$$
$$7 = 2 \times 1 + c$$
$$c = 7 - 2$$
$$= 5$$

The equation is $y = 2x + 5$

Note We used the first point to find the value of c. We can use the second point $(3, 11)$ to check the answer. Put $y = 11$ and $x = 3$.

$$mx + c = 2x + 5$$
$$= 2 \times 3 + 5$$
$$= 11$$

So $\qquad y = mx + c$ This is correct.

SELF TEST 9.10

Find the equation of the straight line which goes through $(-1, 3)$ and $(2, 12)$.

$$y = 3x + 6$$

Negative gradient

The equation of Example 9.10 had a positive value of m. Hence the graph was increasing. If m is negative, then the graph is decreasing. See Figure 9.16.

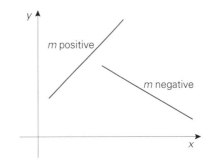

Figure 9.16 Positive and negative gradients

EXAMPLE 9.11

Find the equation of the straight line through $(-2, 6)$ and $(2, 3)$.

Solution
The y change is $3 - 6$, i.e. -3. The x change is $2 - (-2)$, i.e. $+4$. Hence the gradient is $-\frac{3}{4}$.

Use the second point to find c.

$$3 = -\tfrac{3}{4} \times 2 + c$$
$$c = 3 + 1\tfrac{1}{2}$$
$$= 4\tfrac{1}{2}$$

The equation is $y = -\tfrac{3}{4}x + 4\tfrac{1}{2}$

SELF TEST 9.11

Find the equation of the straight line through $(1, 4)$ and $(3, -1)$.

$$y = -2\tfrac{1}{2}x + 6\tfrac{1}{2}$$

9.5 Quadratic graphs

The linear graphs of Section 9.4 were straight lines. You can draw them with a ruler. If the graph is curved, then do not join the points with a ruler. Join them up with a smooth curve.

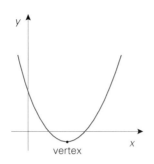

Figure 9.17 Quadratic graph

A quadratic graph has the shape of Figure 9.17. It comes from an equation $y = ax^2 + bx + c$, where a, b and c are constants. This shape is a **parabola**. The point at the bottom is called the **vertex**.

On a quadratic graph, y changes rapidly when x is large. These are examples of quantities which have a quadratic graph.

● Power and current. When a current of I amps passes through a circuit, the power, P watts, generated is given by

$$P = kI^2$$

● Distance and time. When something is thrown downwards, its distance d m after t seconds might be given by

$$d = gt^2 + ct$$

EXAMPLE 9.12

Plot the graph of $y = x^2 - 3x + 1$, taking values of x between 0 and 4.

What is the least value of y?

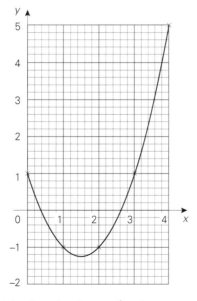

Figure 9.18 Graph of $y = x^2 - 3x + 1$

Solution

We take x values of 0, 1, 2, 3, 4. Put these in a row of a table. For each value of x, evaluate x^2 and $3x$. From these evaluate y.

x	0	1	2	3	4
x^2	0	1	4	9	16
$3x$	0	3	6	9	12
y	1	−1	−1	1	5

Plot the points (0, 1), (1, −1), (2, −1), (3, 1) and (4, 5). Join them up by a smooth curve. The result is shown in Figure 9.18. Note that the lowest point of the graph is (1.5, −1.25).

The least value of y is −1.25.

SELF TEST 9.12

Draw the graph of $y = x^2 - 5x + 3$, taking values of x between 1 and 6.

What is the least value of y?

−3.25

Values of *a*, *b* and *c*

Let us look at some special cases of quadratic graphs. See Figure 9.19.

If $c = 0$, i.e. if $y = ax^2 + bx$, then if $x = 0$, $y = 0$ so the graph goes through the origin.

If $b = 0$, i.e. if $y = ax^2 + c$, then the graph is symmetric about the y-axis.

If a is negative, then the vertex of the graph is at the top.

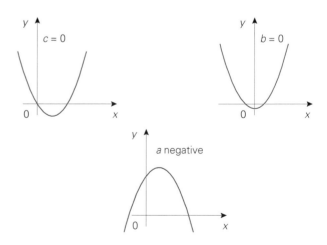

Figure 9.19 Special cases of quadratic graphs

EXAMPLE 9.13

Figure 9.20 shows the graph of $y = ax^2 + bx + c$. What can you say about a, b and c?

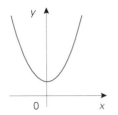

Figure 9.20 Graph of $y = ax^2 + bx + c$

Solution

The graph is symmetric about the y-axis, hence $b = 0$.
  When $x = 0$, y is positive. Hence c is positive.
  The graph has its vertex at the bottom, hence a is positive.

a is positive, $b = 0$, c is positive

SELF TEST 9.13

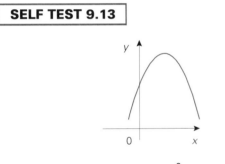

Figure 9.21 Graph of $y = ax^2 + bx + c$

Figure 9.21 shows the graph of $y = ax^2 + bx + c$. What can you say about a, b and c?

a is negative, $b \neq 0$, c is positive

9.6 Reciprocal graphs

Remember that the reciprocal of x is $\frac{1}{x}$. A reciprocal graph comes from an equation $y = \frac{c}{x}$, where c is constant.

It has the shape of Figure 9.22. This shape is a **hyperbola**.

  When x becomes large, y approaches 0. As x approaches 0, y becomes large. x never equals 0, y never equals 0. These are examples of quantities with a reciprocal graph.

● Current and resistance. The current, I amps, which flows through a circuit of resistance R Ω, is given by

$$I = \frac{k}{R}$$

● Pressure and volume. The pressure, P N m^{-2}, of a mass of gas occupying V m^3, is given by

$$P = \frac{k}{V}$$

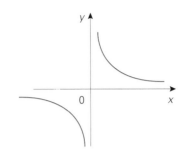

Figure 9.22 Reciprocal graph

EXAMPLE 9.14

Plot the graph of $y = \frac{2}{x}$, for values of x between -3 and 3.

Solution

Set up a table of values as below. Note that $\frac{2}{0}$ is not defined, so we do not include $x = 0$.

x	-3	-2	-1	$-\frac{1}{2}$	$-\frac{1}{4}$	$\frac{1}{4}$	$\frac{1}{2}$	1	2	3
y	$-\frac{2}{3}$	-1	-2	-4	-8	8	4	2	1	$\frac{2}{3}$

Plot the graph as in Figure 9.23. Note that as x tends to 0, the graph climbs up or down the y axis.

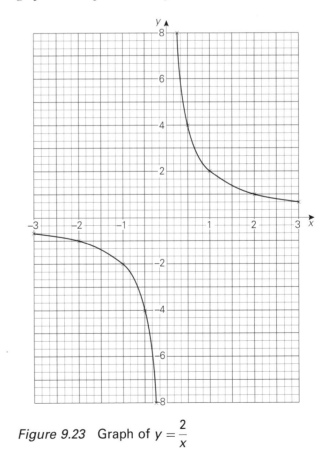

Figure 9.23 Graph of $y = \frac{2}{x}$

SELF TEST 9.14

Plot the graph of $y = \dfrac{\frac{1}{2}}{x}$, for values of x between -4 and 4.

EXAMPLE 9.15

Plot the graph of $y = 4 - \dfrac{1}{x}$, for values of x between 1 and 6.

Solution

Set up a table of values.

x	1	2	3	4	5	6
y	3	$3\frac{1}{2}$	$3\frac{2}{3}$	$3\frac{3}{4}$	$3\frac{4}{5}$	$3\frac{5}{6}$
y	3	3.5	3.$\dot{6}$	3.75	3.8	3.8$\dot{3}$

Plot the graph as in Figure 9.24. Note that as x becomes larger, the graph approaches $y = 4$.

Note   The y values start at 3. Hence the y-axis is labelled from 2 to 4, rather than from 0 to 4.

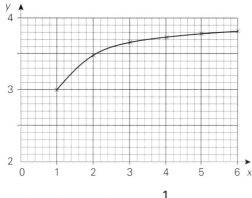

Figure 9.24   Graph of $y = 4 - \dfrac{1}{x}$

SELF TEST 9.15

Plot the graph of $y = 3 - \left(\dfrac{\frac{1}{2}}{x} \right)$, for values of x between $\frac{1}{2}$ and 3.

■ CHECK YOUR UNDERSTANDING

● The two right-angled lines of a graph are the axes. The axes cross at the origin. The coordinates of a point are the x-value and the y-value. The x value is always given first. Take care when reading fractional values.

● A graph can be constructed either from data or from a formula.

● The formula $y = mx + c$ has a straight line (linear) graph. The gradient of the line is m, and it crosses the y-axis at c. The equation of the line can be found from two points on the line.

● A quadratic graph has equation $y = ax^2 + bx + c$. If a is positive the graph has a lowest point, and if a is negative the graph has a highest point.

● A reciprocal graph has equation $y = \frac{c}{x}$. The graph is not defined at $x = 0$. As x tends to 0 then the graph shoots up or down the y-axis.

REVISION EXERCISES AND QUESTIONS

9.1 Plotting graphs

1   Give the coordinates of points A, B and C on Figure 9.25.

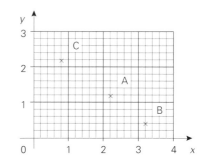

Figure 9.25

2   Give the coordinates of points D, E and F on Figure 9.26.

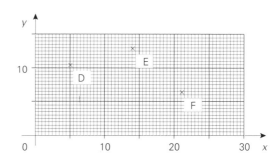

Figure 9.26

3   Give the coordinates of points G, H and I on Figure 9.27.

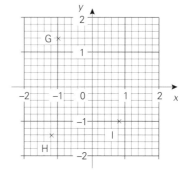

Figure 9.27

4 Copy Figure 9.28. Plot the points (2.7, 1.6) and (1.9, 0.3).

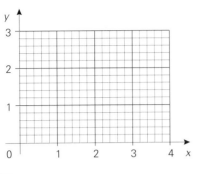

Figure 9.28

5 Copy Figure 9.29. Plot the points (2.7, 25) and (1.1, 19).

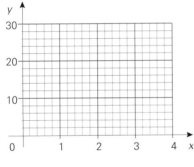

Figure 9.29

6 Copy Figure 9.30. Plot the points (−1, 1.1), (1.3, −0.7) and (−1.8, −1.6).

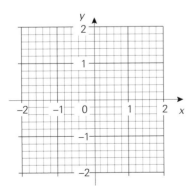

Figure 9.30

9.2 Reading from graphs

7 The graph of Figure 9.31 shows the relationship between t and P.

a) Find P when $t = 2.7$.

b) Find t when $P = 22$.

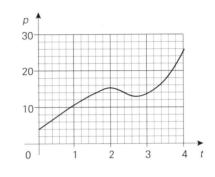

Figure 9.31

9.3 Constructing graphs

8 The table below gives values of x and y. Plot the graph of y against x.

x	0.1	0.2	0.3	0.4	0.5	0.6	0.7	0.8
y	23	31	40	50	63	77	86	104

9 The conversion rate between the £ (British Pound) and the $ (American Dollar) is $1.5 for £1. Construct a conversion chart between the £ and the $.

10 In the Réaumur temperature scale, water freezes at 0° and boils at 80°. Construct a conversion chart between Réaumur temperature and Fahrenheit. (On the Fahrenheit scale water freezes at 32° and boils at 212°.)

9.4 Linear graphs

11 Plot the graph of $y = 3x + 2$, for values of x between −1 and 4.

12 Plot the graph of $y = \frac{2}{3}x - 1$, for values of x between −3 and 3.

13 Plot the graph of $y = -2x + 1\frac{1}{2}$, for values of x between −3 and 2.

14 Figure 9.32 shows three straight line graphs. Below are three equations. Match the equation with the graph.

a) $y = x - \frac{1}{2}$ b) $y = -\frac{1}{4}x + 1\frac{1}{2}$ c) $y = -x + 3$

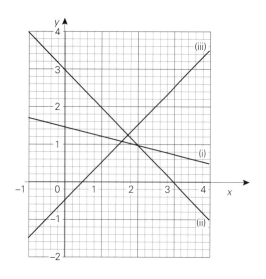

Figure 9.32

15 Find the equations of the following straight lines.

a) with gradient 2, through (1,1)
b) through (1,4) and (3,8)
c) through (3,8) and (5,2)

16   Find the equations of the lines a), b) and c) in Figure 9.33.

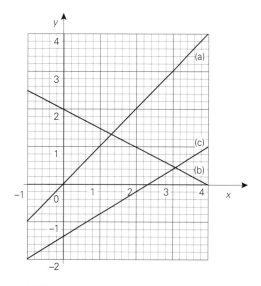

Figure 9.33

9.5 Quadratic graphs

17 Plot the following graphs, for values of x in the given range.

a) $y = 2x^2$ −3 to 3
b) $y = x^2 - 2$ −3 to 3
c) $y = x^2 - 3x$ 0 to 4
d) $y = -3x^2$ −2 to 2
e) $y = 3 - x^2$ −2 to 2
f) $y = 2x - x^2$ −3 to 1
g) $y = x^2 - 2x + 3$ −1 to 4
h) $y = 2x^2 + 3x + 5$ −2 to 2

18 Figure 9.34 shows four graphs of the form $y = ax^2 + bx + c$. Below are four equations. Match the graphs with the equations.

a) $y = 4 - x^2$ b) $y = x^2 - x$

c) $y = 3x^2$ d) $y = x^2 - x + 3$

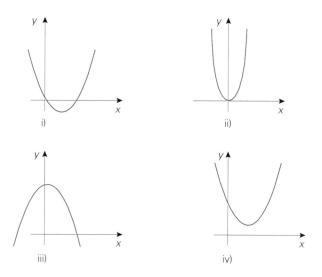

Figure 9.34

9.6 Reciprocal graphs

19 Plot the following graphs, for values of x between −3 and 3.

a) $y = \dfrac{1}{x}$ b) $y = -\dfrac{2}{x}$

c) $y = \dfrac{1}{x} + 2$ d) $y = 3 - \dfrac{2}{x}$

Equations

Introduction

Much technical information consists of formulae. When a formula is put equal to a value, the result is an equation. You need to be able to solve many kinds of equation.

For example, when a wire is under tension T, its length, L m, might be given by

$$L = 0.0012T + 1.1$$

If we want to find the tension for a particular length we need to solve an equation. To find the tension for a length of 1.2 m we solve the equation:

$$1.2 = 0.0012T + 1.1$$

Some equations involve only basic operations like addition, multiplication and so on. Other equations involve functions such as e^x, $\sqrt{x}$ and so on.

10.1 Equations with one unknown

In all equations, there is an unknown. In the equation $7 = 2x - 13$, the unknown is x. You **solve** the equation by finding the value of the unknown. You need to get the unknown x by itself on one side of the equation.

In all equations, there is one rule which you must obey.

> An equation is unchanged if you do to the left what you do to the right.

Imagine an equation is like a set of scales, with the $=$ sign as the pivot. If you add 13 to the right hand side, you must add 13 to the left hand side. If you divide the left hand side by 2, you must divide the right hand side by 2.

The equation $7 = 2x - 13$ is a **linear equation**. It corresponds to a straight line graph. The graph of $y = 2x - 13$ is shown in Figure 10.1.

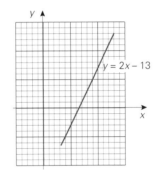

Figure 10.1

EXAMPLE 10.1

Solve the equation $7 = 2x - 13$.

Solution
Add 13 to both sides.

$$7 = 2x - 13$$
$$13 + 7 = 2x$$
$$20 = 2x$$

Divide both sides by 2, obtaining $x = 10$.

The solution is $x = 10$

SELF TEST 10.1

Solve the equation $5x - 3 = 17$.

$x = 4$

When the unknown occurs twice

In the equation $5x + 7 = 2x + 40$, the unknown x occurs twice. Collect the xs together and then proceed as in Example 10.1.

77

EXAMPLE 10.2

Solve the equation $5x + 7 = 2x + 40$.

Solution

Subtract $2x$ from both sides.

$$5x + 7 = 2x + 40$$
$$-2x + 5x + 7 = 40$$
$$3x + 7 = 40$$

Subtract 7 from both sides.

$$3x = 33$$

Divide both sides by 3, obtaining $x = 11$.

The solution is $x = 11$

Check Put the solution into both sides of the original equation.

$$\text{LHS} = 5 \times 11 + 7 = 62 \qquad \text{RHS} = 2 \times 11 + 40 = 62$$

The solution is correct, because the LHS is equal to the RHS.

SELF TEST 10.2

Solve the equation $3x - 7 = 13 - 2x$. Check that your answer is correct.

$x = 4$. Both sides $= 5$

Equations with fractions

An equation with fractions is more complicated. It is easiest to clear up the fractions, by multiplying by the LCM of the fractions.

EXAMPLE 10.3

Solve the equation $\frac{1}{2}x = \frac{3}{8}x + 13$.

Solution

The denominators are 2 and 8. The LCM of 2 and 8 is 8. Multiply both sides of the equation by 8.

$$8 \times \tfrac{1}{2}x = 8 \times \tfrac{3}{8}x + 8 \times 13$$
$$4x = 3x + 104$$
$$4x - 3x = 104$$
hence $$x = 104$$

The solution is $x = 104$

SELF TEST 10.3

Solve the equation $\frac{2}{5}x = \frac{3}{4}x - 28$.

$x = 80$

Equations with brackets

If an equation involves brackets, then expand and collect the like terms.

EXAMPLE 10.4

Solve the equation $2(x - 3) = 5(x - 21)$

Solution

$$2(x - 3) = 5(x - 21)$$

Expand the brackets

$$2x - 6 = 5x - 105$$

Collect the numbers on the left and the xs on the right.

$$105 - 6 = 5x - 2x$$
$$99 = 3x$$
$$\text{Hence } x = 33$$

The solution is $x = 33$

SELF TEST 10.4

Solve the equation $3(x + 7) = 2(x + 29)$

$x = 37$

Unknown denominator

In some equations, the unknown is part of the denominator of a fraction. In this case, multiply by the denominator.

EXAMPLE 10.5

Solve the equation

$$\frac{3}{2x} = 5.$$

Solution

Multiply both sides of the equation by $2x$.

$$2x \times \frac{3}{2x} = 2x \times 5$$
$$3 = 2x \times 5$$
$$3 = 10x$$
$$\text{Hence } x = \tfrac{3}{10}$$

The solution is $x = 0.3$

SELF TEST 10.5

Solve the equation $\dfrac{7}{3x} = 5$.

$x = \frac{7}{15}$

EXAMPLE 10.6

Solve the equation $\dfrac{3}{x+7} = \dfrac{1}{x+1}$.

Solution
Multiply both sides by $(x+7)$ and by $(x+1)$. This technique is called cross-multiplying.

$$(x+7)(x+1) \times \frac{3}{x+7} = (x+7)(x+1) \times \frac{1}{x+1}$$
$$(x+1) \times 3 = (x+7) \times 1$$
$$3x+3 = x+7$$
$$2x = 4$$
Hence $x = 2$

The solution is $x = 2$

SELF TEST 10.6

Solve the equation $\dfrac{5}{x+2} = \dfrac{4}{x-3}$.

$x = 23$

10.2 Simultaneous equations

In Section 10.1 there was one equation with one unknown. Equations with more than one unknown are **simultaneous equations**.

For example, suppose we have an equation linking tension T and length L, of the form

$$L = kT + c$$

where k and c are constants. Suppose we find that tension 5 N gives a length 1.3 m, and that tension 20 N gives a length 1.4 m. We have two simultaneous equations with unknowns k and c.

$$1.3 = 5k + c$$
$$1.4 = 20k + c$$

How to solve simultaneous equations

Suppose the unknowns are x and y. We **eliminate** either x or y.

For example:
1) Adjust the equations so that the coefficients of y are equal.
2) Then add or subtract the equations so that y is eliminated.
3) You will have an equation in x only, which you solve by the methods of Section 10.1.
4) Substitute the value of x into one of the equations, to find the value of y.

Note
a) You may eliminate x rather than y, and then you will have an equation in y only.
b) When you have found x and y, substitute them into the other of the original equations. This lets you check that your answer is correct.

EXAMPLE 10.7

Solve the following simultaneous equations.

$$3x + 2y = 7 \qquad [1]$$
$$5x - 2y = 1 \qquad [2]$$

Solution
Note that there is $+2y$ in [1], and $-2y$ in [2]. We do not need step 1. Add [1] and [2], to eliminate the y terms.

$$\begin{array}{r} 3x + 2y = 7 \\ 5x - 2y = 1 \\ \hline 8x \quad\;\; = 8 \end{array} \quad [1]+[2]$$

Divide by 8, to obtain $x = 1$.
Substitute $x = 1$ into [1].

$$3 + 2y = 7$$

Subtract 3 and divide by 2, obtaining $y = 2$.

The solution is $x = 1$ and $y = 2$

Check Put $x = 1$ and $y = 2$ into [2].

$$\text{LHS} = 5 - 4 = 1 \qquad \text{RHS} = 1$$

The solution is correct.

SELF TEST 10.7

Solve these equations.

$$3x + y = 8$$
$$2x - y = 12$$

$x = 4,\ y = -4$

EXAMPLE 10.8

Solve these equations.

$$5x + 3y = 31 \qquad [1]$$
$$3x + y = 17 \qquad [2]$$

Solution
The coefficients of x are different, and the coefficients of y are different. We cannot quickly eliminate either x or y, hence we do need Step 1.

Multiply [2] by 3 so that the coefficients of y are equal.

$$3 \times (3x + y) = 3 \times 17 \qquad\qquad 3 \times [2]$$
$$9x + 3y = 51 \qquad\qquad [3]$$

Subtract [1] from [3], and the y terms will cancel.

$$9x + 3y = 51$$
$$\underline{5x + 3y = 31}$$
$$4x \quad\quad = 20 \quad [3] - [1]$$

Hence $x = 5$. Substitute into [2]

$$3 \times 5 + y = 17$$
$$y = 17 - 15$$
$$= 2$$

$$\boldsymbol{x = 5 \text{ and } y = 2}$$

SELF TEST 10.8

Solve these equations.

$$4x + 3y = 37$$
$$x + 2y = 13$$

$$\boxed{x = 7, \, y = 3}$$

EXAMPLE 10.9

Solve these equations.

$$3x - 5y = 16 \qquad\qquad [1]$$
$$4x + 3y = 31 \qquad\qquad [2]$$

Solution
Change both equations so that the x coefficients are equal.
Multiply [1] by 4 and [2] by 3.

$$12x - 20y = 64 \qquad\qquad [3] = 4 \times [1]$$
$$12x + 9y = 93 \qquad\qquad [4] = 3 \times [2]$$

Now subtract [3] from [4].

$$12x + 9y = 93$$
$$\underline{12x - 20y = 64}$$
$$29y = 29 \quad [4] - [3]$$

(Note that $9y - (-20y) = 9y + 20y = 29y$.)
Hence $y = 1$. Substitute into [2]

$$4x + 3 \times 1 = 31$$
$$4x = 31 - 3$$
$$4x = 28$$
$$x = 7$$

$$\boldsymbol{x = 7 \text{ and } y = 1}$$

SELF TEST 10.9

Solve these equations.

$$2x + 7y = 39$$
$$5x - 4y = -10$$

$$\boxed{x = 2, \, y = 5}$$

10.3 Equations with powers and roots

Some equations involve powers. You need the rules of powers to solve these equations.

Equating indices

If numbers raised to a certain power are equal, then the indices are equal.

$$\text{If } a^x = a^y, \text{ where } a \neq 0, \text{ then } x = y.$$

For example, if $2^{3x} = 2^{12}$, then $3x = 12$. Hence $x = 4$.

EXAMPLE 10.10

Solve the equation $2^{x+13} = 4^{x-2}$.
Solution
Write 4 as 2^2.

$$2^{x+13} = 4^{x-2}$$
$$= (2^2)^{x-2}$$
$$= 2^{2x-4}$$

Hence $\qquad x + 13 = 2x - 4$
$$13 + 4 = 2x - x$$

This gives $x = 17$.

$$\textbf{The solution is } \boldsymbol{x = 17}$$

SELF TEST 10.10

Solve the equation $9^x = 3^{3x-7}$

$$\boxed{x = 7}$$

Finding roots or powers

If an equation involves the nth power of the unknown, then take the nth root.

$$\text{If } x^n = k, \text{ then } x = \sqrt[n]{k}$$

For example, if $x^2 = 9$, then $x = \sqrt{9}$. $x = 3$.

If an equation involves the nth root of the unknown, then take the nth power.

$$\text{If } \sqrt[n]{x} = k, \text{ then } x = k^n.$$

For example, if $\sqrt[3]{x} = 2$, then $x = 2^3$. $x = 8$

EXAMPLE 10.11

Solve the equation $(3x - 7)^3 = 125$.

Solution

$$3x - 7 = \sqrt[3]{125}$$

The cube root of 125 is 5.

Hence $\quad\quad\quad 3x - 7 = 5$
$$3x = 12$$

The solution is $x = 4$

SELF TEST 10.11

Solve the equation $(11 - 4x)^3 = 27$.

$x = 2$

EXAMPLE 10.12

Solve the equation $\sqrt{(2x - 5)} = 3$.

Solution
Square both sides, obtaining

$$2x - 5 = 9$$
$$2x = 14.$$

The solution is $x = 7$

SELF TEST 10.12

Solve the equation $\sqrt[3]{(4x + 9)} = 5$.

$x = 29$

10.4 Solving equations by graphs

When a graph crosses the x-axis, the value of y is 0. You can use this to solve an equation.

EXAMPLE 10.13

In Example 9.12 of the previous chapter, we drew the graph of $y = x^2 - 3x + 1$. Use this graph to solve the equation $x^2 - 3x + 1 = 0$.

Solution
The graph of $y = x^2 - 3x + 1$ is shown in Figure 9.18 (page 72). The graph crosses the x axis at two values, 0.4 and 2.6. At these points $y = 0$, hence $x^2 - 3x + 1 = 0$.

The solutions are $x = 0.4$ and $x = 2.6$

SELF TEST 10.13

Look at the graph of Self Test 9.12 from Chapter 9. Use the graph to solve the equation $x^2 - 5x + 3 = 0$.

$x = 0.7$ and $x = 4.3$

Solving simultaneous equations using graphs

When two graphs cross, both the corresponding equations are true. This provides a way of solving simultaneous equations.

EXAMPLE 10.14

Plot the graphs of the formulae $y = 3x - 7$ and $y = 2x + 3$. Hence solve the simultaneous equations

$$y = 3x - 7 \quad\quad [1]$$
$$y = 2x + 3 \quad\quad [2].$$

Solution
Plot the graphs, by the methods of Chapter 9. The result is Figure 10.2. Note that the graphs cross at (10, 23). This gives the solution.

The solution is $x = 10$ and $y = 23$

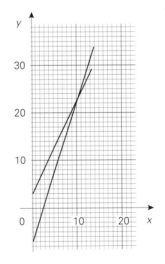

Figure 10.2 Graphs of $y = 3x - 7$ and $y = 2x + 3$

SELF TEST 10.14

Plot the graphs of $y = 3x - 4$ and $y = x + 3$. Hence solve the simultaneous equations.

$$y = 3x - 4$$
$$y = x + 3$$

$$x = 3\tfrac{1}{2}, \; y = 6\tfrac{1}{2}$$

10.5 Problems which lead to equations

Practical problems give rise to equations. In this section we show how to change a practical problem to an equation.

You are given an equation in words. It might be

> The total mass of ten cars and eight lorries is 50 000 kg.

1) Let variable letters stand for the quantities you don't know. Here the unknowns are the mass of each car and the mass of each lorry.

> Let each car have a mass x kg
> Let each lorry have a mass y kg

2) Find the operations which act on the variables. There are 10 cars and 8 lorries. Multiply x by 10, and multiply y by 8. Add the results.

> Total mass $= 10x + 8y$

3) The word 'is' corresponds to the $=$ sign. Write down the equation

> $$10x + 8y = 50\,000$$

EXAMPLE 10.15

A workman receives #3 more for an hour of overtime than for an hour of normal time. In a week he works 38 hours normal time and 6 hours overtime. He receives #238. What is the normal hourly rate?

Solution

1) We do not know the hourly rate. This is the unknown.

> Let the normal hourly rate be #x.

2) Then the overtime hourly rate is #$(x + 3)$. The pay for the normal hours is #$38x$, and the pay for the overtime hours is #$6(x + 3)$.

> Total pay $=$ #$38x +$ #$6(x + 3)$

3) We know that the total pay is #238. This gives the equation.

> $$38x + 6(x + 3) = 238$$

Expand the brackets and simplify.

$$38x + 6x + 18 = 238$$
$$44x + 18 = 238$$
$$44x = 220$$

Hence

$$x = 5$$

The normal hourly rate is #5

SELF TEST 10.15

A lorry's speed along dirt roads is 20 km/hr less than along made-up roads. It travels for 2 hours along a made-up road, then for 3 hours along a dirt road. The total distance it travels is 340 km. Find its speed along made-up roads. (Remember: distance $=$ speed $\times$ time.)

80 km/hr

EXAMPLE 10.16

You have available two alloys of copper and tin. One alloy is 10% tin, the other is 25% tin. How can you obtain 120 kg of an alloy which is 20% tin?

Solution

We don't know the required amount of each alloy. Let variables stand for these amounts.

> Let the amount of the first alloy be x kg
> Let the amount of the second alloy be y kg

The total amount is 120 kg.

$$x + y = 120 \qquad\qquad [1]$$

The total amount of tin in the final alloy is 20% of 120 kg. i.e. 24 kg. This comes from the tin in the original alloys. The amount of tin in the first alloy is 10% of x kg, i.e. $0.1x$ kg. Similarly the amount of tin in the second alloy is $0.25y$ kg. Hence the total amount of tin is given by

$$0.1x + 0.25y = 24 \qquad\qquad [2]$$

[1] and [2] are simultaneous equations. Solve them by the methods of Section 10.2 to find that $x = 40$ and $y = 80$.

Take 40 kg of the first alloy and 80 kg of the second alloy.

SELF TEST 10.16

A firm employs 60 people. The apprentices earn #80 per week, and the qualified staff earn #140 per week. The total wage bill is #7920. Find the number of apprentices employed.

8 apprentices

EXAMPLE 10.17

A square carpet is placed in a square room, with a border of 1.5 m around it. The area of the room is 64 m². Find the side of the carpet.

Solution

The unknown is the side of the carpet. See Figure 10.3.

Let the side of the carpet be x m.

The carpet has two spaces of 1.5 m on either side.

The side of the room is $(x + 3)$ m

We know that the area of the room is 64 m². This gives the equation.

$$(x + 3)^2 = 64$$

Take the square root of both sides, to obtain

$$x + 3 = 8$$

The side of the carpet is 5 m

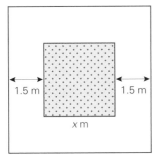

Figure 10.3 Carpet in a room

SELF TEST 10.17

A closed box is a cube made out of material 25 mm thick. The external volume is 343×10^6 mm³. Find the internal side.

650 mm

■ CHECK YOUR UNDERSTANDING

● When one expression is put equal to another, an equation is obtained. You solve the equation by finding the value of the unknown. The basic rule for solving an equation is: do to the left what you do to the right.

● If the unknown occurs more than once, collect together all the terms with the unknown.

● Equations with more than one unknown are simultaneous equations. Eliminate one of the unknowns. You then have an equation with one unknown, which you solve by ordinary methods.

● If an equation involves a function of the unknown, then use the inverse function.

● The solution of an equation can be found from where a graph crosses the x-axis. Simultaneous equations can be solved by finding where two graphs cross.

● A problem in words can often be changed to an equation. Let letters stand for the unknown quantities, identify the operations on the unknowns, and write down the equation.

REVISION EXERCISES AND QUESTIONS

10.1 Equations with one unknown

1 Solve the following equations.
  a) $x - 6 = 11$ b) $x + 7 = 18$ c) $2x + 5 = 23$
  d) $3x - 8 = 16$ e) $9 - x = 2$ f) $17 - x = 4$
  g) $2x + 3 = x + 17$ h) $5x + 9 = 7x - 11$
  i) $x + 12 = 15 - 2x$
  j) $\frac{1}{2}x + \frac{1}{3}x = 15$ k) $\frac{1}{3}x - \frac{1}{4}x = 7$ l) $5(x + 3) = 20$
  m) $6(x - 3) = 7(x - 9)$ n) $3(x + 3) + 5(x - 6) = 7$
  o) $\dfrac{33}{x} = 11$ p) $\dfrac{12}{x + 3} = 5$ q) $\dfrac{x + 7}{x - 3} = 2$

10.2 Simultaneous equations

2 Solve the following pairs of simultaneous equations.
  a) $x + y = 17$ b) $2x + y = 5$ c) $3x + 2y = 6$
  $\ x - y = 5$ $\ 4x + y = 13$ $\ 6x - 2y = 12$
  d) $4x + 3y = 31$ e) $4x + 3y = 15$ f) $4x + y = 15$
  $\ x - 2y = 5$ $\ 5x + y = 16$ $\ 3x - 4y = 16$
  g) $4x + 5y = 23$ h) $7x - 3y = 59$ i) $5x - 9y = -33$
  $\ 3x + 2y = 12$ $\ 4x - 5y = 37$ $\ 2x + 7y = 8$
  j) $\frac{1}{2}x + \frac{1}{3}y = 8$ k) $0.1x + 0.5y = 11$ l) $\frac{5}{8}x + \frac{1}{3}y = 38$
  $\ \frac{1}{2}x - \frac{2}{3}y = 2$ $\ 0.3x + 0.7y = 17$ $\ \frac{2}{3}x + \frac{3}{4}y = 50$

10.3 Equations with powers and roots

3 Solve the following equations.
  a) $2^{x-3} = 2^{2x-7}$ b) $3^{5-x} = 3^{x-9}$ c) $2^{5x} = 8^{x+6}$
  d) $25^{2x-1} = 5^{3x+8}$ e) $(2x + 5)^2 = 100$
  f) $(2 - 3x)^3 = 64$ g) $\sqrt{(3x + 5)} = 4$
  h) $\sqrt{(9 - 2x)} = 2$ i) $\sqrt[3]{(8 - x)} = 6$

10.4 Solving equations by graphs

4 Draw the graphs of $y = 3x + 7$ and $y = 3 - 2x$. Hence solve the equations

$$y = 3x + 7, \quad y = 3 - 2x.$$

5 Draw the graph of $y = x^2 - 3x - 5$, for values of x between -2 and 5. Hence solve the equation

$$x^2 - 3x - 5 = 0.$$

10.5 Problems which lead to equations

6 A nut has a mass 22 mg less than a bolt. The total mass of 13 nuts and 17 bolts is 4304 mg. What is the mass of a bolt?

7 A team of 5 qualified workers and 2 apprentices were paid #244 for a job. Each apprentice was paid #11 less than a qualified worker. How much was each apprentice paid?

8 The three angles of a triangle are $x°$, $(x + 20)°$ and $(x + 40)°$. Find x, given that the sum of the angles of a triangle is 180°.

9 The length of a rectangular field is 30 m greater than its width. The perimeter is 380 m. Find the width of the field.

10 An alloy contains 30% copper. How much of this alloy must be mixed with 20 kg of pure copper to make an alloy which is 60% copper?

11 100 litres of liquid contains water and alcohol in the ratio 2:3. How much water should be added to make the ratio 3:2? How much alcohol should be added to make the ratio 1:5?

12 A firm employs 100 people. Their monthly salaries are either #320 or #490. The total monthly wage bill is #44 070. Find how many people are employed at #320 per month.

13 Two solutions are available. One is 30% alcohol, the other 40% alcohol. How much of each should be mixed to obtain 100 litres which is 32% alcohol?

14 The length, L m, of a wire under tension T N is given by

$$L = kT + c$$

where k and c are constant. The length is 2.7 m for a tension of 20 N, and 2.8 m for a tension of 40 N. Find k and c.

15 The resistance, R Ω, of a wire at $t°$C is given by

$$R = kt + c$$

where k and c are constant. The resistance is 148 Ω at 50°C, and 154 Ω at 80°C. Find k and c.

16 The length k m of a bar at $t°$C is given by $k = k_0 (1 + at)$. At 10°C the length is 1.234 m, and at 100°C the length is 1.241 m. Find k_0 and a.

Further algebra

Introduction

In this chapter we continue the algebra that you need in your work as a technician. Some branches of technology require more complicated algebra. For example, work related to television and radio requires functions involving exponentials, logarithms and so on.

11.1 Algebraic fractions

For an ordinary fraction like $\frac{3}{8}$, the numerator and denominator are numbers. In an **algebraic fraction**, the numerator or the denominator may be algebraic expressions. These are examples of algebraic fractions.

$$\frac{a}{b} \qquad \frac{x}{3} \qquad \frac{1}{x+7} \qquad \frac{x+3y}{x+y^2}.$$

Algebraic fractions obey the same rules as ordinary fractions.

Simplification

A fraction is unchanged if you multiply or divide the numerator and denominator by the same term.

$$\frac{3x}{9y} = \frac{x}{3y} \qquad \text{(dividing top and bottom by 3)}$$

$$\frac{x}{4} = \frac{x^2}{4x} \qquad \text{(multiplying top and bottom by } x\text{)}$$

EXAMPLE 11.1

Simplify the following fractions.

a) $\dfrac{a+a^2}{a+ab}$ b) $\dfrac{3-x}{-4}$

Solution

a) Divide top and bottom by a.

$$\frac{a+a^2}{a+ab} = \frac{1+a}{1+b}$$

b) Multiply top and bottom by -1.

$$\frac{3-x}{-4} = \frac{x-3}{4}$$

SELF TEST 11.1

Simplify the following fractions.

a) $\dfrac{6x}{2x^2}$ b) $\dfrac{3+9x}{3y}$ c) $\dfrac{8-4x}{-2}$

> a) $\dfrac{3}{x}$ b) $\dfrac{1+3x}{y}$ c) $2x-4$

Multiplication and division

Multiplication

Multiply the numerators and multiply the denominators.

$$\frac{a}{b} \times \frac{c}{d} = \frac{ac}{bd}$$

Division

Turn the second fraction upside down and multiply, as you did with numerical fractions.

$$\frac{a}{b} \div \frac{c}{d} = \frac{a}{b} \times \frac{d}{c} = \frac{ad}{bc}$$

EXAMPLE 11.2

Write the following as single fractions.

a) $\dfrac{x}{2} \times \dfrac{y}{3}$ b) $\dfrac{3x}{4y} \div \dfrac{2x}{5y}$

Solution

a) Multiply the numerators and the denominators.

$$\frac{x}{2} \times \frac{y}{3} = \frac{xy}{6}$$

b) Turn the second fraction upside down, then multiply.

$$\frac{3x}{4y} \div \frac{2x}{5y} = \frac{3x}{4y} \times \frac{5y}{2x}$$

$$= \frac{15xy}{8xy}$$

Divide top and bottom by xy.

$$\frac{3x}{4y} \div \frac{2x}{5y} = \frac{15}{8}$$

SELF TEST 11.2

Write the following as single fractions.

a) $\dfrac{3}{x} \times \dfrac{4}{y}$ b) $\dfrac{3x}{y} \div \dfrac{9y}{x}$

a) $\dfrac{12}{xy}$ b) $\dfrac{x^2}{3y^2}$

Addition and subtraction

Before you add or subtract fractions, find a **common denominator**. This is an expression which both denominators will divide into. Then add the numerators. If the denominators have no common factor, the common denominator is their product. For example, the letters b and d have no common factor, hence their common denominator is bd.

$$\frac{a}{b} + \frac{c}{d} = \frac{ad}{bd} + \frac{bc}{db} = \frac{ad + bc}{bd}$$

EXAMPLE 11.3

Write the following as a single fraction.

$$\frac{3}{x} + \frac{4}{y}$$

Solution

Here x and y have no common factor. Hence the common denominator is xy.

$$\frac{3}{x} + \frac{4}{y} = \frac{3y}{xy} + \frac{4x}{xy}$$

$$= \frac{3y + 4x}{xy}$$

$$\frac{3}{x} + \frac{4}{y} = \frac{3y + 4x}{xy}$$

SELF TEST 11.3

Write the following as a single fraction.

$$\frac{5}{a} + \frac{6}{b}$$

$$\frac{5b + 6a}{ab}$$

Least common denominator (LCD)

The **least common denominator** is the simplest expression which the original denominators will divide into. If the original denominators have no common factor, then their LCD is their product. If they do have a factor in common, then a simpler common denominator is possible. For example, the expressions b^2 and bd have the factor b in common. Their LCD is b^2d. Hence

$$\frac{a}{b^2} + \frac{c}{bd} = \frac{ad}{b^2d} + \frac{bc}{b^2d} = \frac{ad + bc}{b^2d}$$

EXAMPLE 11.4

Find the LCD of x, x^2 and x^3. Hence write the following as a single fraction.

$$\frac{y}{x} + \frac{y^2}{x^2} + \frac{y^3}{x^3}$$

Solution

All three terms will divide into x^3.

$$\textbf{The LCD is } x^3$$

Use the least common denominator, x^3.

$$\frac{y}{x} + \frac{y^2}{x^2} + \frac{y^3}{x^3} = \frac{yx^2}{x^3} + \frac{y^2x}{x^3} + \frac{y^3}{x^3}$$

$$= \frac{yx^2 + y^2x + y^3}{x^3}$$

$$\frac{y}{x} + \frac{y^2}{x^2} + \frac{y^3}{x^3} = \frac{yx^2 + y^2x + y^3}{x^3}$$

SELF TEST 11.4

Write the following as a single fraction.

$$\frac{1}{x} + \frac{1}{xy} + \frac{1}{xyz}$$

$$\frac{yz + z + 1}{xyz}$$

Factorising to find the LCD

To find the least common denominator of more complicated expressions, factorise them. Then make the product of the factors which appear in any of the expressions.

EXAMPLE 11.5

Find the LCM of $15a^3b$ and $10ab^3$. Hence write the following as a single fraction.

$$\frac{2}{15a^3b} - \frac{3}{10ab^3}$$

Solution

The factors of $15a^3b$ are 3, 5, a, a, a, b.

The factors of $10ab^3$ are 2, 5, a, b, b, b.

Hence the LCM must have factors 2, 3, 5, a, a, a, b, b, b.

The LCM of $15a^3b$ and $10ab^3$ is $30a^3b^3$

Now give both fractions this LCD.

$$\frac{2}{15a^3b} - \frac{3}{10ab^3} = \frac{2 \times 2b^2}{30a^3b^3} - \frac{3 \times 3a^2}{30a^3b^3}$$
$$= \frac{4b^2 - 9a^2}{30a^3b^3}$$

$$\frac{2}{15a^3b} - \frac{3}{10ab^3} = \frac{4b^2 - 9a^2}{30a^3b^3}$$

SELF TEST 11.5

Find the LCM of $21x^2y^3$ and $28x^3y^2$. Hence write the following as a single fraction.

$$\frac{1}{21x^2y^3} + \frac{1}{28x^3y^2}$$

$$84x^3y^3, \quad \frac{4x + 3y}{84x^3y^3}$$

Fractions within fractions

In some algebraic fractions, there may be fractions in the numerator or in the denominator. To simplify, multiply numerator and denominator by the LCD of these fractions.

EXAMPLE 11.6

Simplify this fraction.

$$\frac{2}{\frac{1}{p} + \frac{1}{q}}$$

Solution

The denominator contains fractions. The LCD of these fractions is pq. Multiply numerator and denominator of the original fraction by pq.

For the denominator,

$$pq \times \left(\frac{1}{p} + \frac{1}{q}\right) = \frac{pq}{p} + \frac{pq}{q}$$
$$= q + p \quad \text{(by cancelling)}$$

For the numerator $pq \times 2 = 2pq$

$$\frac{2}{\frac{1}{p} + \frac{1}{q}} = \frac{2pq}{q + p}$$

SELF TEST 11.6

Simplify this fraction.

$$\frac{\frac{1}{x}}{x + y}$$

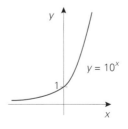

Errors with algebraic fractions

It is easy to make mistakes when using algebraic fractions. We end this section with some common errors concerning algebraic fractions. Be careful of the following

$$\frac{a}{b + c} \neq \frac{a}{b} + \frac{a}{c} \quad \text{Don't split the denominator}$$

$$\frac{a}{c} + \frac{b}{d} \neq \frac{a + b}{c + d} \quad \text{Don't add the numerators and denominators}$$

$$\frac{x + y}{x + z} \neq \frac{y}{z} \quad \text{Don't subtract from numerator and denominators}$$

$$\frac{1}{\frac{1}{x} + \frac{1}{y}} \neq x + y \quad \text{Don't invert the fraction}$$

Algebraic and ordinary fractions obey the same rules. If you are not sure about a rule for algebraic fractions, test it on ordinary fractions. For example, for the first error above:

$$\frac{6}{2 + 3} = \frac{6}{5} = 1\frac{1}{5}$$

but

$$\frac{6}{2} + \frac{6}{3} = 3 + 2 = 5.$$

11.2 Power and logarithmic functions

Power functions

An expression like 10^x is a **power function**. The exponent of 10 is variable. This function grows very quickly. Its graph is shown in Figure 11.1.

Figure 11.1 Graph of $y = 10^x$

Power functions have the same algebraic rules as ordinary powers. Provided that a is positive

$$a^x \times a^y = a^{x+y} \qquad a^x \div a^y = a^{x-y} \qquad (a^x)^y = a^{xy}$$

$$a^0 = 1 \qquad a^{-x} = \frac{1}{a^x} \qquad a^{\frac{1}{x}} = \sqrt[x]{a}$$

EXAMPLE 11.7

Simplify the following.
  a) $10^{3x} \times 10^{5x}$ b) $100^{2x} \div 10^x$

Solution
a) Add the indices.

$$10^{3x} \times 10^{5x} = 10^{8x}$$

b) Write 100 as 10^2.

$$100^{2x} \div 10^x = (10^2)^{2x} \div 10^x$$
$$= 10^{4x} \div 10^x$$
Subtract the indices $= 10^{3x}$

$$100^{2x} \div 10^x = 10^{3x}$$

SELF TEST 11.7

Simplify the following.
  a) $10^{4x+1} \times 10^{2-x}$ b) $1000^{3x} \times 100^{2x}$

a) 10^{3x+3} b) 10^{13x}

Logarithmic functions

The logarithms of algebraic expressions obey the same rules as logarithms of numbers.

$$\log ab = \log a + \log b \qquad \log(a \div b) = \log a - \log b$$

$$\log a^x = x \log a$$

$$\log \tfrac{1}{x} = -\log x \qquad \qquad \log 1 = 0$$

EXAMPLE 11.8

Simplify $\log 10x^2 + \log \frac{100}{x}$.

Solution
Use the rules of logs.

$$\log 10x^2 + \log \tfrac{100}{x} = \log 10 + \log x^2 + \log 100 - \log x$$
$$= 1 + 2\log x + 2 - \log x$$
$$= 3 + \log x$$

$$\log 10x^2 + \log \tfrac{100}{x} = 3 + \log x$$

Note   Here we expanded the log expressions. We could have written the expression as a single log.

$$\log 10x^2 + \log \tfrac{100}{x} = \log \left\{ (10x^2)(\tfrac{100}{x}) \right\}$$
$$= \log \left\{ \frac{10x^2 \times 100}{x} \right\}$$
$$= \log 1000x \quad \text{(by cancelling)}$$
$$= \log 1000 + \log x$$
$$= 3 + \log x$$

SELF TEST 11.8

Simplify $\log 0.1y - \log \frac{y^2}{1000}$.

$\log \frac{100}{y}$ or $2 - \log y$

The exponential function

In advanced work, the number e is very important. This number is approximately 2.7183. The **exponential function** is e^x. Logarithms to the base e are called **natural logarithms** or **Naperian logarithms**, and are often written as ln.

$$\log_e x = \ln x$$

A scientific calculator has a button to evaluate $\ln x$ and e^x. If you use tables there may be a set of natural logarithms, or find their values by converting to 10^x and $\log x$, as follows:

$$e^x = 10^{0.4343x} \qquad \ln x = \log x \times 2.303.$$

EXAMPLE 11.9

Find $e^{2.5}$ and $\ln 4.7$.

Solution
If you have a scientific calculator, you can find $e^{2.5}$ directly. With tables, use the rule above.

$$e^{2.5} = 10^{0.4343 \times 2.5} = 10^{1.086}$$

Hence $\log_{10} e^{2.5} = 1.086$.
    Using antilog tables gives the value of $e^{2.5}$.

$$\text{antilog } 1.086 = 12.19$$

$$e^{2.5} = 12.2$$

You can find $\ln 4.7$ directly with a scientific calculator. Otherwise use the Naperian log tables or use the rule above.

$$\ln 4.7 = \log 4.7 \times 2.303$$

Use log tables to find that $\log 4.7 = 0.6721$.

$$\ln 4.7 = 0.6721 \times 2.303 = 1.548$$

$$\ln 4.7 = 1.548$$

SELF TEST 11.9

Evaluate $e^{3.21}$ and $\ln 28.97$.

24.78, 3.366

EXAMPLE 11.10

Find x, given that $e^x = 6.93$. Find y, given that $\ln y = -0.673$.

Solution

The inverse of e^x is ln. Hence $x = \ln 6.93$.

$$= 1.936$$

The inverse of ln is e^x. Hence $y = e^{-0.673}$.

$$= 10^{0.434 \times -0.673}$$
$$= 10^{-0.2921}$$
$$y = 0.510$$

$$x = 1.936 \text{ and } y = 0.510$$

SELF TEST 11.10

Find x, given that $e^x = 1.465$. Find y, given that $\ln y = 4.210$.

$$x = 0.3819, \ y = 67.36$$

EXAMPLE 11.11

A current is switched on. After t seconds its value, I amps, is given by the formula below. Find the current, to 4 significant figures, after 0.5 seconds.

$$I = 2(1 - e^{-10t})$$

Solution

Substitute 0.5 for t.

$$I = 2(1 - e^{-10 \times 0.5})$$
$$= 2(1 - e^{-5})$$

Find the value of e^{-5} from a calculator or tables.

$$I = 2(1 - 0.006\,738) = 2(0.9933) = 1.9865$$

The current is 1.987 amps (to 4 s.f.)

SELF TEST 11.11

Find the value of the expression $e^{3x+0.7}$ when $x = 0.95$.

$$34.81$$

EXAMPLE 11.12

An electric current in a circuit is switched off. After t seconds, the current is

$$4e^{-5t} \text{ amperes}$$

Find how long it takes for the current to reach 0.1 amperes.

Solution

We want to solve the equation

$$4e^{-5t} = 0.1$$

or

$$e^{-5t} = 0.025.$$

So

$$-5t = \ln 0.025$$
$$= \ln (10^{-2} \times 2.5)$$
$$= \bar{5}.3948 + 0.9163$$
$$= -5 + 0.3948 + 0.9163$$
$$= -3.689$$

Hence

$$5t = 3.689$$
$$t = \frac{3.689}{5}$$
$$= 0.738$$

The current reaches 0.1 A after 0.738 seconds

SELF TEST 11.12

A hot object is placed in a bath of water. After t minutes, its temperature is

$$100e^{-0.9t} \,^{\circ}\text{C}.$$

When will the temperature reach $10\,^{\circ}\text{C}$? Give your answer to 3 significant figures.

$$2.56 \text{ minutes}$$

Solving equations with logs

If you have a calculator, you do not need log tables for calculations. But you need logs (in tables or on your calculator) to solve equations of the form $4^x = 10$.

Take logs of both sides

$$\log 4^x = \log 10$$
$$x \log 4 = \log 10$$
$$x = \frac{\log 10}{\log 4}$$

In the next example, we see that an equation like this can arise naturally.

EXAMPLE 11.13

A population is increasing at 4% per year. How long will it take to double?

Solution

Each year the population is multiplied by $\frac{104}{100}$, i.e. by 1.04. After 2 years the original population will be multiplied by 1.04×1.04, i.e. 1.04^2. After n years it is multiplied by 1.04^n. If the population has doubled

$$1.04^n \times \text{population} = 2 \times \text{population}$$
$$1.04^n = 2$$

Take logs of both sides

$$\log 1.04^n = \log 2$$

Use the rule $\log a^n = n \log a$.

$$n \log 1.04 = \log 2$$
$$n = \frac{\log 2}{\log 1.04}$$
$$= \frac{0.3010}{0.0170}$$
$$= 17.7$$

It takes 17.7 years for the population to double

SELF TEST 11.13

An amount of #1000 is invested so that every year it increases by 8%. How long will it be before it reaches #1500?

5.27 years

11.3 Transposing formulae

The formula below converts temperature in Fahrenheit to Celsius.

$$C = \tfrac{5}{9}(F - 32)$$

We might want to go in the other direction, to convert Celsius to Fahrenheit. This section shows you how to do this.

The **subject** of an algebraic formula is the letter which is expressed in terms of the other letter or letters. In the formula above, the subject is C. If we rearrange the formula so that another letter is the subject, then we **change the subject** of the formula. This is **transposing** the formula. In the formula above, we might want to change the subject to F.

Transposing formulae is similar to solving equations. The basic rule which you must obey is:

Do to the left what you do to the right.

EXAMPLE 11.14

In the formula $y = 4x - 3$, change the subject to x.

Solution
Add 3 to both sides.

$$y + 3 = 4x$$

Divide by 4.

$$\frac{y + 3}{4} = x$$
$$x = \tfrac{1}{4}y + \tfrac{3}{4}$$

SELF TEST 11.14

In the formula $p = 5q + 2$, change the subject to q.

$$q = \tfrac{1}{5}p - \tfrac{2}{5}$$

EXAMPLE 11.15

Make R the subject of the formula $V = IR$.

Solution
Divide both sides by I.

$$\frac{V}{I} = R$$
$$R = \frac{V}{I}$$

SELF TEST 11.15

Make v the subject of the formula $k = \frac{2m}{v}$.

$$v = \frac{2m}{k}$$

Formulae in which the new subject occurs twice

Suppose the new subject occurs more than once. Then we may be able to factorise so that occurs only once.

$$xa + xb = x(a + b)$$

There are two occurrences of x on the left, but only one on the right.

EXAMPLE 11.16

Make x the subject of the formula $ax = bx + c$.

Solution
Subtract bx from both sides, then factorise.

$$ax - bx = c$$
$$x(a - b) = c$$

Divide by $(a - b)$.

$$x = \frac{c}{(a - b)}$$
$$x = \frac{c}{a - b}$$

SELF TEST 11.16

Make y the subject of the formula $3y = 6 - ay$.

$$y = \frac{6}{3 + a}$$

Formulae with algebraic fractions

Some technical formulae involve algebraic fractions. When changing the subject, you will use the rules of Section 11.1. Be careful not to make the mistakes of Section 11.1 (page 87)!

EXAMPLE 11.17

The formula $\frac{1}{u} = \frac{1}{v} - \frac{1}{f}$ refers to lenses. Make v the subject.

Solution

Add $\frac{1}{f}$ to both sides.

$$\frac{1}{u} + \frac{1}{f} = \frac{1}{v}$$

Adding LHS, (LCD = uf)

$$\frac{f + u}{uf} = \frac{1}{v}$$

Invert

$$\frac{uf}{f + u} = \frac{v}{1}$$

$$v = \frac{uf}{f + u}$$

SELF TEST 11.17

When two resistors are connected in parallel, the total resistance is given by the formula below. Change the subject to R_1.

$$\frac{1}{R} = \frac{1}{R_1} + \frac{1}{R_2}$$

$$R_1 = \frac{RR_2}{R_2 - R}$$

EXAMPLE 11.18

When n batteries are connected, the current they produce is given by the formula below. Make n the subject.

$$I = \frac{nE}{R + nr}$$

Solution

Multiply both sides by $R + nr$, then expand.

$$I(R + nr) = nE$$
$$IR + Inr = nE$$

Collect the n terms and factorise.

$$IR = nE - Inr$$
$$= n(E - Ir)$$

Divide by $(E - Ir)$.

$$n = \frac{IR}{E - Ir}$$

SELF TEST 11.18

Make t the subject of the formula

$$k = \frac{t - t_0}{t - t_1}.$$

$$\frac{kt_1 - t_0}{k - 1}$$

Formulae involving inverse functions

Suppose a function $f(x)$ takes x to y. Then a function $g(y)$ is its **inverse** if it takes y back to x.

$$\text{If } y = f(x), \text{ then } x = g(y)$$

If a formula involves f, then when we change the subject we often need its inverse g.

Square and square root functions

These are inverses of each other.

$$\text{If } y = x^2, \text{ then } x = \sqrt{y}$$
$$\text{If } y = \sqrt{x}, \text{ then } x = y^2$$

EXAMPLE 11.19

Change the subject of $h = \sqrt{(x^2 + y^2)}$ to x.

Solution

Square both sides.

$$h^2 = x^2 + y^2$$
$$h^2 - y^2 = x^2$$

Now take the square root of both sides.

$$x = \sqrt{(h^2 - y^2)}$$

SELF TEST 11.19

Make u the subject of the formula $v^2 = u^2 + 2as$.

$$u = \sqrt{(v^2 - 2as)}$$

EXAMPLE 11.20

Change the subject of $s = \sqrt{(\frac{3}{8}x(k-x))}$ to k.

Solution
Square both sides.

$$s^2 = \frac{3}{8}x(k-x)$$

Multiply by $\frac{8}{3}$ and divide by x.

$$\frac{8}{3} \times \frac{s^2}{x} = k - x$$

Rearrange for k.
$$k = \frac{8s^2}{3x} + x$$

$$\mathbf{k = \frac{8}{3}\frac{s^2}{x} + x}$$

SELF TEST 11.20

The following formula occurs in the theory of alternating current. Change the subject to L.

$$Z = \sqrt{[R^2 + (\omega L - \frac{1}{\omega C})^2]}$$

$$\mathbf{L = [\sqrt{(Z^2 - R^2)} + \frac{1}{(\omega C)}]\frac{1}{\omega}}$$

Power and log functions

These are inverses of each other.

If $x = 10^y$, then $y = \log x$ \qquad If $x = \ln y$, then $y = e^x$

EXAMPLE 11.21

Transpose the formula $I = I_0 e^{-1.7t}$ so that t is the subject.

Solution
Divide by I_0.

$$\frac{I}{I_0} = e^{-1.7t}$$

Take ln of both sides.

$$\ln\left(\frac{I}{I_0}\right) = -1.7t$$

From the rules of logs, $\ln x = -\ln\left(\frac{1}{x}\right)$.

Hence \qquad $\ln\left(\dfrac{I}{I_0}\right) = -\ln\left(\dfrac{I_0}{I}\right)$

So \qquad $\ln\left(\dfrac{I_0}{I}\right) = 1.7t$

$$\frac{\ln\left(\frac{I_0}{I}\right)}{1.7} = t$$

$$\mathbf{t = \frac{1}{1.7}\ln\left(\frac{I_0}{I}\right)}$$

SELF TEST 11.21

Make t the subject of the formula $C = C_0(1 - e^{-3t})$

$$\mathbf{t = -\frac{1}{3}\ln\left(1 - \frac{C}{C_0}\right)}$$

EXAMPLE 11.22

Transpose the formula $y = \ln(2x^3 + 7)$ to make x the subject.

Solution
The inverse of ln is the exponential function, e^x. Apply the function to both sides.

$$e^y = 2x^3 + 7$$

Subtract 7, then divide by 2.

$$\frac{e^y - 7}{2} = x^3$$

$$\mathbf{x = \sqrt[3]{\left(\frac{e^y - 7}{2}\right)}}$$

SELF TEST 11.22

Transpose the formula $E = \ln\left(1 - \frac{C_1}{C_0}\right)$ so that C_1 is the subject.

$$\mathbf{C_1 = C_0(1 - e^E)}$$

■ CHECK YOUR UNDERSTANDING

● In an algebraic fraction, either the numerator or the denominator is an algebraic expression. Algebraic fractions obey the same rules as ordinary fractions. Avoid certain common errors.
● In a power function, the index is variable. The inverse of a power function is a logarithmic function.
● The subject of a formula is the letter expressed in terms of the other letters. We change the subject of the formula by making a different letter the subject.
● If a formula involves algebraic fractions, the rules of fractions are used when transposing it. If a formula involves a function, the inverse function may be needed to transpose it.

REVISION EXERCISES AND QUESTIONS

11.1 Algebraic fractions

1 Simplify the following fractions.

a) $\dfrac{2x}{4y}$ \qquad b) $\dfrac{3x}{8x}$ \qquad c) $\dfrac{3x^2}{x}$

d) $\dfrac{\frac{1}{a}}{\frac{1}{b}}$ \qquad e) $\dfrac{x + x^2}{x}$ \qquad f) $\dfrac{x + y}{\frac{1}{x} + \frac{1}{y}}$

2 Write the following as single fractions. Simplify your answers if possible.

a) $\dfrac{a}{b} \times \dfrac{x}{y}$ 　　 b) $\dfrac{2x}{y} \times \dfrac{3x}{z}$ 　　 c) $\dfrac{2x}{y} \times \dfrac{y}{3x}$

d) $\dfrac{p}{q} \div \dfrac{r}{t}$ 　　 e) $\dfrac{5x}{3y} \div \dfrac{2y}{7x}$ 　　 f) $\dfrac{x^2}{y} \div \dfrac{y^2}{2x}$

g) $\dfrac{x}{y} + \dfrac{a}{b}$ 　　 h) $\dfrac{x}{3} + \dfrac{x}{4}$ 　　 i) $\dfrac{2}{x} - \dfrac{3}{y}$

3 Find the LCMs of the following sets of expressions.

a) ab, ac 　　 b) $6x, 9y$ 　　 c) a, ab, a^2

d) mn, m^2n, mn^2 　　 e) $15x^2, 20xy, 25y^2$

4 Use the results of Question 3 to write the following as single fractions.

a) $\dfrac{1}{ab} + \dfrac{1}{ac}$ 　　 b) $\dfrac{a}{6x} - \dfrac{b}{9y}$ 　　 c) $\dfrac{1}{a} + \dfrac{1}{ab} + \dfrac{1}{a^2}$

d) $\dfrac{2}{mn} + \dfrac{3}{m^2n} + \dfrac{4}{mn^2}$ 　　 e) $\dfrac{y}{15x^2} + \dfrac{1}{20xy} + \dfrac{x}{25y^2}$

11.2 Power and logarithmic functions

5 Evaluate the following.

a) $e^{2.532}$ 　　 b) $e^{-0.2173}$ 　　 c) $\ln 34.563$

6 Find x from the following equations.

a) $e^x = 8.453$ 　　 b) $e^x = 0.352$
c) $\ln x = 2.179$ 　　 d) $\ln x = -2.675$

7 Evaluate the following.

a) e^{2x-7}, for $x = 2.1$
b) e^{x^2+3}, for $x = -0.647$
c) $\ln\left(\dfrac{B_1}{B_0}\right)$, for $B_1 = 2.674$ and $B_0 = 1.045$
d) $\ln[R + \sqrt{(R^2 - L^2)}]$, for $R = 4.978$ and $L = 3.299$

8 Solve the following equations.

a) $e^{2x} = 6.47$ 　　 b) $e^{\frac{1}{4}x} = 0.0561$ 　　 c) $\ln \frac{1}{2}x = 1.256$
d) $\ln 3x = -2.958$ 　　 e) $e^{2x-4} = 10.8$
f) $e^{7-3x^2} = 0.000\,354$ 　　 g) $\ln(1 + 7x) = 0.954$
h) $\ln(3 + 4x^2) = 3.19$ 　　 i) $2^x = 10$
j) $4.2^x = 5.123$ 　　 k) $4^{1+x} = 6$ 　　 l) $4^{x+1} = 5^x$

9 A current is switched off. After t seconds the current is $3e^{-4.7t}$ A. Find when the current reaches 0.5 A.

10 A current is switched on. After t seconds, the current is $5.5(1 - e^{-2.7t})$ A. Find when the current reaches 5 A.

11 The inductance of an aerial is given by $\frac{1}{500}\left(\ln\left(\dfrac{4l}{d}\right) - 1\right)$. Let $d = 1.5$.

a) Find the inductance when $l = 6000$.
b) What value of l will give an inductance of 0.016?

12 E is given by $E = 2\ln\left(\dfrac{B_1}{B_0}\right)$.

a) Find E when $B_1 = 3.54$ and $B_0 = 1.73$
b) Find B_1 when $E = 1.06$ and $B_0 = 2.97$
c) Find B_0 when $E = 3.012$ and $B_1 = 9.674$

13 A population is increasing at 3% each year. How long will it take to be multiplied by 3?

14 A sum of money is invested at 7%. How long will it take for #1000 to increase to #2500?

Section 11.3 Transposing formulae

15 In each of the following formulae, transpose so that the letter in brackets is the subject.

a) $y = 3x - 10$ 　(x) 　　 b) $y = 7 - 2z$ 　(z)
c) $a = \frac{1}{3}b + 5$ 　(b) 　　 d) $p = \frac{1}{2}q - \frac{3}{4}$ 　(q)
e) $a = b - c + d$ 　(d) 　　 f) $y = xz$ 　(x)
g) $C = \pi ab$ 　(a) 　　 h) $y = \dfrac{x}{z}$ 　(x)
i) $a = \frac{1}{4}\dfrac{b}{c}$ 　(b) 　　 j) $y = \dfrac{x}{z}$ 　(z)
k) $a = \dfrac{2}{b}$ 　(b) 　　 l) $E = \dfrac{TR}{P}$ 　(T)
m) $k = \pi a^2 b$ 　(b) 　　 n) $y = 7\dfrac{t}{r}$ 　(r)
o) $y = \dfrac{5}{x+1}$ 　(x) 　　 p) $y = \dfrac{7}{\frac{1}{2}x - 5}$ 　(x)
q) $V = \frac{1}{3}\pi r^2 h$ 　(h) 　　 r) $S = \dfrac{kL^2}{4r}$ 　(r)
s) $y = ax + bx$ 　(x) 　　 t) $ax - 3 = bx + 7$ 　(x)
u) $y = \dfrac{x+2}{x}$ 　(x) 　　 v) $T = \dfrac{R}{R+1}$ 　(R)
w) $\dfrac{1}{f} = \dfrac{1}{v} + \dfrac{1}{u}$ 　(u) 　　 x) $P = \dfrac{f-t}{f+t}$ 　(f)
y) $A = \pi r^2$ 　(r) 　　 z) $y = \frac{1}{8}x^2 - 7$ 　(x)
aa) $b^2 = a^2(e^2 - 1)$ 　(e) 　　 bb) $E = \frac{1}{2}mv^2$ 　(v)
cc) $c^2 = a^2 + b^2$ 　(b) 　　 dd) $V = \frac{4}{3}\pi r^3$ 　(r)
ee) $E = mgd + \frac{1}{2}mv^2$ 　(v) 　　 ff) $F = \dfrac{k}{r^2}$ 　(r)
gg) $y = \sqrt{2x}$ 　(x) 　　 hh) $a = \sqrt{(b+c)}$ 　(b)
ii) $Q = \frac{1}{2}\sqrt{(a^2 + b^2)}$ 　(a) 　　 jj) $y = 5\sqrt{z} + 2\sqrt{x}$ 　(x)
kk) $T = 2\pi\sqrt{\left(\dfrac{l}{g}\right)}$ 　(l) 　　 ll) $T = 2\pi\sqrt{\left(\dfrac{l}{g}\right)}$ 　(g)
mm) $S = \sqrt{[\frac{1}{3}d(l - d)]}$ 　(l) 　　 nn) $R = \sqrt{(\frac{1}{4}r^2 + \frac{1}{12}b^2)}$ 　(b)
oo) $y = 10^{2x}$ 　(x) 　　 pp) $p = 5e^x$ 　(x)
qq) $I = 8e^{2x+1}$ 　(x) 　　 rr) $V = 0.9e^{-\frac{t}{3}}$ 　(t)
ss) $A = e^{5x-3}$ 　(x) 　　 tt) $I = I_0(1 - e^{-\frac{t}{L}})$ 　(t)
uu) $y = \log(x + 1)$ 　(x) 　　 vv) $k = \ln(5i^2)$ 　(i)
ww) $E = 2\ln\left(\dfrac{B_1}{B_0}\right)$ 　(B_1) 　　 xx) $E = 2\ln\left(\dfrac{B_1}{B_0}\right)$ 　(B_0)

Proportion and linear laws

Introduction

The photograph in Figure 12.1 shows an ammeter and a voltmeter attached to the same electrical circuit. There is a current of 2.5 amps flowing through the circuit, and the potential difference across the voltmeter is 10 volts.

If the potential difference is doubled to 20 volts, then the current also doubles, to 5 amps. If the potential difference is halved to 5 volts, then the current also halves, to 1.25 amps.

The quantities being measured, potential difference and current, increase and decrease at the same rate. They are proportional to each other.

12.1 Direct proportion

In many situations, one quantity increases directly with another. They are **directly proportional** to each other. You may have met the following quantities.

- The current through a circuit and the voltage across it.
- The extension of a spring and the mass suspended from it.

Suppose you suspend different masses from a spring. The greater the mass, the longer the spring. If you plot the mass m grams against the extension e mm, the result might be like Figure 12.2. There are two important things to note about the points on this graph.

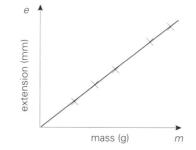

Figure 12.2

- The points lie on a straight line.
- The straight line goes through the origin.

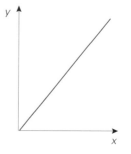

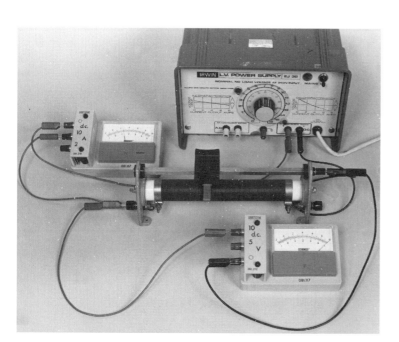

Figure 12.1 Ammeter and voltmeter

Figure 12.3 Graph of proportional quantities

> If two quantities are proportional, their graph is a straight line through the origin.

The symbol used for proportion is $\propto$. If y is proportional to x, write

$$y \propto x$$

In terms of the examples above

● The voltage V volts across a circuit is proportional to the current I amps through it.

$$V \propto I$$

● The extension e mm of a spring is proportional to the mass m N suspended from it.

$$e \propto m$$

The first example is *Ohm's Law*. The second example is *Hooke's Law*.

Note   When y is proportional to x, the ratio $y{:}x$ is constant.

Solving problems of proportion

Suppose y is proportional to x, and two pairs of values of x and y are (x_1, y_1) and (x_2, y_2). The ratios between the values are the same.

$$\frac{y_1}{x_1} = \frac{y_2}{x_2}$$

If we know three of the values, then we can find the fourth.

EXAMPLE 12.1

The quantities x and y are proportional to each other. When $x = 5.6$ then $y = 0.262$. Find the value of y when $x = 9.8$.

Solution
Here $y \propto x$. Use the ratio equation above.

$$\frac{y}{9.8} = \frac{0.262}{5.6}$$

$$y = \frac{0.262 \times 9.8}{5.6} = 0.4585$$

The new value of y is 0.4585

SELF TEST 12.1

The quantities R and T are proportional. When $R = 56$, then $T = 0.43$. Find T when $R = 7$.

0.053 75

Equations of direct proportion

The expression $y \propto x$ is not an equation. It can be converted to an equation by putting in a constant.

$y \propto x$ is equivalent to $y = kx$, where k is a constant.

The constant k is the **constant of proportionality**. It is the constant ratio $y{:}x$. It is the slope of the graph.
Consider again our examples.

● The voltage, V volts, across a circuit is proportional to the current, I amps, flowing through it.

$$V = kI$$

The constant k is the *resistance* of the circuit. It is measured in ohms (Ω).

● The mass, m N, suspended from a spring is proportional to the extension, e mm, of the spring.

$$m = ke$$

The constant k is the *stiffness* of the spring.

The constant can be found from a pair of values of the variables. Suppose that a mass of 40 g extends the spring by 5 mm.

$$40 = k5$$
$$\text{Hence } k = 40 \div 5 = 8.$$

The stiffness of the spring is 8 g mm^{-1}.

EXAMPLE 12.2

The voltage in a circuit is proportional to the current. Suppose a voltage of 12 volts will cause a current of 10 amps. Find an equation giving the voltage V in terms of the current I.

Solution
Here $V \propto I$. This is equivalent to the equation $V = kI$, where k is the constant of proportionality. In this case k is the resistance of the circuit. Put in the values

$$12 = k10$$
$$\text{Hence} \quad k = 12 \div 10 = 1.2.$$

The equation is $V = 1.2I$

SELF TEST 12.2

The volume V m^3 of a mass of gas under constant pressure is proportional to the absolute temperature $T°$K. At 300°K the volume is 3.24 m^3. Find an equation giving V in terms of T.

$$V = 0.0108T$$

12.2 Inverse proportion

Consider several copper wires, all of the same length but different thicknesses. The electrical resistance will depend on the area of cross-section of the wire. If the area is doubled then the resistance is halved. If the area is divided by three then the resistance is multiplied by three. The resistance goes up when the area goes down, and the resistance goes down when the area goes up.

In general, suppose that y is proportional to the reciprocal of x. i.e., suppose that:

$$y \propto \frac{1}{x}$$

Then y is **inversely proportional** to x.

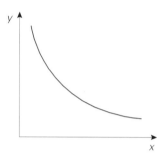

Figure 12.4   Graph of inversely proportional quantities

Section 9.6 of Chapter 9 discussed graphs of this type.

If two quantities are inversely proportional, their graph is a hyperbola, or reciprocal graph.

The proportionality statement is equivalent to an equation.

$$y \propto \frac{1}{x} \text{ is equivalent to } y = \frac{k}{x}.$$

Here k is the constant of proportionality. It can be found from a pair of values of x and y.

Note   If two quantities are inversely proportional, then their *product* is constant. The product is the constant of proportionality.

EXAMPLE 12.3

Boyle's Law states that:

    The volume of a fixed quantity of gas at constant temperature is inversely proportional to its pressure.

Letting the volume be $V\,\mathrm{m}^3$ and the pressure $P\,\mathrm{N/m}^2$, write down the law as a proportionality statement. If $2.5\,\mathrm{m}^3$ of gas has pressure $1600\,\mathrm{N/m}^2$, find the law as an equation.

Solution

The volume V is inversely proportional to the pressure P.

$$V \propto \frac{1}{P}$$

Write this as an equation.

$$V = \frac{k}{P}$$

Put in the values given.

$$2.5 = \frac{k}{1600}$$

Hence $k = 2.5 \times 1600 = 4000$.

$$\textbf{The equation is } V = \frac{4000}{P}$$

SELF TEST 12.3

The quantities y and x are inversely proportional to each other. When $x = 43.2$, then $y = 0.85$. Find an equation giving y in terms of x.

$$y = \frac{36.72}{x}$$

12.3 Proportion to powers

If the radius of a circle increases, then its area also increases. But the relationship is not simple proportion. If the radius is doubled, then the area is multiplied by 4. The area is proportional to the **square** of the radius.

$$A \propto r^2$$

As in the previous sections, this statement of proportionality can be converted to an equation. In this case the constant of proportionality is π.

$$A = \pi r^2$$

The graph of A against r is a quadratic graph, like that of $y = x^2$ in Figure 12.5.

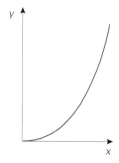

Figure 12.5   Quadratic graph $y = x^2$

Section 9.5 of Chapter 9 discussed quadratic graphs.

> If one quantity is proportional to the square of another quantity, their graph is a quadratic through the origin.

A quantity can be inversely proportional to a power of another quantity. *Newton's law of gravity* is of this form.

The attraction between two objects is inversely proportional to the square of the distance between them.

$$F \propto \frac{1}{d^2}$$

EXAMPLE 12.4

The electrical resistance of wire of fixed length is inversely proportional to the square of its diameter. A length of wire of diameter 0.5 mm has resistance 10 Ω. Find an equation linking the diameter d mm with the resistance R Ω. Hence find the resistance of a length of diameter 0.1 mm.

Solution
The relationship is

$$R \propto \frac{1}{d^2}$$

This is equivalent to the equation

$$R = \frac{k}{d^2}$$

We know that $R = 10$ when $d = 0.5$. Substitute these values.

$$10 = \frac{k}{0.5^2}$$

This gives $k = 10 \times 0.5^2 = 2.5$.

$$\textbf{The equation is } R = \frac{2.5}{d^2}$$

Now put $d = 0.1$.

$$R = \frac{2.5}{0.1^2} = 250$$

The resistance is 250 Ω

SELF TEST 12.4

The mass m g of a metal sphere is proportional to the cube of its radius, r mm. A sphere of radius 1.2 mm has mass 0.05 g. Find an equation giving m in terms of r. Find the mass of a sphere of radius 0.8 mm.

$$m = 0.028\,94r^3, \; 0.014\,81 \text{ g}$$

12.4 Linear laws

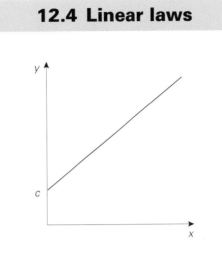

Figure 12.6   Linear relationship $y = mx + c$

Figure 12.6 shows the relationship between two quantities x and y. Note that

- The graph is a straight line.
- The graph does *not* go through the origin.

Hence the relationship is not direct proportion. It is of the form

$$y = mx + c$$

where m and c are constant. The constant m is the gradient of the graph. The constant c is the value of y when $x = 0$, i.e. the point where the line cuts the y-axis. We discussed linear graphs in Chapter 9, Section 9.4.

The relationship between y and x is a **linear law**. There are two unknown constants, m and c. Hence to find the law we need two pairs of values of x and y. Use simultaneous equations to find the values of m and c.

EXAMPLE 12.5

The pressure, P N/m^2, of a closed volume of gas and its temperature, $T°$C, are connected by a law of the form

$$P = aT + b$$

where a and b are constants. At 10°C the pressure is 28 N/m^2, and at 50°C it is 31 N/m^2.
  a) Find the law connecting P and T.
  b) Find the pressure at 100°C.

Solution
a)   Substitute the values given into the equation above.

$$28 = a10 + b \qquad [1]$$
$$31 = a50 + b \qquad [2]$$

Subtract [1] from [2], to obtain $3 = 40a$. Hence $a = 0.075$.
Subtstitute this value into [1].

$$28 = 0.75 + b$$

Hence $b = 27.25$.

The law is $P = 0.075\,T + 27.25$

b)   Put $T = 100$, obtaining $P = 34.75$.

At $100°$C the pressure is 34.75 N/m^2

SELF TEST 12.5

The load, L N, and the effort, E N, of a machine are related by
a law of the form

$$L = aE + b$$

where a and b are constant. An effort of 20 N will raise a load
of 84 N, and an effort of 40 N will raise a load of 210 N. Find
the law connecting L and E.

$$L = 6.3E - 42$$

12.5 Exponential growth and decay

Exponential increase

Consider a population which is growing steadily through
natural increase. The larger the population, the larger the
increase in population. The increase in population is proportional to the population itself.

In this, and in many important cases, the rate of increase of
a quantity is proportional to the quantity itself. This is
exponential growth. Examples are

● A sum of money invested at a constant percentage rate.
● The length of a rod being heated.

If y is increasing exponentially as a function of t, then it is
given by

$$y = Ae^{kt}$$

where A and k are constant.

● The value of A is the value of y when $t = 0$.
● The value of k is the constant of proportionality between y
and its rate of increase.
● The number e, introduced in Chapter 11, is approximately
2.718.

Figure 12.7 shows the graph of a quantity increasing
exponentially. Note that

● The graph starts at $y = A$.
● As t tends to infinity, y also tends to infinity.

We can find A and k from two pairs of values of t and y.

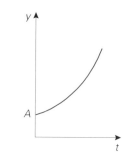

Figure 12.7   Exponential growth

EXAMPLE 12.6

A growth of bacteria is increasing exponentially. At time $t = 0$
the mass is 5×10^{-9} g, and after 1 hour it is 1.7×10^{-8} g. Find
the mass after t hours.

Solution

Let the mass be m g. Then after t hours the mass is given by
$m = Ae^{kt}$. Put in the information given.

$$5 \times 10^{-9} = Ae^{k0} \qquad [1]$$
$$1.7 \times 10^{-8} = Ae^{k1} \qquad [2]$$

In [1], note that $e^{k0} = 1$. Hence $A = 5 \times 10^{-9}$.
    Put this value into the second equation.

$$1.7 \times 10^{-8} = 5 \times 10^{-9} \times e^{k}$$
$$e^{k} = 1.7 \times 10^{-8} \div (5 \times 10^{-9}) = 3.4$$

Hence $$k = \ln 3.4 = 1.22$$

The mass after t hours is $5 \times 10^{-9} e^{1.22t}$ g

SELF TEST 12.6

The population of a city is growing exponentially. When $t = 0$
the population was 120 000, and ten years later it was 174 000.
Find the population P in terms of time t.

$$P = 120\,000 e^{0.0372t}$$

Exponential decrease

If the rate of decrease of a quantity is proportional to the
quantity, then it is **exponentially decreasing** or exponentially decaying. The formula for the quantity is

$$y = Ae^{-kt}$$

Examples of exponential decrease are

● The mass of a radioactive material.
● The electrical charge held by a capacitor while it is
discharging.

Figure 12.8 shows the graph of a quantity decreasing
exponentially. Note that

• The graph starts at $y = A$, i.e. the value of y when $t = 0$
• As t tends to infinity, y tends to 0.

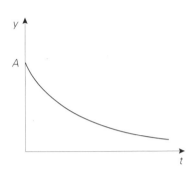

Figure 12.8 Exponential decay

EXAMPLE 12.7

A current of 4 amps flows in a circuit. When it is switched off, the rate of decrease of the current is 7 times the current. After t seconds, the current is I amps. Find I in terms of t. Hence find

a) the current after $\frac{1}{2}$ second
b) the time by which the current has fallen to 0.001 amps.

Solution
The current is decreasing exponentially with time. Hence its value is given by

$$I = A e^{-kt}$$

At $t = 0$, $I = 4$ amps. Hence $A = 4$. The constant of proportionality is 7, hence $k = 7$.

After t seconds the current is $4e^{-7t}$ amps

a) Put $t = \frac{1}{2}$ into this formula.

$$I = 4e^{-7 \times \frac{1}{2}} = 4e^{-3.5} = 0.121$$

After $\frac{1}{2}$ second the current is 0.121 amps

b) Put $I = 0.001$ into the formula.

$$0.001 = 4e^{-7t}$$
$$0.000\,25 = e^{-7t}$$

Hence

$$-7t = \ln 0.000\,25 = -8.294$$
$$t = 1.18$$

The current has fallen to 0.001 amps after 1.18 seconds

SELF TEST 12.7

An object at $80°C$ is placed in a bath of water at $0°C$. The rate of decrease of the object's temperature, in $°C$ per minute, is equal to 0.3 times the temperature. Find an equation giving the temperature, $T°C$, in terms of time, t minutes. Hence find

a) the temperature after 4 minutes
b) the time to reach a temperature of $10°C$.

$$T = 80e^{-0.3t}, \ 24.1°C, \ 6.93 \text{ min}$$

■ CHECK YOUR UNDERSTANDING

• If quantities x and y are proportional, then $y \propto x$. This is equivalent to the equation $y = kx$, where k is the constant of proportionality. The graph of y against x is a straight line through the origin, with gradient k.
• If quantities x and y are inversely proportional, then $y \propto \frac{1}{x}$. This is equivalent to the equation $y = \frac{k}{x}$, where k is the constant of proportionality. The graph of y against x is a reciprocal graph.
• If y is proportional to the nth power of x, then $y \propto x^n$, or $y = kx^n$. If $n = 2$, the graph of y against x is a quadratic graph.
• A linear law connecting y and x is of the form $y = mx + c$, where m and c are constant. The graph of y against x is a straight line, not necessarily through the origin. The line has gradient m and cuts the y axis at $(0, c)$.
• If the rate of growth of y is proportional to y, then $y = Ae^{kt}$, where A and k are constant. This is exponential growth. If the rate of decrease of y is proportional to y, then $y = Ae^{-kt}$. This is exponential decay. In both cases A is the value of y when $t = 0$, and k is the constant of proportionality.

REVISION EXERCISES AND QUESTIONS

12.1 Direct proportion

1 The quantities x and y are directly proportional. When $x = 10$, then $y = 26$. Find an equation giving y in terms of x. Find y when x is 15, and find x when y is 52.

2 T is directly proportional to R. $T = 20$ for $R = 0.5$. Find an equation giving T in terms of R. Find T when $R = 1.5$.

3 The electrical resistance of a wire is directly proportional to its length. A piece 1.2 m long has a resistance of $0.7\ \Omega$. Find an equation giving the resistance $R\ \Omega$ in terms of the length l m. Find the resistance of a wire of length 0.3 m, and the length of a wire with resistance $2.8\ \Omega$.

4 Under a tension of 250 N, the extension of a wire is 0.15 mm. Use Hooke's Law (page 95) to write the tension T N in terms of the extension e mm. Find the tension for an extension of 0.4 mm.

12.2 Inverse proportion

5 The quantities y and x are inversely proportional. When $x = 55$, then $y = 22$. Find an equation giving y in terms of x. Find y when $x = 11$, and x when $y = 44$.

6 A mass of gas occupies 7.8 m^3 under 300 000 pascals of pressure. Use Boyle's Law (page 96) to find the volume of the gas when the pressure is changed to 120 000 pascals.

7 The electrical resistance, R Ω, of a wire is inversely proportional to its area of cross-section, A mm^2. The resistance is 0.002 Ω for an area of 0.1 mm^2. Find an equation giving R in terms of A. Find the value of A which gives a resistance of 0.000 15 Ω.

8 The current, I A, in a conductor, is inversely proportional to the resistance, R Ω. For $R = 20$, $I = 35$. Find an equation giving I in terms of R. Find I when $R = 4$.

12.3 Proportion to powers

9 The quantity y is proportional to the square of x. When $x = 2.5$, then $y = 12.5$. Find y in terms of x. Find y when $x = 1.5$.

10 The quantity q is inversely proportional to the square of p. When $p = 0.2$, then $q = 129$. Find q when $p = 0.3$. Find p when $q = 68$.

11 The electrical resistance, R Ω, of a circular wire is inversely proportional to the square of its radius of cross-section, r mm. The resistance is 25 Ω for a radius of 0.8 mm. Find an equation giving R in terms of r. Find the value of r which gives a resistance of 500 Ω.

12 The period, t seconds, of a simple pendulum is proportional to the square root of its length, l m. A pendulum of length 1.5 m has a period of 2.46 s. What length of pendulum would give a period of 1 s?

12.4 Linear laws

13 The length, L m, of a bar at temperature $T°$C, is given by an equation of the form $L = aT + b$. At 20°C the length is 1.65 m, and at 200°C the length is 1.68 m. Find the law, and hence find

a) the length at 100°C
b) the temperature for a length of 1.66 m.

14 Something is thrown downwards. After t seconds its velocity, v m/s, is given by $v = u + at$. After 1 second $v = 12$ m/s, and after 1.5 seconds it is 16 m/s. Find the values of u and a. Find when the velocity reaches 30 m/s.

15 The Réaumur temperature scale is such that 0° Réaumur is equivalent to 32°F, and 80° Réaumur is equivalent to 212°F. Find an equation of the form $R = aF + b$, giving Réaumur temperature R in terms of Fahrenheit temperature F.

16 The resistance, R Ω, of a wire at $T°$C is given by $R = R_0 (1 + aT)$. At 5°C the resistance is 28 Ω, and at 85°C it is 33 Ω. Find R_0 and a.

12.5 Exponential growth and decay

17 The quantity y is growing exponentially with time t. At $t = 0$, $y = 45$, and at $t = 10$, $y = 58$. Find an equation giving y in terms of t. Hence

a) find y when $t = 6$
b) find t when $y = 102$.

18 A quantity m is decreasing exponentially with time t. Initially $m = 7$, and at $t = 3$, $m = 3$. Find an equation giving m in terms of t. Hence

a) find m when $t = 0.7$
b) find t when $m = 0.3$.

19 The charge, Q, held by a capacitor decreases exponentially with time t. Initially the charge is 0.4 coulombs, and after 3.2 seconds it is 0.1 coulombs. Find an equation giving Q in terms of t. Hence

a) find the charge after 7 seconds
b) the time for the charge to reduce to 0.05 coulombs.

20 A bar has length l_0 at 0°C, and its length at $\theta°$C is $l = l_0 e^{a\theta}$, where a is the constant coefficient of expansion. If the bar has length 1.0001 l_0 m at 20°C, find a.

21 The population of a city is increasing exponentially with time. Initially it is 7.3 million, and after 10 years it is 9.7 million. Find the population after t years. When will the population reach 12 million?

22 The value of a machine is decreasing exponentially. It was bought for #20 000, and after 2 years it was worth #15 000. Find its value after t years. When will it be worth #10 000?

Laws from experimental data

Introduction

When a wire is heated, its electrical resistance increases. If the temperature of the wire is $T°C$, and the resistance $R\ \Omega$, the relationship might be of the form

$$R = mT + c$$

where m and c are unknown constants. To find m and c, you could perform experiments by measuring the temperature and the resistance. The results, plotted on a graph, might look like Figure 13.1. The points do not lie exactly on a straight line. There are reasons why this might happen.

- The relationship is not *exactly* of the form $R = mT + c$.
- The experimental data is inaccurate.

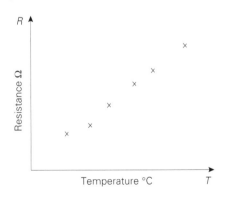

Figure 13.1

When finding a law from experimental data, the result might be inaccurate.

13.1 Linear laws from experimental data

Suppose there is a linear relationship between two quantities, of the form $y = mx + c$, where m and c are constant. The graph of the relationship has gradient m, and it crosses the y-axis at $(0, c)$. We can find the two constants m and c from two pairs of values of x and y. We did this in Section 9.4 of Chapter 9.

But suppose we find the values of x and y by experiment. Then they might not be accurate. They might not obey the equation exactly. If we find m and c from these values, then the results might not be correct.

To avoid this, do the following. Collect *several* pairs of values of x and y. Plot the pairs on a graph. Draw the straight line which seems close to the points. This is a **line of best fit**. Figure 13.2 shows the result. The points lie roughly on a straight line, verifying that x and y approximately follow a linear law.

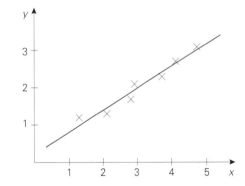

Figure 13.2 Line of best fit for experimental data

Notes

1. There should be about as many points above the line as below the line.
2. The line does not have to go through the first and last points. Possibly the line does not go through any of the points.
3. You use your own judgement when drawing the line. Someone else might draw a different line.

101

The equation of the line has the form $y = mx + c$. We find the values of m and c from the line. Pick two points on the line. For example, in Figure 13.3, the points $(0.5, 5)$ and $(5, 32)$ lie on the line. The value of m is the gradient of the line. This is found by dividing the y-change by the x-change, i.e.

$$\text{gradient} = \frac{32 - 5}{5 - 0.5} = \frac{27}{4.5} = 6$$

Hence the equation of the line is of the form $y = 6x + c$. The line goes through $(5, 32)$. Put $x = 5$ and $y = 32$ into the equation.

$$32 = 6 \times 5 + c$$

Hence $c = 2$. The equation of the line is $y = 6x + 2$.

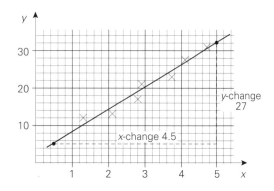

Figure 13.3

Notes

1 For greater accuracy, pick points which are as far apart as possible.
2 The points must be on the line. They are not necessarily the plotted points.
3 If the line crosses the y-axis, the intercept gives the value of c directly. If the line does not cross the y-axis, then find the gradient m first and then find c.
4 Drawing a line of best fit is an approximate procedure. Do not give the answers to a high degree of accuracy.

EXAMPLE 13.1

The resistance, R Ω, of a length of wire depends on its temperature, $T°C$. The relationship is of the form $R = aT + b$, where a and b are constant. The following values were found by experiment. Plot the points on a graph, draw a line of best fit, and find the relationship.

Temperature T (°C)	20	40	60	80	100
Resistance R (Ω)	10.8	11.2	11.9	13.2	14.0

Solution

Plot the points, with temperature along the horizontal axis and resistance up the vertical axis. Figure 13.4 shows the results.

Draw a line of best fit. This line goes through the points $(0, 9.7)$ and $(100, 13.9)$. Hence the intercept is 9.7. The gradient is given by

$$\frac{13.9 - 9.7}{100 - 0} = 0.042$$

Hence $a = 0.042$ and $b = 9.7$.

The relationship is $R = 0.042\,T + 9.7$

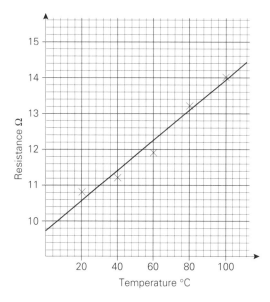

Figure 13.4 $R = aT + b$

Notes

1 The line does not go through any of the original points. A line through the first and last points would be too high for the other points.
2 The vertical scale does not start at $R = 0$. It goes from $R = 9$ to $R = 15$. We get greater accuracy by taking a greater distance on the graph paper between the R values.
3 A scientific calculator may have a facility to evaluate the line of best fit. Often this is by using the LR (Linear Regression) mode.

SELF TEST 13.1

The relationship between x and y is of the form $y = ax + b$, where a and b are constant. The table below gives experimental values of x and y. Plot the points and draw a line of best fit. From your line estimate a and b.

x	3	4	5	6	7	8	9	10
y		48	61	71	85	95	110	117	123

$$a = 11, b = 17$$

Finding errors

Experiments can be inaccurate. You can use the process of drawing a line of best fit to find an inaccurate measurement. If one point lies away from the line then it probably comes from an inaccurate measurement.

EXAMPLE 13.2

The breaking stress, F N/mm^2, of certain wire is thought to depend on the temperature, $T°$C, by a law of the form $F = aT + b$, where a and b are constant. The table below gives experimental values of T and F. One value of F is inaccurate. Plot the points and identify the inaccurate value. Draw a line of best fit and find the correct value.

T (°C)	20	50	100	200	300
F (N/mm^2)	0.1020	0.1012	0.0998	0.0962	0.0943

Solution

Plot the points as in Figure 13.5. Notice that most points lie on a straight line. The fourth point lies below the line, hence the fourth value of F is inaccurate.

Ignore this point, and draw the line for the other points. On the line, find the value of F corresponding to $T = 200$.

The correct value of F is 0.097

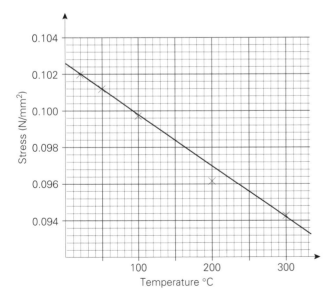

Figure 13.5 $F = aT + b$

SELF TEST 13.2

The table below gives experimental values of x and y, which should obey a law of the form $y = ax + b$. One value of y is inaccurate. Plot the points and find the inaccurate value. Use a line of best fit to find the correct value.

x	10	20	30	40	50	60
y	21.2	41.6	58.7	77.4	96.2	114.9

$$\text{For } x = 20, y = 40$$

Interpolation and extrapolation

When we have found a line of best fit, we can use it to predict other values. This can be done either from the graph, or from the equation of the line.

● **Interpolation** is finding a new value within the range of the experimental data.
● **Extrapolation** is finding a new value outside the range of the experimental data.

Figure 13.6 shows a line of best fit through five points. The x-values of the points lie between 0 and 20.

The point on the line for $x = 15$ is $(15, 1.3)$. The interpolated value of y is 1.3.

The point on the line for $x = 25$ is $(25, 1.7)$. The extrapolated value of y is 1.7.

Note The dotted line of Figure 13.6 corresponds to x-values well beyond 20. The y-value corresponding to $x = 45$ is 2.7, but this is very unreliable.

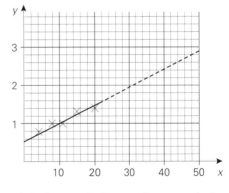

Figure 13.6 Interpolation and extrapolation (with dotted line)

Extrapolation might not be reliable outside the range of the experimental data. The line of Figure 13.6 might be a good fit for low values of x, but not for higher values.

EXAMPLE 13.3

Using the data in Example 13.1, predict the resistance of the wire at a temperature of 150°C.

Solution

This is an example of extrapolation, as 150 lies outside the range of the original data. In Example 13.1 we found the law

$$R = 0.042T + 9.7$$

Put $T = 150$ into this equation.

$$R = 0.042 \times 150 + 9.7 = 16$$

We predict that the resistance is 16 Ω

Note　As 150 is well beyond the original range of values, the prediction is not very reliable.

SELF TEST 13.3

Use your result from Self Test 13.1 to predict the value of y when $x = 12$.

149

EXAMPLE 13.4

From the figures given in Example 13.2, predict the breaking stress of the wire at a temperature of 80°C.

Solution

This is an example of interpolation, as 80 lies within the range of the original data. On Figure 13.5, find the point on the line corresponding to $T = 80$. We obtain 0.1004

We predict that the breaking stress is 0.1004 N/mm^2

Note　The value of 80 is inside the range of the original values, and these values were close to the line. Hence the prediction is reliable.

SELF TEST 13.4

Use your result from Self Test 13.1 to predict the value of y when $x = 4.5$.

66

13.2 Reduction to linear form

If two quantities obey a linear law, the points on their graph lie on a on a straight line, which can be joined with a ruler. But there are many relationships which are not linear. The relationship between the current through a circuit and the power of the circuit is shown in Figure 13.7. The points lie on a curve, and it is difficult to draw an accurate curve through the points.

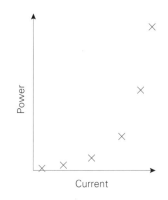

Figure 13.7　Points which lie on a curve

In many cases, taking new variables X and Y changes the equation to the form $Y = aX + b$. This transforms the curve to a straight line. For example:

- If the relationship is parabolic, of the form $y = ax^2 + b$, where a and b are unknown constants.
  Let $X = x^2$, and $Y = y$.
  The relationship is now $Y = aX + b$.
- If the relationship is of the form $y = \dfrac{a}{x} + b$.
  Let $Y = y$ and $X = \dfrac{1}{x}$.
  The relationship is now $Y = aX + b$.
- If the relationship is of the form $y = ax^2 + bx$. Divide by x, to obtain $\dfrac{y}{x} = ax + b$.
  Let $Y = \dfrac{y}{x}$ and $X = x$.
  The relationship is now $Y = aX + b$.

In all cases $Y = aX + b$ is the equation of a straight line. Find values of X and Y. Plot them on a graph. If the original relationship is correct, the points will lie roughly on a straight line. Now proceed as in Section 13.1.

EXAMPLE 13.5

A belt slides over a pulley at v m/s. The coefficient of friction, μ, between the belt and the pulley is thought to obey a law of the form $\mu = a\sqrt{v} + b$. Experimental values are given below. Reduce the equation to linear form, and find the law.

v (m/s)	5	10	15	20	25
μ	0.289	0.303	0.314	0.323	0.331

Solution

If we let $X = \sqrt{v}$, then the law becomes $\mu = aX + b$. This is a linear law. The first value of X is the square root of 5, i.e. 2.24.

Write out a new row of the table for values of X.

| X | 2.24 | 3.16 | 3.87 | 4.47 | 5 |

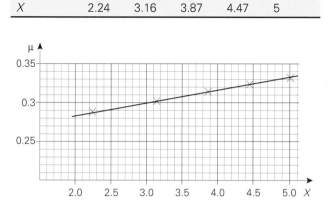

Figure 13.8 $\mu = aX + b$

Plot μ against X, as in Figure 13.8. Notice that the points lie on a straight line, which confirms that the law is correct. Two points on the line are $(2, 0.283)$ and $(5, 0.332)$. The gradient, a, is

$$\frac{0.332 - 0.283}{5 - 2} = 0.0163$$

To find b, put $\mu = 0.283$, $X = 2$ and $a = 0.0163$ into the equation $\mu = aX + b$.

$$0.283 = 0.0163 \times 2 + b. \text{ Hence } b = 0.25.$$

The law is $\mu = 0.0163 \sqrt{v} + 0.25$

SELF TEST 13.5

The relationship between y and x is of the form $y = ax^3 + b$, where a and b are constant. The table below gives values of x and y found by experiment. Write out an extra row for the values of x^3. Plot y against x^3 and draw a line of best fit. Hence estimate a and b.

x	1	2	3	4	5	6
y	6.2	27.1	80.4	182.1	346.1	603.8

$a = 2.8, \ b = 4.2$

EXAMPLE 13.6

Suppose a projectile is moving at v m/s. The air resistance is R N, where the relationship between v and R is of the form

$$R = av^2 + bv$$

Here a and b are unknown constants. The table below gives experimental values of v and R. Divide both sides of the equation by v.

Let $T = \dfrac{R}{v}$. By plotting T against v find the relationship between R and v.

Speed (m/s) (v)	10	20	30	40	50
Resistance (N) (R)	1.1	2.5	4.2	6.0	8.3

Solution

After division by v, the equation is

$$\frac{R}{v} = av + b$$

Letting $T = \dfrac{R}{v}$, the equation is linear.

$$T = av + b$$

To find the values of T, divide R by v. The first value is $1.1 \div 10 = 0.11$. Write an extra row of values for T.

| T | 0.11 | 0.125 | 0.14 | 0.15 | 0.166 |

Plot the values of T and v on a graph as shown in Figure 13.9. Draw a line of best fit between them. This line goes through $(10, 0.111)$ and $(50, 0.167)$. Hence the gradient is given by

$$\frac{0.167 - 0.111}{50 - 10} = 0.0014$$

Hence $a = 0.0014$. To find the value of b, put this into the equation, using $T = 0.111$ and $v = 10$.

$$0.111 = 10 \times 0.0014 + b$$

Hence $b = 0.097$.

The relationship is $R = 0.0014v^2 + 0.097\,v$

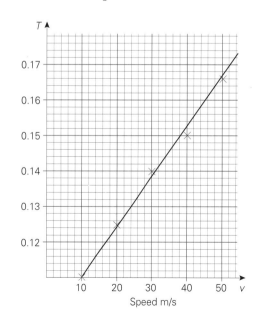

Figure 13.9 $T = av + b$

V (volts)	10	12	14	16	18
L (candelas)	21	45	85	150	240

The relationship between x and y is of the form $y = ax^2 + bx$. Experimental values are given below. Reduce the equation to linear form, and by drawing a line of best fit find the relationship.

x	2	3	4	5	6	7
y	9.8	15.6	22.0	28.3	35.4	42.7

$a = 0.24$, $b = 4.5$

13.3 Use of logarithms

In some cases we must use logarithms to reduce an equation to linear form. We need the following properties of logarithms, from Chapter 4.

$$\log xy = \log x + \log y$$
$$\log x^n = n \log x$$

Consider the following examples.

1 Suppose y is proportional to an unknown power of x, i.e. the curve is of the form $y = ax^n$, where a and n are unknown constants. Apply logs to both sides.

$$\log y = \log ax^n$$
$$= \log a + \log x^n$$
$$= \log a + n \log x$$

Let $Y = \log y$ and $X = \log x$.
The relationship is now $Y = \log a + nX$.

2 Suppose y increases exponentially with x, i.e. the curve is of the form $y = ab^x$, where a and b are unknown constants. Apply logs to both sides.

$$\log y = \log ab^x$$
$$= \log a + \log b^x$$
$$= \log a + x \log b$$

Let $Y = \log y$ and $X = x$.
The relationship is now $Y = \log a + X \log b$.

In both cases the relationship is now linear. Proceed as in Section 13.1 to find the constants. When you have found $\log a$, use antilogs to find a itself.

The voltage applied to a lamp is V volts. The luminosity is L candelas. The luminosity is proportional to an unknown power of the voltage, i.e. the relationship is of the form $L = aV^n$, where a and n are constant. The table below gives experimental values. Reduce the equation to linear form and hence find the law.

Solution

Apply logs to the equation $L = aV^n$. It becomes

$$\log L = \log aV^n$$
$$= \log a + n \log V$$

This is a linear relationship between $\log L$ and $\log V$. Write out rows for the values of $\log L$ and $\log V$

$\log V$	1	1.08	1.15	1.20	1.26
$\log L$	1.32	1.65	1.93	2.18	2.38

Plot these values on a graph as in Figure 13.10. Notice that they now lie roughly on a straight line. Draw a line through the points.

Two points on the line are $(1, 1.32)$ and $(1.26, 2.4)$. Hence the gradient is given by

$$\frac{2.4 - 1.32}{1.26 - 1} = 4.15$$

Hence the value of n is 4.15. This is the unknown power. To find a, substitute into the equation above, for the first of the points.

$$1.32 = \log a + 4.15 \times 1$$

Hence $\log a = -2.83$ (or $\bar{3}.17$). Take antilogs, giving $a = 0.0015$.

The relationship is $L = 0.0015V^{4.15}$

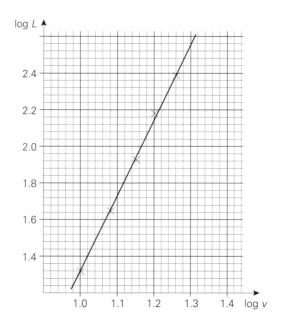

Figure 13.10 $\log L = \log a + n\log V$

SELF TEST 13.7

The relationship between x and y is of the form $y = ax^b$, where a and b are constant. The table below gives experimental values. Use logs to estimate the values of a and b.

x	20	30	40	50	60
y	3.97	4.77	5.45	6.01	6.53

$a = 1.02, b = 0.45$

EXAMPLE 13.8

A hot object is placed in a large bath of water. After t seconds, its temperature, $T°C$, is given by

$$T = ab^t$$

where a and b are unknown constants. The table below gives experimental values. Reduce the equation to linear form, and hence find the equation.

Time (s) (t)	10	20	30	40	50
Temperature (°C) (T)	75	62	51	41	33

Solution
Take logs of both sides.

$$\log T = \log ab^t = \log a + t \log b$$

Let $Y = \log T$. The relationship between t and Y is now $Y = \log a + t \log b$. This is the equation of a straight line.
Write a new row of the table, for Y.

Y	1.875	1.792	1.708	1.613	1.519

Plot Y against t, as in Figure 13.11. Notice that the points lie roughly in a straight line. Note also that the line has negative gradient.
Draw a line through the points. This line goes through $(10, 1.88)$ and $(50, 1.52)$. Hence the gradient is given by

$$\frac{1.52 - 1.88}{50 - 10} = -0.009$$

Hence $\log b = -0.009$. Substitute this value into the equation, and use the fact that the line goes through $(10, 1.88)$.

$$1.88 = \log a - 10 \times 0.009$$

This gives $\log a = 1.97$. Now find a and b by antilogs, hence $a = 93.3$ and $b = 0.979$.

The formula is $T = 93.3 \times 0.979^t$

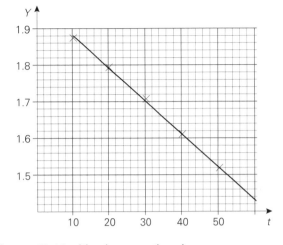

Figure 13.11 $Y = \log a + t\log b$

SELF TEST 13.8

The quantity y is growing exponentially. Its value in terms of time t is given by $y = ab^t$, where a and b are constant. The table below gives experimental values of t and y. Use logs to estimate the values of a and b.

t	0	1	2	3	4	5
y	54	66	83	105	130	161

$a = 54, b = 1.25$

EXAMPLE 13.9

A belt passes round a peg. One side is kept at a constant tension T_0 N. The tension T N, in the other side is dependent on the angle $\theta°$ subtended by the belt in contact with the peg, as shown in Figure 13.12. The relationship is of the form

$$T = ab^\theta.$$

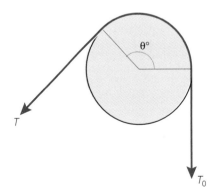

Figure 13.12 Belt passing over peg

The table below gives experimental values of T and θ. One value of T is inaccurate. Find it and correct it.

θ (°)	10	20	30	40	50	60
T (N)	7.7	10.2	10.6	12.4	14.6	17.0

Solution

When we take logs, the relationship becomes
$$\log T = \log a + \theta \log b$$
Let $Y = \log T$. The relationship is now $Y = \log a + \theta \log b$. Write out an extra row for the values of Y.

Y	0.89	1.01	1.03	1.09	1.16	1.23

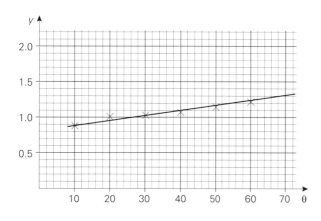

Figure 13.13 $Y = \log a + \theta \log b$

Plot the values of θ and Y as in Figure 13.13. Notice that they lie roughly on a straight line, except for the second point. This corresponds to the inaccurate value of T.

Draw a straight line through the other points. On the line, the value of Y corresponding to $\theta = 20$ is 0.95.
$$Y = \log T = 0.95. \text{ Hence } T = 8.9$$

The second value of T should be 8.9

SELF TEST 13.9

The data below should follow the law $y = ax^b$. One of the y-values is inaccurate. Take logs to reduce the equation to linear form. Identify the inaccurate value and correct it.

x	0.1	0.2	0.3	0.4	0.5	0.6
y	0.14	0.29	0.45	0.61	0.81	0.93

For $x = 0.5$, $y = 0.77$

EXAMPLE 13.10

Using the figures in Example 13.8, predict the temperature of the object after 60 seconds.
Solution
We found the law $T = 93.3 \times 0.979^t$. Put $t = 60$ into this equation.
$$T = 93.3 \times 0.979^{60} = 26.11....$$
We predict that the temperature will be $26°$C

SELF TEST 13.10

Using the figures in Self Test 13.7, predict the value of y when $x = 45$.

5.7

CHECK YOUR UNDERSTANDING

● Suppose x and y obey a linear law, of the form $y = ax + b$. Values found by experiment might be inaccurate. Plot the values and draw a line of best fit through them.
● If a point lies away from the line of best fit, then it might come from inaccurate measurement.
● The line of best fit can be used to find the value of y for other values of x. If the new value of x lies within the range of the old values, the process is interpolation. If the new value lies outside the range, the process is extrapolation. If the new value of x is far from the old values, extrapolation is not reliable.
● Some non-linear laws can be reduced to linear form. In some cases it is necessary to divide by x.
● Laws of the form $y = ax^b$ and $y = ab^x$ can be reduced to linear form by taking logarithms.

REVISION EXERCISES AND QUESTIONS

13.1 Linear laws from experimental data

1 The tables below give values of x and y which approximately obey a law of the form $y = ax + b$, where a and b are constant. In each case plot the values, draw a line of best fit, and find the law.

a)
x	1	2	3	4	5
y	5.9	6.4	6.8	7.3	7.7

b)

x	20	30	40	50	60	70
y	-0.7	-0.4	0.0	0.4	0.7	1.1

c)

x	-0.3	-0.2	-0.1	0	0.1	0.2
y	34.2	32.6	31.0	29.5	27.9	26.3

2 The tables below give experimental values of x and y which obey a law of the form $y = ax + b$, where a and b are constant. In each case there is an inaccurate value of y. Find this value and correct it.

a)

x	10	20	30	40	50	60
y	7.2	8.9	10.7	12.8	14.1	15.8

b)

x	-2	-1	0	1	2	3
y	2.4	6.3	7.4	10.0	12.4	14.8

c)

x	0.1	0.2	0.3	0.4	0.5	0.6
y	50	140	200	240	280	330

3 a) For Question 1a, predict the value of y when $x = 3.5$.
   b) For Question 1b, predict the value of y when $x = 80$.
   c) For Question 1c, predict the value of y when $x = -0.4$.

4 The length, L m, of an elastic string is related to its tension, T N, by a law of the form $L = aT + b$. The table below gives values found by experiment. Find the law.

T(N)	10	15	20	25	30
L(m)	1.32	1.45	1.56	1.70	1.86

5 The load, W N, and the effort, E N, of a pulley-system are related by a law of the form $E = aW + b$, where a and b are constant. Experimental values are given below. Find the law.

W(N)	10	20	30	40	50
E(N)	3.1	5.3	8.2	10.7	13.3

6 The solubility of a certain chemical, y grams per litre of water, varies according to the temperature $T°C$, by a law of the form $y = aT + b$. Experimental values are given below. Find the law. Predict the solubility at $90°C$.

T(°C)	0	20	40	60	80
C(g/l)	33	36	40	43	48

13.2 Reduction to linear form

7 In each of the following the relationship between y and x is given. In each case reduce the relationship to linear form by the suggested change of variables. Plot the new variables, draw a line of best fit, and hence find the relationship.

a) $y = a\sqrt{x} + b$. Change to $Y = y$, $X = \sqrt{x}$.

x	1	2	3	4	5	6
y	11.0	14.2	16.4	18.6	20.2	21.8

b) $y = ax^2 + bx$. Change to $Y = \dfrac{y}{x}$, $X = x$.

x	10	20	30	40	50
y	35	100	185	300	450

c) $\dfrac{1}{y} = \dfrac{a}{x} + b$. Change to $Y = \dfrac{1}{y}$, $X = \dfrac{1}{x}$.

x	0.02	0.03	0.04	0.05	0.06	0.07
y	0.07	0.13	0.22	0.34	0.57	1.23

8 A circuit carries a current of I amps. The power dissipated, P watts, obeys a law of the form $P = aI^2 + bI$, where a and b are constant. Experimental values are given below. Reduce the equation to linear form, and hence find the law.

I (amps)	5	10	15	20	25
P (watts)	31	49	55	43	22

13.3 Use of logarithms

9 In each of the following the variable y is proportional to an unknown power of x. Hence the relationship is of the form $y = ax^n$, where a and n are unknown. Values of x and y are given below. Take logs to reduce the equation to linear form. By plotting a line of best fit find the equation.

a)

x	1	2	3	4	5	6
y	2.4	5.7	9.6	13.8	18.4	23.2

b)

x	1.1	1.2	1.3	1.4	1.5
y	2.6	3.9	5.5	7.5	9.9

c)

x	10	20	30	40	50	60
y	240	590	970	1400	1850	2310

10 In each of the following, y varies exponentially with x, i.e. $y = ab^x$, where a and b are constant. Take logs to reduce the equation to linear form. By plotting the line of best fit find the equation.

a)

x	1	2	3	4	5	6
y	3.79	4.03	4.29	4.57	4.80	5.21

b)

x	20	25	30	35	40	45
y	0.065	0.070	0.077	0.084	0.092	0.100

c)

x	10	20	30	40	50
y	40.9	26.3	16.9	10.8	7.0

11 An insulator is d mm thick, and the voltage at which it will break down is V kV. These are related by $V = ad^n$, where a and n are constant. Experimental values are given below. Find the law by reducing the equation to linear form.

d (mm)	1	3	4	6	8	10
V (kV)	100	230	280	380	460	540

12 The frictional force, F N, in a lubricated system depends on the temperature, $T°$C, of the lubricant. The law is approximately of the form $F = aT^n$, where a and n are constant. Experimental values are given below. Find the law.

T (°C)	10	20	30	40	50	60
F (N)	0.009	0.002	0.001	0.0005	0.0003	0.0002

13 A battery is discharging slowly. After t minutes, its voltage is V volts, where $V = ab^t$. The values are given below. Find a and b.

t (mins)	0	20	40	60	80
V (volts)	12.6	6.3	3.1	1.5	0.8

14 A current of i amps passes through a circuit containing a capacitor and a resistor. The value of i after t seconds is given by $i = ab^t$, where a and b are constant. Experimental values are given below. Find the law.

t (secs)	0.01	0.02	0.03	0.04	0.05
i (amps)	0.054	0.050	0.047	0.044	0.042

15 A voltage, V volts, is applied to a circuit. The resulting current, I milliamperes, is given by $I = aV^n$, where a and n are unknown constants. The following values of V and I were found by experiment. Find the law.

V (volts)	2	3	4	5	6
I (amps)	38	55	66	81	90

Quadratics

Introduction

A linear expression in x has only a single power of x. If the expression also involves x^2, then it is a quadratic expression. These quadratic expressions occur often in technology and science. For example:

● Air resistance. The resistance felt by an object moving at speed v might be $av + bv^2$.
● Height of a projectile. The height of a projectile after time t might be $40t - 5t^2$.

We dealt with the graphs of these expressions in Chapter 9. In this chapter we will look at the algebra involved. We will solve quadratic equations. From this, we will be able to find when the air resistance reaches a certain value. We will be able to find when a projectile reaches a certain height.

14.1 Factorising quadratic expressions

A **quadratic expression** in x is of the form $ax^2 + bx + c$, where a, b and c are constant. Note that the square of x is involved. The graph of a quadratic expression has the shape shown in Figure 14.1.

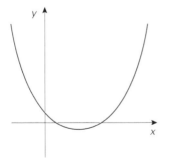

Figure 14.1 Graph of a quadratic expression

Consider the quadratic expression $x^2 + 7x + 12$. There is no common factor to the three terms. But it can be factorised, as the product of a pair of brackets, as below.

$$x^2 + 7x + 12 = (x + 3)(x + 4)$$

Note that $3 \times 4 = 12$, and that $3 + 4 = 7$. The product of the numbers is 12, and their sum is 7.

> To factorise $x^2 + bx + c$, look for two numbers whose product is c, and whose sum is b.

EXAMPLE 14.1

Factorise $x^2 + 8x + 15$.

Solution
The c term is 15. This can be written either as 1×15 or as 3×5. Note that the sum of 3 and 5 is 8, which is the b term.

$$x^2 + 8x + 15 = (x + 3)(x + 5)$$

Check by multiplying the factors.

$$(x + 3)(x + 5) = x(x + 5) + 3(x + 5)$$
$$= x^2 + 5x + 3x + 15$$
$$= x^2 + 8x + 15$$

SELF TEST 14.1

Factorise $x^2 + 7x + 10$.

$(x + 2)(x + 5)$

If b is negative

If the middle term b is negative, and the constant term c positive, then the factors of c are both negative.

EXAMPLE 14.2

Factorise $x^2 - 7x + 12$.

Solution
The factors of 12 are: $1 \times 12 \qquad 2 \times 6 \qquad 3 \times 4$

Of these, 3 and 4 add up to 7. Because the 7 term is negative, take −3 and −4.

$$x^2 - 7x + 12 = (x - 3)(x - 4)$$

SELF TEST 14.2

Factorise $x^2 - 11x + 30$.

$$(x - 5)(x - 6)$$

If c is negative

If the constant term c is negative, then one of its factors is negative. Hence look for factors whose *difference* is b.

EXAMPLE 14.3

Factorise $x^2 + 5x - 24$.

Solution
The c term is −24. 24 can be written as the following

$$1 \times 24 \qquad 2 \times 12 \qquad 3 \times 8 \qquad 4 \times 6$$

The c term is negative. Hence one factor is negative. Look for a pair of factors whose *difference* is 5. The correct pair is 3 and 8. The b term is +5, hence take +8 and −3.

$$x^2 + 5x - 24 = (x - 3)(x + 8)$$

SELF TEST 14.3

Factorise $x^2 - 7x - 30$.

$$(x - 10)(x + 3)$$

Summary

The following summary shows whether the factors are positive or negative.

b positive	c positive	both factors positive
b negative	c positive	both factors negative
b positive	c negative	larger factor positive, smaller negative
b negative	c negative	larger factor negative, smaller positive

Expressions of the form $ax^2 + bx^2 + c$

These expressions are more complicated, as both a and c may have factors.

Find the product ac. Find factors of ac whose sum is b. Use the summary above to decide whether the factors are positive or negative. Group the terms and factorise, as shown in the next two examples.

EXAMPLE 14.4

Factorise $6x^2 + 7x + 2$.

Solution
Here $a = 6$, $b = 7$ and $c = 2$. The product ac is 12. The factors of 12 which add up to 7 are 3 and 4.

$$6x^2 + 7x + 2 = 6x^2 + 3x + 4x + 2$$

Factorise the first two terms and the last two terms.

$$3x(2x + 1) + 2(2x + 1)$$

Now there is a common factor of $(2x + 1)$. Factorise again.

$$6x^2 + 7x + 2 = (2x + 1)(3x + 2)$$

SELF TEST 14.4

Factorise $6x^2 + 11x + 3$.

$$(2x + 3)(3x + 1)$$

EXAMPLE 14.5

Factorise $2x^2 + x - 15$.

Solution
Here the product ac is −30. We want factors of 30 whose *difference* is 1. These are 6 and 5. The value of b is positive, hence put +6 and −5.

$$2x^2 + x - 15 = 2x^2 + 6x - 5x - 15$$
$$= 2x(x + 3) - 5(x + 3)$$

$$2x^2 + x - 15 = (x + 3)(2x - 5)$$

SELF TEST 14.5

Factorise $3x^2 - x - 10$.

$$(x - 2)(3x + 5)$$

Difference of two squares

A **difference of two squares** is an expression which consists of one square subtracted from another. You can factorise these expression immediately. For example

$$x^2 - a^2 = (x+a)(x-a)$$

Check: $(x+a)(x-a) = x\,(x-a) + a(x-a)$
$$= x^2 - ax + ax - a^2$$
$$= x^2 - a^2$$

EXAMPLE 14.6

Factorise $2x^2 - 18$.

Solution
Take out a common factor of 2.
$$2x^2 - 18 = 2(x^2 - 9)$$
This is now the difference of two squares.
$$\mathbf{2x^2 - 18 = 2(\,x+3)(\,x-3)}$$

SELF TEST 14.6

Factorise $3z^2 - \frac{3}{4}$.

$$3(z + \tfrac{1}{2})(z - \tfrac{1}{2})$$

14.2 Completing the square

Some quadratics are perfect squares. (i.e. they factorise to a square of one factor.)
$$x^2 - 8x + 16 = (x-4)(x-4) = (x-4)^2$$
Consider $x^2 - 8x + 22$. This is 6 greater than the expression above.
$$x^2 - 8x + 22 = x^2 - 8x + 16 + 6 = (x-4)^2 + 6$$
This process is **completing the square**
 When a quadratic is in this form, we can find its least value, and we can easily sketch its graph.

Least value

Note that $(x-4)^2$ is never negative. Hence the least value of $x^2 - 8x + 22$ is reached when $(x-4)^2 = 0$, or $x = 4$. The least value of $x^2 - 8x + 22$ is 6.

Graph

The graph of $y = (x-4)^2 + 6$ has a lowest point at (4, 6). Figure 14.2 shows its graph.

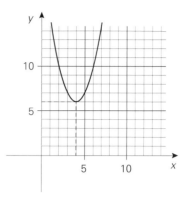

Figure 14.2 $y = (x-4)^2 + 6$

In general, a method for completing the square of $x^2 + bx + c$, is to consider the expansion of $(x + \frac{1}{2}b)^2$. Adjust by adding c and subtracting $\frac{1}{4}b^2$.

$$x^2 + bx + c = (x + \tfrac{1}{2}b)^2 + c - \tfrac{1}{4}b^2$$

EXAMPLE 14.7

Express $x^2 + 4x - 3$ in completed square form. Hence sketch the graph of $y = x^2 + 4x - 3$.

Solution
Here $b = 4$ and $c = -3$. Consider $(x+2)^2$. Adjust by adding -3 and subtracting $\frac{1}{4} \times 4^2$.
$$x^2 + 4x - 3 = (x+2)^2 - 3 - \tfrac{1}{4} \times 4^2$$
$$\mathbf{x^2 + 4x - 3 = (\,x+2)^2 - 7}$$
The least value of this expression is -7, reached when $x = -2$. Hence the graph of $y = x^2 + 4x - 3$ has a lowest point at $(-2, -7)$. Figure 14.3 shows a sketch of its graph.

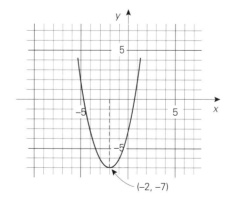

Figure 14.3 $y = x^2 + 4x - 3$

SELF TEST 14.7

Express $x^2 + 3x - 5$ in completed square form. Hence sketch the graph of $y = x^2 + 3x - 5$.

$$(x + 1\tfrac{1}{2})^2 - 7\tfrac{1}{4}$$

Completing the square for $ax^2 + bx^2 + c$

In the examples so far, the coefficient of x^2, the a term, was always 1. If $a \neq 1$, then factorise by a and then proceed as above.

If a is positive, the graph has a lowest point.

If a is negative, the graph has a highest point. See Figure 14.4, and Chapter 9 page 72.

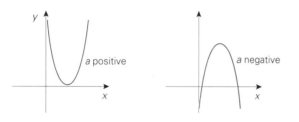

Figure 14.4

EXAMPLE 14.8

Complete the square of $2x^2 + 6x + 5$.

Solution

Factorise the first two terms by 2.

$$2x^2 + 6x + 5 = 2(x^2 + 3x) + 5$$

Complete the square of $x^2 + 3x$ by the method above, obtaining $(x + 1\tfrac{1}{2})^2 - 2\tfrac{1}{4}$.

$$2x^2 + 6x + 5 = 2[(x + 1\tfrac{1}{2})^2 - 2\tfrac{1}{4}] + 5$$
$$= 2(x + 1\tfrac{1}{2})^2 - 4\tfrac{1}{2} + 5$$
$$2x^2 + 6x + 5 = 2(x + 1\tfrac{1}{2})^2 + \tfrac{1}{2}$$

SELF TEST 14.8

Complete the square of $3x^2 + 15x - 4$.

$$3(x + 2\tfrac{1}{2})^2 - 22\tfrac{3}{4}$$

Greatest value

If the a term is negative, then the expression will have a greatest value instead of a least value.

EXAMPLE 14.9

A stone is thrown vertically upwards. After t seconds, its height, h m, is given by

$$h = 40t - 5t^2$$

Complete the square for this expression. Hence find the greatest height reached. Sketch the graph of h against t.

Solution

Factorise by -5.

$$40t - 5t^2 = -5(t^2 - 8t)$$

Now complete the square of $t^2 - 8t$, by the method above.

$$t^2 - 8t = (t - 4)^2 - 16$$
So $$40t - 5t^2 = -5[(t - 4)^2 - 16]$$
$$= -5(t - 4)^2 + 80$$

The completed square form is $h = 80 - 5(t - 4)^2$

The greatest value of this expression occurs when $t = 4$, and then $h = 80$.

The greatest height reached is 80 m

The graph has a highest value at $(4, 80)$. It is shown in Figure 14.5.

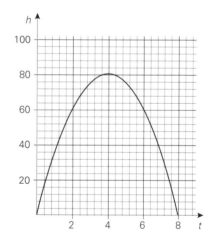

Figure 14.5 $h = 80 - 5(t - 4)^2$

SELF TEST 14.9

Complete the square of $3 + 8x - 2x^2$. Hence find the greatest value of this expression. Sketch the graph of $y = 3 + 8x - 2x^2$.

$$11 - 2(x - 2)^2, \ 11$$

14.3 Quadratic equations

When a quadratic expression is put equal to a fixed value, the result is a **quadratic equation**. Usually all the terms are collected on one side of the equation, so that it is of the form

$$ax^2 + bx + c = 0$$

For example, suppose the height of a projectile is given by $h = 40t - 5t^2$. When it is 30 m high, the following quadratic equation holds

$$30 = 40t - 5t^2$$

This can be rewritten as $5t^2 - 40t + 30 = 0$. When we solve this equation, we find the times when the projectile is 30 m high.

The graph of a quadratic expression is shown in Figure 14.6. Notice that it crosses the x-axis at two places. Hence a quadratic equation may have two solutions.

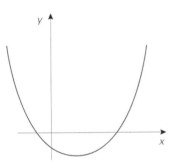

Figure 14.6 Graph of a quadratic expression

Solution by factors

If the product of two terms is 0, then one of the terms must be zero.

$$\text{If } ab = 0, \text{ then } a = 0 \text{ or } b = 0$$

This applies to a factorised quadratic.

$$\text{If } (x - 5)(x - 3) = 0, \text{ then } x - 5 = 0 \text{ or } x - 3 = 0$$

Hence

$$x = 5 \text{ or } x = 3$$

EXAMPLE 14.10

Solve the equation $x^2 + 5x - 36 = 0$.

Solution
The expression factorises, to $(x + 9)(x - 4) = 0$.
  Hence

$$x + 9 = 0 \text{ or } x - 4 = 0$$

The solution is $x = -9$ or $x = 4$

SELF TEST 14.10

Solve the equation $x^2 + 3x - 10 = 0$.

$$x = 2 \text{ or } x = -5$$

Solution by completing the square

Suppose we want to solve the equation $x^2 + bx + c = 0$.
  Complete the square of $x^2 + bx + c$, as $(x + \frac{1}{2}b)^2 - d$.

$$(x + \tfrac{1}{2}b)^2 - d = 0, \text{ hence } (x + \tfrac{1}{2}b)^2 = d$$

If d is positive, we can take the square root of both sides. Remember that you get both $+\sqrt{d}$ and $-\sqrt{d}$.
  If d is negative, there are no solutions.

EXAMPLE 14.11

Solve the equation $x^2 + 4x - 7 = 0$, by completing the square. Give your answers correct to three decimal places.

Solution
Complete the square, so that we get

$$(x + 2)^2 - 11 = 0$$
$$(x + 2)^2 = 11$$

Hence $x + 2 = \sqrt{11}$ or $x + 2 = -\sqrt{11}$

or $x = -2 + \sqrt{11}$ or $x = -2 - \sqrt{11}$

The solution is $x = 1.317$ or $x = -5.317$ (corr to 3 d.p.)

SELF TEST 14.11

Solve the equation $x^2 - 5x + 2 = 0$, by completing the square. Give your answers to 3 decimal places.

$$x = 0.438 \text{ or } x = 4.562$$

Solution by formula

The formula for solving a quadratic equation is

$$\text{if } ax^2 + bx + c = 0, \text{ then } x = \frac{-b \pm \sqrt{(b^2 - 4ac)}}{2a}.$$

Notes

1 Be careful if any of the terms are negative. For example, if b is negative, then $-b$ is positive.
2 The two roots are obtained by either adding or subtracting $\sqrt{(b^2 - 4ac)}$. Do not multiply.

3 The $b^2 - 4ac$ term tells us whether the equation can be solved. If it is positive, there are two solutions. If it is 0, there is one solution. If it is negative, there are no solutions.
4 The formula method is the usual way to solve a quadratic equation. If the equation has solutions, then the formula method will find them.
5 If the coefficients in a quadratic equation are large, don't waste time trying to factorise. It is quicker to use the formula. If the $b^2 - 4ac$ term is a perfect square, then the quadratic expression factorises.

EXAMPLE 14.12

Solve the equation $2.8x^2 - 7.3x - 10.7 = 0$.
Solution
Here $a = 2.8$, $b = -7.3$ and $c = -10.7$. Substitute into the formula above. Be careful with the negative values of b and c.

$$x = \frac{-(-7.3) \pm \sqrt{[(-7.3)^2 - 4 \times 2.8 \times (-10.7)]}}{2 \times 2.8}$$
$$= \frac{7.3 \pm \sqrt{(53.29 + 119.84)}}{5.6}$$
$$= \frac{7.3 \pm \sqrt{173.13}}{5.6}$$

Hence $x = \dfrac{7.3 + 13.16}{5.6} = 3.653$ or $x = \dfrac{7.3 - 13.16}{5.6} = -1.046$

The solution are $x = 3.653$ or $x = -1.046$

SELF TEST 14.12

Use the formula to solve the equation $7x^2 - 8x + 1.8 = 0$. Give your answers to 4 significant figures.

$x = 0.3080$ or $x = 0.8348$

Rearranging equations

You may have to rearrange a quadratic equation to make it fit the formula.

EXAMPLE 14.13

After t seconds, the height, h m, of a projectile is given by
$$h = 50t - 5t^2$$
When is the projectile 83 m high?
Solution
Put $h = 83$ into the expression.
$$83 = 50t - 5t^2$$
Rearrange this equation so that all the terms are on the left.
$$5t^2 - 50t + 83 = 0$$

Use the formula to solve this equation.
$$t = 2.10 \text{ or } t = 7.90$$

The projectile will be 83 m high after 2.1 secs and 7.9 secs

SELF TEST 14.13

Solve the equation $x^2 = 7x + 9$. Give your answers to 4 significant figures.

$x = -1.110$ or $x = 8.110$

EXAMPLE 14.14

Solve the equation
$$\frac{x - 3}{x - 1} = 12x.$$

Solution
Multiply by $x - 1$, then expand, then rearrange.
$$x - 3 = 12x(x - 1)$$
$$x - 3 = 12x^2 - 12x$$
So $12x^2 - 13x + 3 = 0$
Solve this by the formula or by factorising.
$$x = \tfrac{1}{3} \text{ or } x = \tfrac{3}{4}$$

The solution is $x = \frac{1}{3}$ or $x = \frac{3}{4}$

SELF TEST 14.14

Solve the equation $\dfrac{2x + 3}{x - 2} = x + 3$.

$x = -2.541$ or $x = 3.541$

Simultaneous linear and quadratic equations

In Chapter 10 we dealt with simultaneous linear equations. Consider the following pair of equations, in which one equation is linear and the other equation is quadratic.
$$x + y = 4$$
$$y = x^2 - 4x + 5$$
Figure 14.7 shows the graphs of both equations. Notice that they cross in two places, at approximately $(0.4, 3.6)$ and at $(2.6, 1.4)$.

From the graph the solution of these equations is $x = 0.4$ and $y = 3.6$ or $x = 2.6$ and $y = 1.4$.

It is more accurate to solve equations by using algebra. Proceed as follows:
1 Use the linear equation to write y in terms of x.

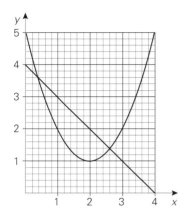

Figure 14.7 Graphs of $x + y = 4$ and $y = x^2 - 4x + 5$

2 Substitute into the quadratic equation, to obtain an equation in x alone.

3 Solve this equation to find x. Find the corresponding value of y.

Note If it is easier, you can write x in terms of y, and then find an equation in y alone.

EXAMPLE 14.15

Solve the simultaneous equations $y + 2x = 4$ and $y = x^2 + x - 3$.

Solution
Make y the subject of the first equation.

$$y = 4 - 2x$$

Substitute into the second equation.

$$4 - 2x = x^2 + x - 3$$

So

$$x^2 + 3x - 7 = 0$$

Solve using the formula.

$$x = -4.541 \text{ or } x = 1.541$$

Find the corresponding values of y by substituting into the first equation.

$$y = 4 - 2 \times -4.541 = 13.08$$

or

$$y = 4 - 2 \times 1.541 = 0.9172$$

$x = -4.541$ and $y = 13.08$, or $x = 1.541$ and $y = 0.9172$

SELF TEST 14.15

Solve the simultaneous equations

$$y - 3x = 5 \text{ and } y = 2x^2 + 7x + 1.$$

Give your answers to 3 decimal places.

$x = -2.732$ and $y = -3.196$,
or $x = 0.732$ and $y = 7.196$

CHECK YOUR UNDERSTANDING

● A quadratic expression is of the form $ax^2 + bx + c$, where a, b and c are constant

● A quadratic expression $x^2 + bx + c$ can sometimes be factorised to $(x + \alpha)(x + \beta)$, where $\alpha + \beta = b$ and $\alpha\beta = c$.

● To factorise $ax^2 + bx + c$, find factors of ac whose sum is b. Rewrite the bx terms using these factors, and factorise the first two terms and the last two terms.

● To complete the square of $x^2 + bx + c$, write it as

$$(x + \tfrac{1}{2}b)^2 + c - \tfrac{1}{4}b^2.$$

● To complete the square of $ax^2 + bx + c$, take out a factor of a and then proceed as above.

● When a quadratic is in completed square form, its maximum or minimum value can be found, and the value of x at which the maximum or minimum is reached.

● A quadratic equation is obtained when a quadratic expression is equal to 0. If the expression is factorised, then the solutions can be written down.

$$\text{If } (x + \alpha)(x + \beta) = 0, \text{ then } x = -\alpha \text{ or } x = -\beta$$

● The formula for solving a quadratic equation is

$$\text{if } ax^2 + bx + c = 0, \text{ then } x = \frac{-b \pm \sqrt{(b^2 - 4ac)}}{2a}.$$

● You may have to rearrange the equation to get it in the correct form.

● With simultaneous equations, one linear and one quadratic, use the linear equation to write one variable in terms of the other. Substitute into the quadratic equation and solve.

REVISION EXERCISES AND QUESTIONS

14.1 Factorising quadratic expressions

1 Factorise the following quadratics.

a) $x^2 + 7x + 12$ b) $x^2 + 9x + 18$ c) $x^2 + 17x + 60$
d) $x^2 - 5x + 6$ e) $x^2 - 8x + 15$ f) $x^2 - 4x + 4$
g) $x^2 + 4x - 12$ h) $x^2 - 8x - 33$ i) $x^2 - 6x - 72$
j) $2x^2 + 5x + 2$ k) $3x^2 - 7x + 4$ l) $5x^2 + 11x + 2$
m) $2x^2 + 5x - 3$ n) $5x^2 - 8x - 4$ o) $3x^2 - 7x - 6$
p) $x^2 - 16$ q) $2x^2 - 50$ r) $\tfrac{1}{2}x^2 - 18$

14.2 Completing the square

2 Complete the square of the following expressions.

a) $x^2 + 4x + 6$ b) $x^2 - 6x - 6$ c) $x^2 + 3x + 1$
d) $2x^2 + 8x + 1$ e) $3x^2 + 4x - 5$ f) $5 - 4x - x^2$

3 For each of the expressions of Question 2, find the maximum or minimum values of the quadratics. Find the values of x which give these maximum or minimum values.

4 Sketch the graphs of the expressions of Question 2.

14.3 Quadratic equations

5   Solve the following equations, where relevant giving your answer correct to 4 significant figures.

a) $x^2 + 7x + 10 = 0$ b) $x^2 - 6x + 8 = 0$

c) $x^2 + 9x - 20 = 0$ d) $x^2 + 8x + 5 = 0$

e) $3x^2 - 15x + 7 = 0$ f) $0.23x^2 + 0.7x + 0.17 = 0$

g) $x^2 + 3x = 11$ h) $x + 7 + \dfrac{1}{x} = 0$

i) $(x + 2)(x - 1) = 17$ j) $\dfrac{x + 3}{x} = x$

k) $\dfrac{1}{x + 4} + \dfrac{1}{x + 5} = 7$ l) $\dfrac{2x + 3}{x - 4} - = \dfrac{x - 4}{x + 7}$

6   Solve the following pairs of simultaneous equations.

a) $y = 2x - 3, y = x^2 + 4x - 5$

b) $2y + 3x = 6, y = x^2 - x - 1$

c) $y = 3x - 4, y^2 + x^2 = 12$

d) $3y - 2x = 1, x^2 + 2xy + 2y^2 = 5$

7   When a body is moving at speed v m/s, the force of air resistance is $0.2v + 0.003v^2$ N. Find the air resistance at 10 m/s. Find the speed if the air resistance is 23 N.

8   The volume of a frustum of a cone is $\frac{1}{3}\pi h(R^2 + Rr + r^2)$, where h is the height and the top and bottom radii are r and R respectively. (See Figure 14.8.) If the top radius is 18 mm, the height is 48 mm and the volume is 64 000 mm³, find the bottom radius.

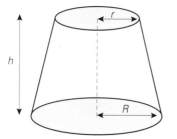

Figure 14.8   Frustum of a cone

9   The surface area of a cylinder is $2\pi rh + 2\pi r^2$, where h is the height and r is the radius. If the height is 1.5 m and the surface area is 0.89 m², find the radius.

10 A boiler consists of a cylinder of height h and radius r, with hemispheres of radius r at both ends. The surface area of the boiler is $4\pi r^2 + 2\pi rh$. A particular boiler has $h = 1.3$ m and has surface area 11.56 m². Find r.

11 Figure 14.9 shows a rectangle in which the length is 12 mm greater than the width.

a) If the area is 15 400 mm², find the width.

b) If the diagonal is 163 mm, find the width. (The length of the diagonal is given by the formula $d^2 = l^2 + w^2$.)

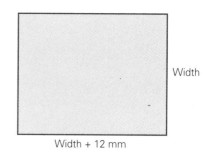

Width

Width + 12 mm

Figure 14.9

12 Figure 14.10 shows a metal tray with a square base. The sides are 0.3 m high. The total area of metal is 4 m². Find the side of the base. (Hint: Draw a diagram of the flat sheet of metal needed to make the tray, i.e. the *net* of the tray.)

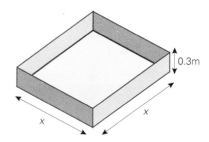

0.3m

x x

Figure 14.10   Metal tray

13 Figure 14.11 shows a rectangular template with quarter circles of radius r mm removed at each corner. The distances, in mm, are as shown, and the total area is 900 mm². Find r.

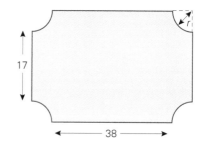

17

38

Figure 14.11   Template

14 Figure 14.12 shows a wire of length L m stretched between two supports x m apart. The sag is s m. It can be shown that $L = x + 2\frac{2}{3}\dfrac{s^2}{x}$. If $L = 200$ and $s = 8$, find x.

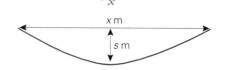

x m

s m

Figure 14.12   Stretched wire

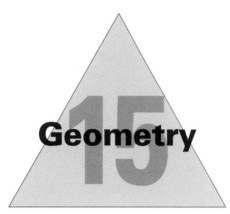

Geometry

Introduction

Technicians need to take measurements of the objects they work on. They also need to make diagrams of these objects, in order to plan their work.

Measurements involve angles and lengths, and diagrams involve several basic shapes such as squares, circles and so on. Geometry is the study of angles, lengths, squares, circles and so on.

In this chapter we give the names and the basic properties of shapes. In the next chapters we use the properties for calculations.

15.1 Lines and angles

A technical drawing is made mainly with straight lines. We label a straight line by letters at its ends. The straight line of Figure 15.1 is labelled AB.

Figure 15.1

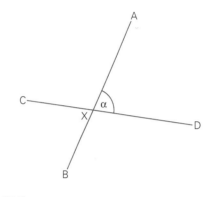

Figure 15.2

In Figure 15.2 two lines AB and CD meet at a point X. We label angles by giving the letters of points around them. In Figure 15.2 the angle labelled α is $A\hat{X}D$. Often we use the sign ˆ above the middle letter.

Usually angles are measured in **degrees**. (We looked at angles in Chapter 7.) The symbol for a degree sign is a small circle, °. 360 degrees is written 360°.

The instrument to measure angles is a **protractor**. Its use is shown in Figure 15.3. One line lies along the base line. The other line passes through 20°, hence the angle between the two lines is 20°.

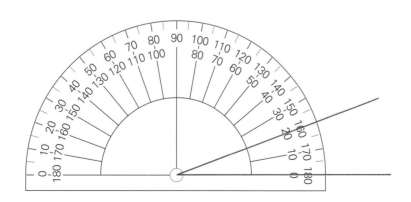

Figure 15.3 A protractor

Special sorts of angle

Some special sorts of angle are listed below. See Figures 15.4, 15.5 and 15.6

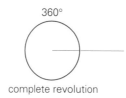

straight line   complete revolution

Figure 15.4

right angle

Figure 15.5

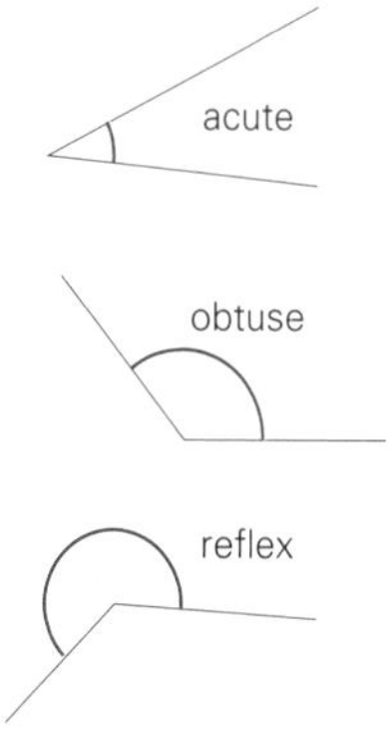

Figure 15.6

● There are 180° in a straight line. AB̂C = 180°.
● A complete revolution, i.e. a full turn, contains 360°. XŶZ = 360°.
● Half of 180° is a **right angle**. Hence there are 90° in a right angle. A right-angle is shown by the symbol in Figure 15.5.
● An angle less than 90° is **acute**.
● An angle between 90° and 180° is **obtuse**
● An angle greater than 180° is **reflex**.

We show that two angles are equal by marking them with the same symbols, such as the dots and curves in Figure 15.7.

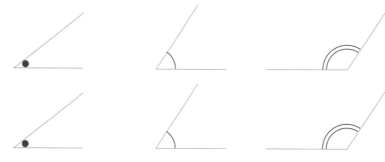

Figure 15.7 Equal angles

● Two angles which make up a right angle are **complementary**. Their sum is 90°. For example, 30° and 60° are complementary angles. See Figure 15.8.
● Two angles which make up a straight line are **supplementary**. Their sum is 180°. For example, 30° and 150° are supplementary. See Figure 15.8.

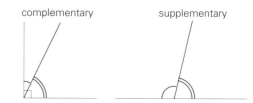

complementary   supplementary

Figure 15.8

EXAMPLE 15.1

Three lines cross so that the angles between them are equal. What is the angle between each pair of lines?

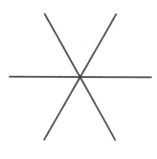

Figure 15.9

Solution
There are 6 angles surrounding the meeting point. Hence each angle is 360° ÷ 6, i.e. 60°.

The angle is 60°

SELF TEST 15.1

From point X, point A is due north, and point B is north-east, i.e. halfway between north and east. Find the angle AX̂B.

45°

EXAMPLE 15.2

Figure 15.10 shows the floor of a room. The lines joining opposite corners meet at X. From the figure identify an acute angle. Find two angles which are supplementary.

Solution
The angle AX̂D is less than 90°.

AX̂D is an acute angle

The angles AX̂B and BX̂C together make up the straight line AC.

AX̂B and BX̂C are supplementary

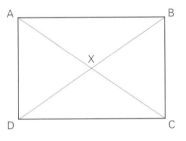

Figure 15.10

SELF TEST 15.2

From the diagram of Figure 15.11 identify an acute angle. Find two angles which are complementary.

CB̂D. BĈD & AĈD (others possible)

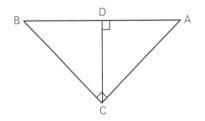

Figure 15.11

Types of line

We show that two lines are **equal** in length by marks across them, as in Figure 15.12.

Two lines going in the same direction are **parallel**. We show that lines are parallel by arrow symbols.

Two lines making 90° with each other are **perpendicular**. We show that lines are perpendicular by the right angle sign.

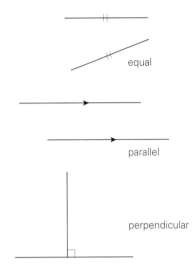

Figure 15.12

When two lines cross at a point, as in Figure 15.13, the angles on **opposite** sides of the point are equal.

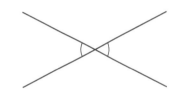

Figure 15.13   Opposite angles

Figure 15.14 shows two parallel lines, with a third line crossing. The angles a and b are equal. They are called **alternate angles**. The angles a and c are equal. They are called **corresponding angles**.

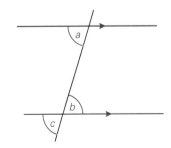

Figure 15.14   Alternate and corresponding angles

EXAMPLE 15.3

Find the angles labelled x and y in Figure 15.15.

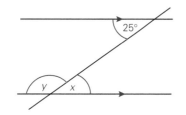

Figure 15.15

Solution
The angle x is alternate to the angle of $25°$.

$$x = 25°$$

The angles x and y are supplementary. Subtract $25°$ from $180°$, obtaining $155°$.

$$y = 155°$$

SELF TEST 15.3

Find the angles labelled a, b and c in Figure 15.16.

40°, 40°, 50°

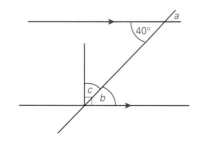

Figure 15.16

Fractions of a degree

We can measure an angle which is not a whole number of degrees by decimals or fractions. A quarter of a right angle is $22.5°$ or $22\frac{1}{2}°$.

Sometimes we measure fractions of a degree in **minutes** and **seconds**. There are 60 minutes in a degree, and 60 seconds in a minute. The symbols for minutes and seconds are $'$ and $''$ respectively.

$5°\ 12'\ 37''$ means 5 degrees, 12 minutes and 37 seconds.

Each minute is $\frac{1}{60}$ of a degree, and each second is $\frac{1}{3600}$ of a degree. Hence the angle above is

$$5 + \frac{12}{60} + \frac{37}{3600} = 5.2103°$$

We dealt with the arithmetic of minutes and seconds in Chapter 7.

EXAMPLE 15.4

A cog wheel has 32 teeth. If A and B are the points of adjacent teeth, what angle does AB subtend at the centre of the wheel? Give your answer as a decimal and also in terms of minutes.

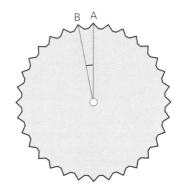

Figure 15.17   Cog wheel

Solution
Divide 360 by 32, obtaining 11.25. This is the angle.

AB subtends 11.25°

To convert $0.25°$ to minutes, multiply by 60, obtaining $15'$.

AB subtends $11°\ 15'$

SELF TEST 15.4

A cog wheel has 54 teeth. Find the angle subtended at the centre of the wheel by adjacent teeth. Give your answer as a decimal and also in terms of minutes.

6.67°, 6° 40′

15.2 Triangles

A **triangle** is a figure with three sides. Some special triangles are as follows. See Figure 15.18.

● In an **acute-angled** triangle, all the angles are acute.
● In an **obtuse-angled** triangle, one of the angles is obtuse.
● In a **right-angled** triangle, one of the angles is 90°.

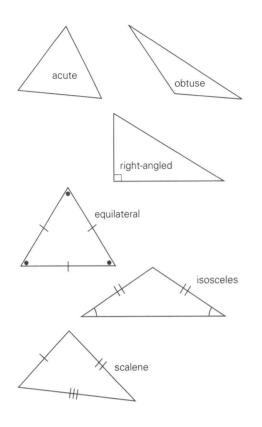

Figure 15.18 Special triangles

- In an **equilateral** triangle all the sides are equal and all the angles are equal.
- In an **isosceles** triangle two sides are equal and two angles are equal.
- In a **scalene** triangle all the sides and all the angles are different.

EXAMPLE 15.5

In Figure 15.19 ABCD is a square. What sort of triangle is ABC?

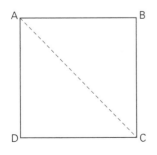

Figure 15.19

Solution
The sides AB and BC are equal. The angle $\hat{B}$ is 90°.

ABC is isosceles and right-angled

SELF TEST 15.5

In Figure 15.20, ABCD is a square and M is the midpoint of AB. What sort of triangle is MDC?

isosceles

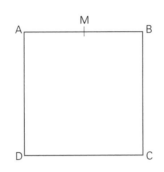

Figure 15.20

Angles in a triangle

(a) In any triangle, the sum of the angles is 180°. In Figure 15.21,

$$\hat{A} + \hat{B} + \hat{C} = 180°.$$

(b) In Figure 15.21, a is the **exterior** angle. It is the sum of the opposite interior angles, $b + c$.

$$a = b + c$$

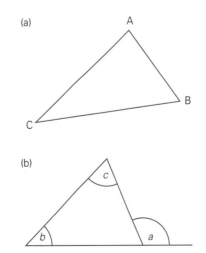

Figure 15.21 Sum of angles

124 Essential mathematics for technicians

EXAMPLE 15.6

Figure 15.22 shows the section of a roof. The two sides of the roof are equal, and make an angle of 150° with each other. Find the slope of the roof.

Figure 15.22 Section of roof

Solution
The section is an isosceles triangle. Hence the two angles at the base are equal.

Subtract 150° from 180°, obtaining 30°.

Divide 30° by 2, obtaining 15°.

The slope of the roof is 15°

SELF TEST 15.6

Find the unknown angles in the triangles of Figure 15.23.

$a = 50°, b = 70°$

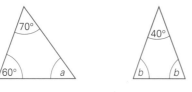

Figure 15.23

Congruent triangles

Two triangles are **congruent** if they have the same shape and the same size. Their sides are the same and their angles are the same. In Figure 15.24 triangles ABC and DEF are congruent.

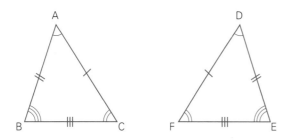

Figure 15.24 Congruent triangles

It follows that

$$AB = DE \qquad BC = EF \qquad CA = FD$$
$$\hat{A} = \hat{D} \qquad \hat{B} = \hat{E} \qquad \hat{C} = \hat{F}$$

Note The order of letters is important. When we say that triangle ABC is congruent to triangle DEF, then $\hat{A} = \hat{D}$, $\hat{B} = \hat{E}$ and $\hat{C} = \hat{F}$.

There are four sets of conditions for two triangles to be congruent.

SSS The three sides of one triangle are equal to the three sides of the other triangle. (See Figure 15.25.)

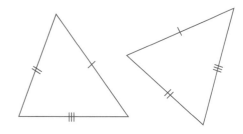

Figure 15.25

SAS Two sides and the enclosed angle of one triangle are equal to two sides and the enclosed angle of the other triangle. (See Figure 15.26.)

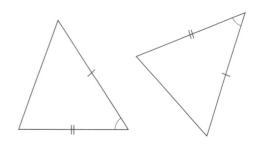

Figure 15.26

ASA Two angles and the enclosed side of one triangle are equal to two angles and the enclosed side of the other triangle. (See Figure 15.27.)

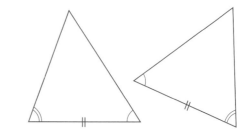

Figure 15.27

RHS Both triangles are right angled, with equal hypotenuses and one other side equal. (See Figure 15.28.)

Figure 15.28

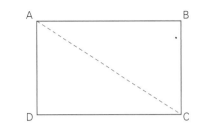

Figure 15.31

Solution

AC is in both ACB and ACD.
AB is parallel to DC, hence $B\hat{A}C = D\hat{C}A$ (alternate).
Similarly $A\hat{C}B = D\hat{A}C$.
Hence triangle ACB is congruent to triangle CAD (ASA).

ACB is congruent to CAD

Note The order of the letters is important. It is not true that ABC is congruent to CAD.

EXAMPLE 15.7

In Figure 15.29, which pair of triangles are congruent?

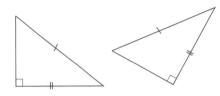

Figure 15.29

Solution

In pair (a), the equal angle is enclosed within the equal sides for the first triangle, but not for the second triangle.

In pair (b), the sides of one triangle are equal to the sides of the other triangle. (SSS).

The triangles in (b) are congruent

SELF TEST 15.7

In Figure 15.30, which pair of triangles are congruent?

Pair (a)

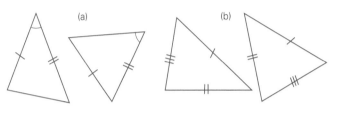

Figure 15.30

EXAMPLE 15.8

In Figure 15.31, ABCD is a rectangle. AC is a diagonal. Find a pair of congruent triangles.

SELF TEST 15.8

Figure 15.32 shows an isosceles triangle, for which AB = AC. The midpoint of BC is M. Find a pair of congruent triangles.

ABM, ACM (SSS)

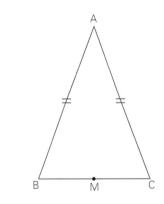

Figure 15.32

15.3 Quadrilaterals

A **quadrilateral** is a figure with four sides. Some special quadrilaterals are as follows. See Figure 15.33.

- A **square** has equal sides, each angle is 90°.
- A **rectangle** has all angles equal to 90°
- A **rhombus** has equal sides.

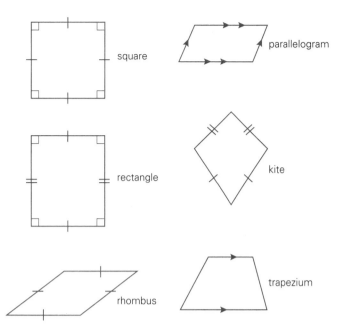

Figure 15.33   Special quadrilaterals

- A **parallelogram** has opposite sides equal and parallel and opposite angles equal.
- A **kite** has two pairs of adjacent sides equal.
- A **trapezium** has one pair of opposite sides parallel.

EXAMPLE 15.9

In Figure 15.34 ABCDEF is a regular (all the sides are equal) six sided figure. (A hexagon). What sort of quadrilaterals are
    a) ABCD   b) BCEF?

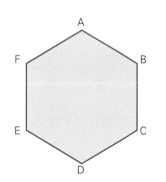

Figure 15.34

Solution
a) In ABCD, BC and AD are parallel, but AB and CD are not parallel.

         ABCD is a trapezium

b) All the angles of BCEF are 90°.

         BCEF is a rectangle

SELF TEST 15.9

In Figure 15.35, X is the centre of the hexagon. Give the names of AFXB and ACDE.

rhombus, kite

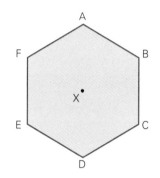

Figure 15.35

Angles in a quadrilateral

The angles in a quadrilateral add up to 360°.

EXAMPLE 15.10

In the quadrilateral ABCD of Figure 15.36, $\hat{A} = 75°$ and $\hat{B} = \hat{C} = \hat{D}$. Find $\hat{B}$.

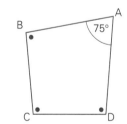

Figure 15.36

Solution
The sum of all four angles is 360°.
Hence
$$75° + 3\hat{B} = 360°$$
So
$$3\hat{B} = 285°$$
$$\hat{B} = 95°$$
Hence
$$\hat{B} = 95°$$

SELF TEST 15.10

In a quadrilateral PQRS, $\hat{P} = 84°$, $\hat{Q} = 78°$ and $\hat{R} = \hat{S}$. Find $\hat{R}$.

99°

15.4 Polygons

A **polygon** is a figure with straight sides. Triangles and quadrilaterals are examples of polygons. The next two polygons are listed below. See Figure 15.37.

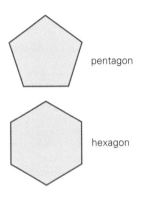

pentagon

hexagon

Figure 15.37

● A **pentagon** has five sides.
● A **hexagon** has six sides.

With each extra side, the sum of the angles increases by 180°. Hence the angles in a pentagon add up to 540°, and the angles in a hexagon add up to 720°.

If a polygon has n sides, the sum of its **interior** angles is $(180n - 360)°$.

The angles going round the outside of a polygon are the **exterior** angles. When going round, a full circle is completed. Hence for all polygons, the sum of the exterior angles is 360°. See Figure 15.38.

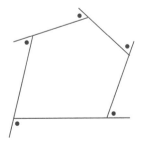

Figure 15.38   Exterior angles

In a **regular** polygon, all the sides are equal and all the angles are equal. For example, the sum of the internal angles of a hexagon is 720°. Hence if the hexagon is regular, each internal angle is 720 ÷ 6, i.e. 120°.

EXAMPLE 15.11

A window is made in the shape of a regular octagon (8 sides). Find the interior angles. See Figure 15.39.

Figure 15.39   Octagonal window

Solution
The sum of the interior angles is given by the formula

$$\text{Sum of interior angles} = (180n - 360)°$$

For an octagon,

$$\text{Sum of interior angles} = 180° \times 8 - 360° = 1080°$$

Divide 1080 by 8, obtaining 135.

Each interior angle is 135°

SELF TEST 15.11

Find the interior angle of a regular decagon (10 sides).

144°

EXAMPLE 15.12

Each interior angle of a regular polygon is 160°. How many sides does it have?

Solution
Each exterior angle is 180° − 160°, i.e. 20°. Divide 360 by 20, obtaining 18.

The polygon has 18 sides

SELF TEST 15.12

Each interior angle of a regular polygon is 150°. Find the number of sides of the polygon.

12 sides

15.5 Circles

The shapes considered so far all have straight line sides. The simplest curved figure is a circle. All the points on a circle are the same distance from one fixed point, the centre. Some lines within the circle are as follows. See Figures 15.40 and 15.41.

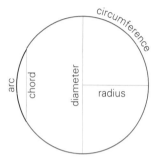

Figure 15.40

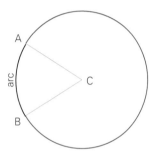

Figure 15.41 Subtended angle

● The **radius** is the distance from a point on the circle to the centre.
● The **diameter** is the distance across the circle. It is twice the radius.
● A **chord** is a line joining two points on the circle.
● An **arc** is the part of the circle between two points on it.
● The **circumference** or **perimeter** is the length around the circle.
● If AB is an arc of a circle centre C, then the angle **subtended** at the centre is $A\hat{C}B$.

The ratio of the circumference to the diameter is the same for all circles. Its value is π (pronounced *pie*).

For any circle
$$\text{circumference} \div \text{diameter} = \pi$$

π is a decimal which has an infinite number of decimal places, it goes on for ever. Approximate values for π are 3.142 and $\frac{22}{7}$. A scientific calculator has a button which gives π to more decimal places.

EXAMPLE 15.13

A running track is a circle with radius 90 m. Find its diameter and the length of one circuit of the track.

Solution
The diameter is twice the radius.

The diameter is 180 m

The length of the track is the circumference of the circle.
$$\frac{\text{circumference}}{\text{diameter}} = \pi$$
[Multiply both sides by the diameter]
$$\text{circumference} = 180 \times \pi = 565 \text{ m}$$

The length of the track is 565 m

SELF TEST 15.13

The diameter of a pipe is 43 mm. Find its radius and its circumference.

21.5 mm, 135 mm

EXAMPLE 15.14

A label of width 88 mm will just wrap around a can. Find the radius of the can.

Solution
The width of the label is the same as the circumference of the can.

The circumference is the diameter multiplied by π. Hence
$$\text{diameter} = \text{circumference} \div \pi$$
$$\text{diameter} = 88 \div \pi = 28 \text{ mm}$$

The radius is 14 mm

SELF TEST 15.14

A running track is to be a circle of circumference 700 m. What should its radius be?

111.4 m

Regions of circles

Figure 15.42 shows some regions within a circle.

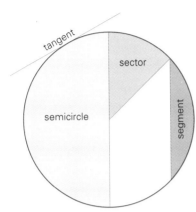

Figure 15.42

- A **sector** is a region between two radii.
- A diameter cuts a circle into two **semicircles**.
- A **segment** is a region cut off by a chord.
- A **tangent** is a line which touches the circle.

The tangent is perpendicular to the radius. Hence if two circles touch each other, the line joining their centres goes through the point of contact. See Figure 15.43.

Figure 15.43

EXAMPLE 15.15

Two walls meet at X, making 80° with each other. A cylindrical pipe is placed so that it meets the walls at A and B. Find the angle $\hat{AOB}$, where O is the centre of the cylinder. See Figure 15.44.

Solution

The walls are tangents to the cylinder. Hence both $X\hat{A}O$ and $X\hat{B}O$ are 90°. Subtract from 360°

$$\hat{AOB} = 360° - 90° - 90° - 80° = 100°$$

The angle $\hat{AOB}$ is 100°

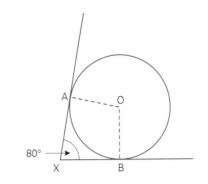

Figure 15.44

SELF TEST 15.15

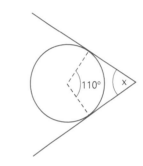

Figure 15.45

Find the angle x of Figure 15.45.

70°

15.6 Solids

So far, we have dealt with flat shapes. Real objects are solid. When you cut a solid, the region exposed is a **cross-section**. For example, when you saw through a plank, the rectangle exposed is a cross-section of the plank. See Figure 15.46.

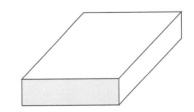

Figure 15.46 **Cross-section**

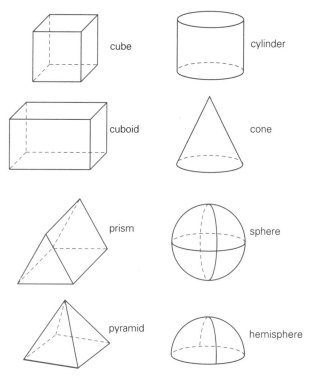

Figure 15.47   Special solids

Some types of solids are listed below. See Figure 15.47.

● A **cube** has six square faces.
● A **cuboid** has six rectangular faces.
● A **prism** has a constant cross-section. If the cross-section is a triangle, then it is a **triangular** prism.
● A **pyramid** tapers to a point from its base. The famous pyramids of Egypt have square bases.
● A **cylinder** has a constant circular cross-section.
● A **cone** tapers to a point from a circular base.
● A **sphere** is a perfectly round object, like a ball.
● A **hemisphere** is half a sphere.

(a)   (c)

Top
Blend
Coffee

200g

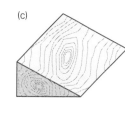

(b)

Figure 15.48

EXAMPLE 15.16

What are the mathematical names for the following objects, shown in Figure 15.48?
    a) a coffee tin
    b) the tip of a sharpened pencil
    c) a wedge

Solution

a) The cross-section of a tin is a circle.

           A coffee tin is a cylinder

b) The pencil is sharpened so that it tapers to a point.

           The tip is a cone

c) A wedge has a cross-section which is a triangle.

           A wedge is a triangular prism

SELF TEST 15.16

Figure 15.49 shows a concrete pillar. Give the names of the sloping part at the top, and of the part underneath.

                     pyramid, cuboid

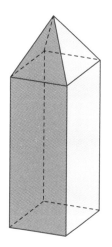

Figure 15.49   Concrete pillar

EXAMPLE 15.17

A block of wood is shaped as the cuboid ABCDEFGH. (See Figure 15.50). What shapes are obtained if it is cut along ABGH?

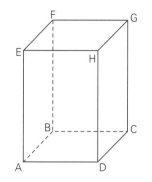

Figure 15.50

Solution

The cross-section of both halves are triangles.

The block is cut into two triangular prisms

SELF TEST 15.17

The block of Example 15.17 is cut along the plane AFH. What is the smaller shape obtained?

triangular-based pyramid

■ **CHECK YOUR UNDERSTANDING**

● There are 360° (360 degrees) in a circle. An angle less than 90° is acute. An angle between 90° and 180° is obtuse. An angle greater than 180° is reflex. An angle of 90° is a right angle. Angles whose sum is 180° are supplementary. Angles whose sum is 90° are complementary.

● Lines in the same direction are parallel. Lines at 90° to each other are perpendicular.

● An equilateral triangle has equal sides and equal angles. An isosceles triangle has two equal sides and two equal angles. A right-angled triangle has one angle equal to 90°. The sum of the angles in a triangle is 180°.

● Triangles are congruent if they have the same shape and the same size. Two triangles are congruent if any of the following sets of conditions hold.

SSS   All sides are equal.

SAS   Two sides and the enclosed angle equal.

ASA   Two angles and the enclosed side equal.

RHS   Both triangles right-angled, hypotenuse and another side equal.

● A rectangle has all angles equal to 90°. A square is a rectangle with equal sides. A parallelogram has opposite sides parallel. A trapezium has one pair of opposite sides parallel. A rhombus has equal sides. A kite has two pairs of adjacent sides equal. The sum of the angles in a quadrilateral is 360°.

● A five sided figure is a pentagon. A six sided figure is a hexagon. If a figure has n sides, the sum of its interior angle is $n180° - 360°$. The sum of the exterior angles is always 360°.

● The diameter of a circle is twice the radius. The circumference of a circle is π times the diameter. A tangent to a circle is perpendicular to a radius of the circle.

● A cuboid has six rectangular faces. A cube is a cuboid with six square faces. A prism has constant cross-section. A pyramid tapers to a point. A cylinder has circular cross-section. A cone tapers to a point from a circle. A sphere is a perfectly round object.

REVISION EXERCISES AND QUESTIONS

15.1 Lines and angles

1   Find the angles in the diagrams of Figure 15.51.

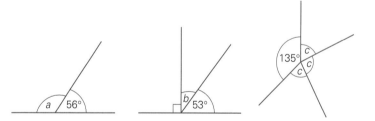

Figure 15.51

2   In Figure 15.52 the horizontal lines are parallel. Find the angles.

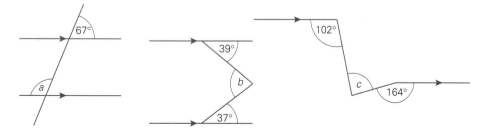

Figure 15.52

3 In Figure 15.53 12 holes are drilled in a circular plate. Find the angle subtended by holes next to each other, at the centre of the plate.

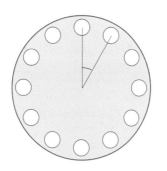

Figure 15.53

4 Figure 15.54 shows a chisel point. The angle of the point of the chisel is 48°, and the clearance angle is 15°. Find the angle of inclination.

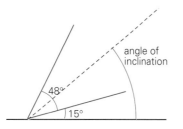

Figure 15.54 Chisel point

5 Find the angle which is supplementary to 68°. Find the angle which is complementary to 42°.

6 A machine turns through 3.3 revolutions per minute. How many degrees does it pass through per second?

15.2 Triangles

7 Figure 15.55 shows a rectangle ABCD. AC and BD meet at X. Give the names of the triangles AXB and ABD.

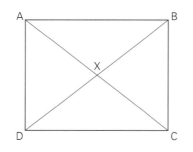

Figure 15.55

8 Find the unknown angles in the triangles of Figure 15.56.

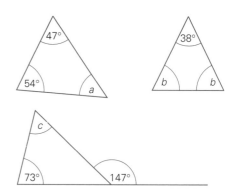

Figure 15.56

9 Figure 15.57 shows a kite. Write down a pair of congruent triangles.

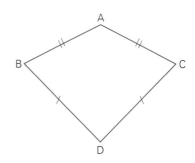

Figure 15.57

10 ABCDE is a regular pentagon (5 sides). Show that ABD and BCE are congruent.

15.3 Quadrilaterals

11 Figure 15.58 shows a regular decagon with X its centre. Give the names of the quadrilaterals ACGI and JAXH.

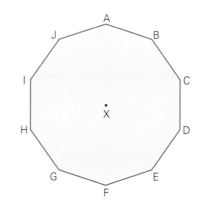

Figure 15.58

12 Find the unknown angles in the quadrilaterals of Figure 15.59.

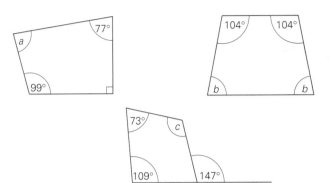

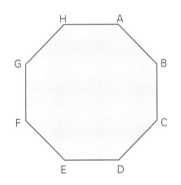

Figure 15.59

13 Figure 15.60 shows a regular octagon, ABCDEFGH. Identify on the figure

a) a rectangle   b) a trapezium   c) a kite.

Figure 15.60

15.4 Polygons

14 Find the sum of the interior angles of a 12-sided figure.

15 Find each internal angle of a regular 15-sided figure.

16 A regular n sided polygon has internal angle $140°$. Find n.

15.5 Circles

(For these question take $\pi = 3.142$ or use the π button on your calculator.)

17 In Figure 15.61 A and B are two points on a circle with centre C. What are the names of

a) the straight line AB
b) the curved line AB
c) the region enclosed by AC, BC and the curved line AB
d) the region enclosed by the straight line AB and the curved line AB.

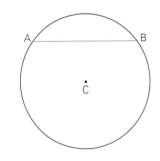

Figure 15.61

18 A circular roundabout has radius 50 m. Find its diameter and its circumference.

19 The circumference of a circle is 256 mm. Find its diameter and its radius.

15.6 Solids

20 Give the names of the solids of Figure 15.62.

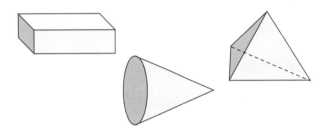

Figure 15.62

21 Figure 15.63 is a diagram of a house. What are the mathematical names of

a) the roof section EFGHIJ
b) the section below the roof, ABCDEFGH.

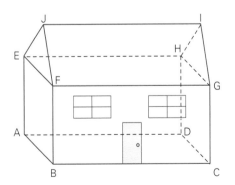

Figure 15.63

Area and volume

Introduction

You often need to make accurate measurements of areas and volumes. When preparing to paint a house, you need to know the area of its walls. When preparing to fill a swimming pool, you need to know its volume.

You need to know the areas and volumes of basic shapes, so that you can plan the quantities you use.

16.1 Units

Length

In the SI system the basic unit of length is the metre (m). Other units of length are the millimetre (mm) and the kilometre (km). The units of area and volume are found from the units of length. For each length unit there is an area unit and a volume unit. (See Table 16.1.)

Area

The area of a rectangle is the product of the two sides. Figure 16.1 shows a rectangle which is 4 m by 5 m. There are 4×5, i.e. 20, square metres in the rectangle.

Figure 16.1

Volume

The volume of a cuboid is the product of the three sides. Figure 16.2 shows a cuboid which is 4 m by 5 m by 2 m. There are $4 \times 5 \times 2$, i.e. 40, cubic metres in the cuboid.

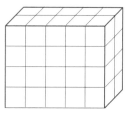

Figure 16.2

Mixed measurements

When combining measurements, make sure they are in the same units.

Table 16.1

Length	Area	Volume
metre (m)	square metre (m^2)	cubic metre (m^3)
millimetre (mm)	square millimetre (mm^2)	cubic millimetre (mm^3)
kilometre (km)	square kilometre (km^2)	cubic kilometre (km^3)

Adding

If you add two distances, say 2.1 km and 365 m, put them both in metres or both in kilometres.

Converting to km: 2.1 km + 0.365 km
= 2.465 km

Converting to m: 2100 m + 365 m
= 2465 m

Multiplying

If a rectangular sheet of wood is 1.5 m by 480 mm, change both lengths to the same units before finding the area.

Converting to m: 1.5 m × 0.480 m
= 0.72 m^2

Converting to mm: 1500 mm × 480 mm
= 720 000 mm^2

EXAMPLE 16.1

A road is 5 m wide. What is the area of a 30 km length of this road?

Solution
Convert the km to m. The road is 30 000 m long. Multiply by 5, obtaining 150 000.

The area is 150 000 m^2

SELF TEST 16.1

A roll of fax paper is 216 mm wide and 40 m long. What is the area of paper, in m^2?

8.64 m^2

Conversion between mm^2, m^2 and km^2

When converting between square units, square the number.

There are 1000 mm in 1 m
and 1000^2, i.e. 1 000 000 mm^2 in 1 m^2.
There are 1000 m in 1 km
and 1000^2, i.e. 1 000 000 m^2 in 1 km^2.

Look at the result above, about a rectangle of wood. In mm^2, its area was 720 000 mm^2. In m^2, its area was 0.72 m^2. There are 1 000 000 mm^2 in 1 m^2.

720 000 = 1 000 000 × 0.72

Remember Do *not* convert from mm^2 to m^2 by taking 1000 mm^2 in 1 m^2. If you do this your answer will be 1000 times too large or too small!

Conversion between mm^3, m^3 and km^3

Similarly, when converting between cubic units, cube the number.

There are 1000^3, i.e. 1 000 000 000 mm^3 in 1 m^3.
Again, be careful not to take 1000 mm^3 in 1 m^3.

EXAMPLE 16.2

A rectangular piece of wood is 1045 mm by 2180 mm. Find its area in mm^2. Convert your answer to m^2.

Solution
Both measurements are in mm.
Multiply 1045 by 2180, obtaining 2 278 100.

The area is 2 278 100 mm^2

Divide by 1000^2 obtaining 2.2781.

The area is 2.2781 m^2

Note We would get the same answer if we converted the lengths to 1.045 m and 2.18 m, and then multiplied.

SELF TEST 16.2

A region of land is a rectangle with sides 0.65 km and 0.46 km. Find the area of the region in km^2. Convert your answer to m^2.

0.299 km^2. 299 000 m^2

16.2 Areas of straight line figures

Basic shapes occur in everyday life. A door is a rectangle. The side of a shed might be a trapezium. (See Figure 16.3.) You need to know how to find the areas of these shapes.

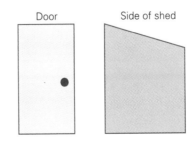

Figure 16.3

Table 16.2 gives the formulae for finding areas of some basic shapes.

Table 16.2 Areas of simple shapes

Shape	Area	
Rectangle with breadth b and height h (breadth is another word for width)	bh	
Square with side x	x^2	
Triangle with base b and height h	$\frac{1}{2}bh$	
Parallelogram with base b and height h	bh	
Trapezium with parallel sides a and b, height h	$\frac{1}{2}(a+b)h$	

EXAMPLE 16.3

Find the area of the metal plate shown in Figure 16.4. Lengths are in mm.

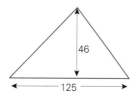

Figure 16.4

Solution

The plate is a triangle, with base 125 mm and height 46 mm. Apply the formula Area $= \frac{1}{2}bh$.

$$\text{Area} = \tfrac{1}{2} \times 125 \times 46 = 2875 \text{ mm}^2$$

The area is 2875 mm^2

SELF TEST 16.3

Find the area of the triangular field shown in Figure 16.5.

79 200 m^2

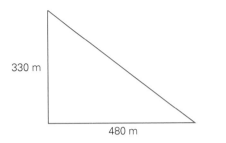

Figure 16.5

EXAMPLE 16.4

A swimming pool is 1 m at the shallow end, and 3.5 m at the deep end. The length of the pool is 25 m. Find the area of a side wall.

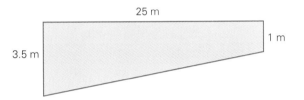

Figure 16.6 Side wall of a swimming pool

Solution
Figure 16.6 shows the side wall. This is a trapezium, with the parallel sides of length 1 m and 3.5 m, at a distance apart of 25 m. Apply the formula for the area of a trapezium.

$$\text{Area} = \tfrac{1}{2}(a + b)h$$
$$\text{Area} = \tfrac{1}{2}(1 + 3.5)\,25 = 56.25 \text{ m}^2$$

The area is 56.25 m^2

SELF TEST 16.4

Figure 16.7 shows the side wall of a shed. The shed is 2.2 m

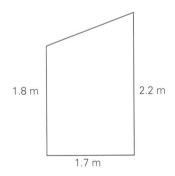

Figure 16.7

---

high at the front, 1.8 m high at the back, and 1.7 m from back to front. Find the area of the wall.

3.4 m^2

16.3 Area of circles

The simplest shape with a curved side is a circle. If a circle has radius r, its area is πr^2. An approximate value for π can be found from a button on a calculator, or taken as 3.142.

If the diameter of the circle is d, then its area is $\tfrac{1}{4}\pi d^2$.

Note In the formula πr^2, you square r and then multiply by π. Do not multiply by π and then square.

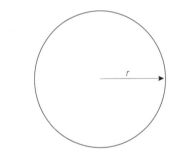

Figure 16.8

EXAMPLE 16.5

A circular running track has diameter 100 m. Find the area within the track.

Solution
Here the diameter is 100 m. Apply the formula Area $= \tfrac{1}{4}\pi d^2$.

$$\text{Area} = \tfrac{1}{4}\pi 100^2 = 7854 \text{ m}^2$$

The area is 7854 m^2

SELF TEST 16.5

A circular carpet has radius 1.9 m. Find the area of the carpet.

11.34 m^2

Finding the radius from the area

The formula $A = \pi r^2$ gives A in terms of r. When we change the subject to r, this will give r in terms of A.

Suppose you know the area of a circle. To find its radius, divide by π and take the square root.

$$\text{If } \pi r^2 = A, \text{ then } r = \sqrt{\left(\frac{A}{\pi}\right)}$$

EXAMPLE 16.6

A circular roof has area 80 m². What is its radius?

Solution
Here $A = 80$ m². Hence $\pi r^2 = 80$, giving $r = \sqrt{\left(\dfrac{80}{\pi}\right)}$.

$$r = \sqrt{25.46} = 5.05$$

The radius is 5.05 m

SELF TEST 16.6

The area of the top of a cylindrical soup can is 9850 mm².
Find its diameter.

112 mm

16.4 Combinations of shapes

Complicated shapes can be built up from simple shapes. To
find the area of a complicated shape, add or subtract the areas
of the simpler shapes.

In Figure 16.9, there is a triangle on top of a rectangle. *Add* the
areas.

Figure 16.9

In Figure 16.10, a circle has been removed from a square.
Subtract the areas.

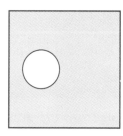

Figure 16.10

EXAMPLE 16.7

Figure 16.11 shows the side wall of a swimming pool.
Distances are in m. Find the area of the side wall.

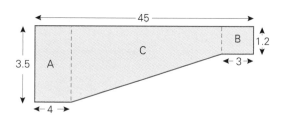

Figure 16.11 Wall of a swimming pool

Solution
The shape can be cut up into two rectangles A and B and a
trapezium C, as shown.

$$\text{Area of A} = 3.5 \times 4 = 14 \text{ m}^2$$
$$\text{Area of B} = 1.2 \times 3 = 3.6 \text{ m}^2$$
$$\text{Area of C} = \tfrac{1}{2}(3.5 + 1.2) \times 38 = 89.3 \text{ m}^2$$
$$\text{Whole area} = \text{A} + \text{B} + \text{C} = 14 + 3.6 + 89.3 = 106.9$$

The area is 106.9 m²

SELF TEST 16.7

Figure 16.12 shows the cross-section of a steel girder.
Distances are in mm. Find the area of cross-section.

2391 mm²

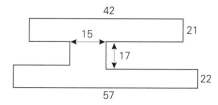

Figure 16.12

EXAMPLE 16.8

A hole of diameter 16 mm is drilled through a square plate of
side 115 mm. Find the area of the remaining plate.

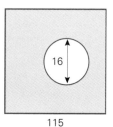

Figure 16.13

Solution

Subtract the area of the circular hole from the area of the square plate.

$$\text{Area of square} = 115^2 \text{ mm}^2 = 13\,225 \text{ mm}^2$$
$$\text{Area of hole} = \tfrac{1}{4}\pi\,16^2 \text{ mm}^2 = 201 \text{ mm}^2$$

The area remaining is 13 024 mm^2

SELF TEST 16.8

A circular washer of diameter 2.7 mm has a square hole of side 0.9 mm removed from its centre. Find the remaining area.

4.916 mm^2

16.5 Volumes

Table 16.3 gives the formulae for finding volumes of some basic shapes.

EXAMPLE 16.9

An oil drum is 1.1 m high, and has radius 0.2 m. Find its volume.

Table 16.3 Volumes of simple solids

Shape	Volume	
Cuboid with sides *a*, *b* and *c*	abc	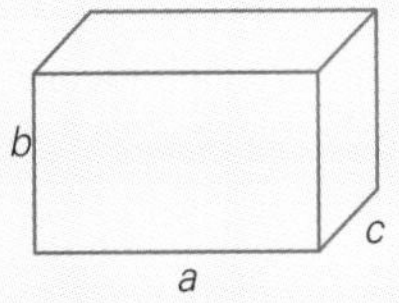
Cube with side *x*	x^3	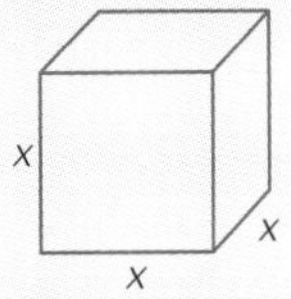
Prism with cross-sectional area *A* and height *h*	Ah	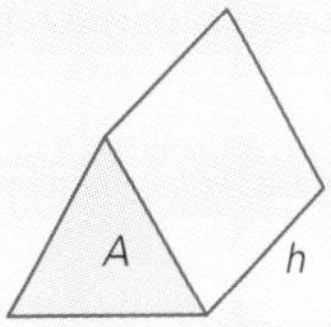
Pyramid with base area *A* and height *h*	$\tfrac{1}{3}Ah$	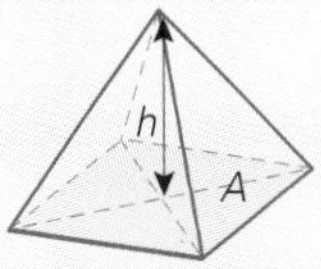
Sphere with radius *r*	$\tfrac{4}{3}\pi r^3$	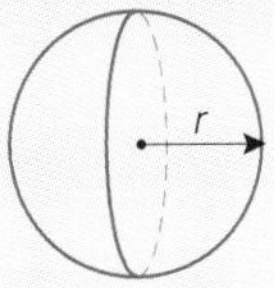
Cylinder with base radius *r*, height *h*	$\pi r^2 h$	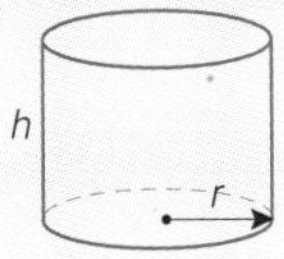
Cone with base radius *r*, height *h*	$\tfrac{1}{3}\pi r^2 h$	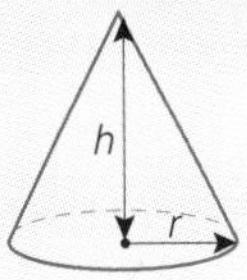

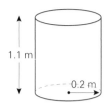

Figure 16.14   Oil drum

Solution

The drum is a cylinder, with $h = 1.1$ m and $r = 0.2$ m. Use the formula

$$V = \pi r^2 h$$
$$\text{Volume} = \pi \times 0.2^2 \times 1.1 = 0.138 \text{ m}^3$$

The volume is 0.138 m³

SELF TEST 16.9

A can of fish is a cylinder with radius 56 mm and height 68 mm. Find its volume. Give your answer to 2 significant figures.

670 000 mm³

EXAMPLE 16.10

Sand is poured from a lorry onto the ground. It forms a cone with diameter 3.8 m and height 0.8 m. Find the volume of sand.

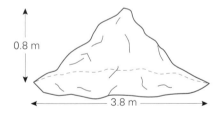

Figure 16.15   Pile of sand

Solution

The cone has radius 1.9 m and height 0.8 m. Apply the formula

$$V = \tfrac{1}{3}\pi r^2 h$$
$$\text{Volume} = \tfrac{1}{3}\pi \times 1.9^2 \times 0.8 = 3.02 \text{ m}^3$$

The volume is 3.02 m³

SELF TEST 16.10

Find the volume of a cone which is 34 mm high and has base radius 18 mm. Give your answer to 2 significant figures.

12 000 mm³

EXAMPLE 16.11

Figure. 16.16 shows the cross section of a girder, with the measurements in mm. If the girder is 3 m long, find its volume in mm³.

Solution

The girder is a prism. Split the cross-section into three rectangles, A, B and C and find their areas.

$$\begin{aligned}
\text{A:} \quad & 300 \times 25 = 7500 \text{ mm}^3 \\
\text{B:} \quad & 200 \times 25 = 5000 \text{ mm}^3 \\
\text{C:} \quad & 400 \times 25 = 10\,000 \text{ mm}^3
\end{aligned}$$

The total cross-section area is 22 500 mm³

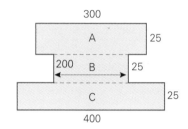

Figure 16.16   Cross-section of a girder

The length of the girder is 3 m, i.e. 3000 mm. Multiply by the cross-section area,

$$22\,500 \times 3000 = 67\,500\,000 \text{ obtaining } 6.75 \times 10^7 \text{ mm}^3.$$

The volume is 6.75 × 10⁷ mm³

SELF TEST 16.11

The shed of Self Test 16.4 is 2.5 m from side to side. Find its volume.

8.5 m³

16.6 Combinations of volumes

If a solid is built up out of basic solids, we can find its volume by adding or subtracting the basic volumes.

EXAMPLE 16.12

The boiler of Figure 16.17 consists of a cylinder of diameter 440 mm and length 1500 mm, with hemispheres (half spheres) at both ends. Find the volume of the boiler, in m³.

Figure 16.17   Boiler

Solution

The two hemispheres make a sphere, of radius 220 mm or 0.22 m. The cylinder has radius 0.22 m and length 1.5 m. Apply the formulae:

$$\text{Volume of sphere} = \tfrac{4}{3}\pi \times 0.22^3 = 0.0446 \text{ m}^3$$
$$\text{Volume of cylinder} = \pi \times 0.22^2 \times 1.5 = 0.2281 \text{ m}^3$$

Add the volumes to find the volume of the boiler.

The volume of the boiler is 0.273 m³

SELF TEST 16.12

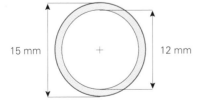

Figure 16.18   Ice cream cone

Figure 16.18 shows an ice-cream cone. It consists of a hemisphere of radius 35 mm on top of a cone with radius 35 mm and height 83 mm. Find its volume, correct to 3 significant figures.

196 000 mm³

EXAMPLE 16.13

A copper pipe is 5 m long, and has inner diameter 12 mm and outer diameter 15 mm. Find the volume of copper in the pipe.

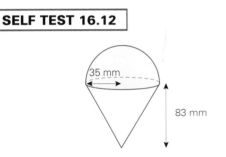

Figure 16.19   Copper pipe

Solution

First find the cross-section area. Subtract the area of a circle of radius 6 mm from the area of a circle of radius 7.5 mm.

$$\text{Area of circle} = \pi r^2$$
$$\text{Cross-section area} = \pi\,7.5^2 - \pi 6^2 = 63.6 \text{ mm}^2$$

Multiply by the length, 5000 mm, obtaining 318 000 mm³.

The volume of copper is 318 000 mm³

SELF TEST 16.13

A hollow rubber ball is a sphere with inner radius 45 mm and outer radius 50 mm. Find the volume of rubber it contains.

142 000 mm³

EXAMPLE 16.14

The volume of a sphere is 3400 mm³. Find its radius.

Solution

The volume of a sphere is given by $V = \tfrac{4}{3}\pi r^3$. Make r the subject by multiplying by 3, dividing by 4π, then taking the cube root.

$$3V = 4\pi r^3$$

so

$$\frac{3V}{4\pi} = r^3$$

so

$$\sqrt[3]{\left(\frac{3V}{4\pi}\right)} = r$$

Hence

$$r = \sqrt[3]{\left(\frac{3 \times 3400}{4\pi}\right)} = 9.33$$

The radius is 9.33 mm

SELF TEST 16.14

Find the radius of a sphere with volume 0.645 m³.

0.536 m³

EXAMPLE 16.15

The volume of a car cylinder is 320 cm³. The radius of the cylinder is 34 mm. How far does the piston move in one stroke?

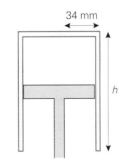

Figure 16.20   Car cylinder

Solution

The piston moves through a cylinder of radius 3.4 cm. The cylinder has a volume of 320 cm^3. Hence if the distance is h cm

$$V = \pi r^2 h$$
$$320 = \pi \times 3.4^2 h$$
$$h = \frac{320}{\pi 3.4^2} = 8.81$$

The distance moved is 8.81 cm

SELF TEST 16.15

The volume of a cone is 0.107 m^2, and its height is 0.623 m. Find its radius, correct to 3 significant figures.

0.405 m

16.7 Density

The **density** of a solid object is its mass per unit volume. For example, 1 m^3 of water has mass 1000 kg. Hence the density of water is 1000 kg/m^3. If you know the density of an object, you can find its mass from its volume, or find its volume from its mass.

$$D = \frac{M}{V}$$

To find the mass, multiply the volume by the density.
$$M = V \times D$$

To find the volume, divide the mass by the density.
$$V = \frac{M}{D}$$

EXAMPLE 16.16

A tank has height 0.8 m, and has a square base of side 0.6 m. If it is full of water, find the mass of the water.

Solution

The volume of water is 0.8×0.6^2 m^3, i.e. 0.288 m^3.
The density of water is 1000 kg/m^3.
Multiply the volume by the density.

$$M = 0.288 \times 1000$$

The mass of water is 288 kg

SELF TEST 16.16

A cylinder of wood is 1.6 m high and has radius 0.12 m. Find its mass, given that the density of the wood is 975 kg/m^3. Give your answer to 3 significant figures.

70.6 kg

EXAMPLE 16.17

Find the mass in kg of the pipe of Example 16.13, given that the density of copper is 8900 kg/m^3.

Solution

Volume = 318 000 mm^3

First find the volume of copper in m^3. Divide 318 000 by 1000^3.

Volume = 0.000318 m^3

Mass = Volume × Density, so now multiply by 8900, obtaining 2.83.

The mass of copper is 2.83 kg

SELF TEST 16.17

A cylinder of concrete is 650 mm high, and has base radius 220 mm. Find its mass, given that the density of the concrete is 3660 kg/m^3. Give your answer to the nearest kg.

362 kg

EXAMPLE 16.18

10 kg of copper is made into cylindrical wire of diameter 1.1 mm. Find the length of the wire, correct to 3 significant figures.

Solution

Volume = Mass ÷ Density

To find the volume of copper, divide 10 by 8900.

Volume of copper = 0.00112 m^3

The radius of cross-section is 0.55 mm, i.e. 0.00055 m.

volume = cross-section area × length
So   length = vol ÷ c-s area
                 = $0.00112 \div (\pi 0.00055^2)$
                 = 1180 to 3 s.f.

The length of wire is 1180 m (corr to 3 s.f.)

SELF TEST 16.18

A sphere is made from 2.5 kg of steel. Find its radius, given that the density of the steel is 9600 kg/m^3. Give your answer to 3 significant figures.

0.0396 m

EXAMPLE 16.19

The density of a metal is 9.8 grams/cm^3. Find the mass to the nearest milligram of a ball-bearing of radius 2.1 mm.

Solution
The radius is 0.21 cm. Find the volume.

$$\text{Volume} = \tfrac{4}{3}\pi \times 0.21^3 = 0.0388 \text{ cm}^3$$

Multiply this by the density, obtaining 0.38024 grams. To convert to milligrams, multiply by 1000.

The mass is 380 mg to the nearest mg

SELF TEST 16.19

The density of a liquid is 0.98 grams/cm^3. Find the mass to the nearest kg of a cylinder of the liquid which is 650 mm high and with a base radius of 290 mm.

168 kg

Mass per area and mass per length

The density of a flat sheet may be expressed as mass per *area*, rather than as mass per volume. The density of a wire may be expressed as mass per *length*, rather than as mass per volume.

EXAMPLE 16.20

A thin metal sheet has density 10.5 kg/m^2. Find the mass of a rectangle which is 2.1 m long and 0.6 m wide.

Solution
The area of the sheet is 2.1 × 0.6 m^2, i.e. 1.26 m^2.

Density = 10.5 kg/m^2

So

$$\text{Mass} = 10.5 \times 1.26 \text{ kg}$$

The mass is 13.23 kg

SELF TEST 16.20

The metal of Example 16.20 is used to make a disc of radius 0.045 m. Find the mass of the disc, to the nearest gram.

67 g

EXAMPLE 16.21

The density of a length of copper wire is 0.027 kg/m. Find the mass of 1.2 km of the wire.

Solution
Convert 1.2 km to m, obtaining 1200 m. Multiply this by 0.027.

Mass = Density × Length

Hence

$$M = 0.027 \times 1200$$

The mass is 32.4 kg

SELF TEST 16.21

A piece of the wire of Example 16.21 has mass 100 kg. Find its length in km. Give your answer to 2 significant figures.

3.7 km

■ CHECK YOUR UNDERSTANDING

● Each length unit has a corresponding area unit and a volume unit.
● Do not mix different units in one calculation.
● There are 1000^2 mm^2 in 1 m^2. There are 1000^3 mm^3 in 1 m^3.
● Area of basic shapes are as follows

rectangle ab	square x^2
triangle $\frac{1}{2}bh$	parallelogram bh
trapezium $\frac{1}{2}(a+b)h$	circle πr^2 or $\frac{1}{4}\pi d^2$

● Find the area of a compound figure by adding or subtracting basic areas.
● Volume of basic shapes are as follows

cuboid abc	cube x^3
prism Ah	pyramid $\frac{1}{3}Ah$
cylinder $\pi r^2 h$	sphere $\frac{4}{3}\pi r^3$
cone $\frac{1}{3}\pi r^2 h$	

● The density of a substance is its mass per unit volume. The density of a flat sheet may be given as the mass per unit area. The density of a wire may be given as the mass per unit length.

REVISION EXERCISES AND QUESTIONS

16.1 Units

1 Evaluate the following, with your answer in the units given.

  a) 456 m + 1.654 km (km)
  b) 1231 mm + 2.123 m (mm)
  c) 23 m × 2.1 km (m^2)
  d) 76 mm × 29 m (m^2)
  e) 0.03 km × 0.045 km (m^2)
  f) 4657 mm × 2098 mm (m^2)

2 A sheet of cloth is a rectangle of width 120 mm and length 2.8 m. Find its area in m^2.

3 A slab of concrete is 2 m wide, 3.8 m long, and 25 mm thick. Find its volume in m^3.

16.2 Areas of straight line figures

4 Find the areas of the shapes of Figure 16.21. Lengths are in mm.

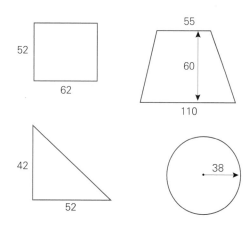

Figure 16.21

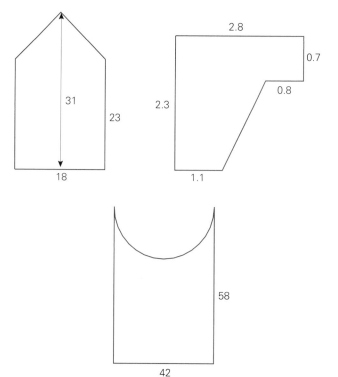

Figure 16.22

5 A can of paint can cover 30 m^2. If it is used to paint a wall which is 2.4 m high, what length of wall can be painted?

6 The area of a rectangle is 386 mm^2. Find its length, given that its width is 18 mm.

7 The parallel sides of a trapezium are 25 mm and 35 mm. Find its height, given that its area is 1200 mm^2.

16.3 Areas of circles

8 Find the areas of the circles with

  a) radius 26 mm
  b) diameter 1.6 m
  c) circumference 27 km.

9 A circle has area 4.36 m^2. Find its radius.

10 A circle has area 295 mm^2. Find its circumference.

16.4 Combinations of shapes

11 Find the areas of the shapes in Figure 16.22. Distances are in m.

12 A semicircle of diameter 140 mm is on top of a square of side 140 mm. Find the total area, to 3 significant figures.

13 A rectangular lawn is 29 m by 39 m. A path of width 1.2 m is made round it. What is the area of the path to 3 significant figures?

14 Figure 16.23 shows seven cables contained within a circular tube. The radius of the tube is 26 mm. Find the area of cross-section *not* occupied by the cables.

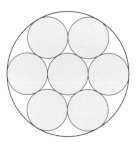

Figure 16.23 Cables

15 A circular swimming pool has radius 15 m. It is surrounded by a tiled walkway, 0.8 m wide. Find the area of tiles to 3 significant figures.

16 A steel disc has radius 38 mm. Three small holes of radius 2.1 mm are drilled out of it. Find the area remaining.

16.5 Volumes

17 Find the volumes of the shapes in Figure 16.24. The distances are in m.

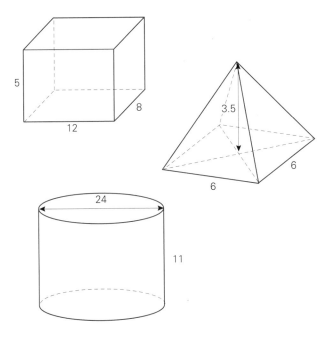

Figure 16.24

18 Find the volumes of the following.

a) a cube of side 1.6 m
b) a sphere of diameter 48 mm
c) a cylinder of height 75 mm and radius 23 mm
d) a pyramid with height 2.6 m and a square base of side 1.8 m
e) a cone of height 880 mm and radius 385 mm

19 A rectangular area of length 10.8 m and width 6.6 m is to be covered with concrete 0.2 m thick. Find the volume of concrete.

20 Bricks are cuboids, 65 mm by 102.5 mm by 215 mm. Find the volume of a brick. How many are needed to fill a space of volume 180 m^3?

21 Figure 16.25 shows the cross-section of a trench. Distances are in m. If the trench is 120 m long, find the volume of earth removed.

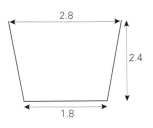

Figure 16.25   Cross-section of a trench

22 A girder has the cross-section shown in Figure 16.26. Distances are in mm. Find the volume if the girder is 3.5 m long.

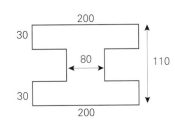

Figure 16.26   Cross-section of a girder

23 A tent is a cone with diameter 4.3 m and height 3.8 m. Find the volume it contains.

24 Find the volume of a hemisphere of diameter 0.98 m.

25 Concrete is poured into a mould with a rectangular cross-section, which is 2.2 m by 2.6 m. Find the height of the concrete if its volume is 0.564 m^3.

26 A wooden moulding has the cross-section shown in Figure 16.27. Distances are in mm. Find the volume of 1.6 m of the moulding.

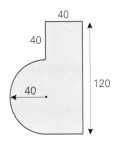

Figure 16.27   Wooden moulding

27 A hollow plastic cylinder is open at both ends. It has length 2.5 m, inside radius 36 mm and outside radius 44 mm. Find the volume of plastic.

16.6 Combinations of volumes

28 A cube of steel, of side 250 mm, is melted and recast into a pyramid. The pyramid has a square base of side 120 mm. Find the height of the pyramid.

29 A concrete post consists of a cylinder 1.8 m high with radius 0.2 m, with a hemisphere of radius 0.2 m on top. Find the volume of the post.

30 A sphere is to be made from 18.95 mm^3 of glass. Find the radius of the sphere.

31 Four tennis balls, of radius 31 mm, are packed into a cylindrical tube. Find the volume of the tube *not* occupied by the balls.

32   A pencil consists of a cylinder of length 60 mm, and radius 6 mm. Find its volume. The pencil is sharpened, so that 15 mm at the end becomes a cone. Find the lost volume.

33   A water tank has an internal square base of side 1.4 m. A volume of 0.4 m³ of concrete is poured into the tank. Assuming that the water does not overflow, how much does it rise by?

16.7 Density

For the following questions assume the density of water = 1000 kg/m³.

34   An aquarium is a cuboid with base 500 mm by 200 mm. If the depth of the water is 340 mm find the mass of the water.

35   A water trough is 2.8 m long. Its cross-section is a triangle, with sides of 0.38 m meeting at a right-angle, as shown in Figure 16.28. Find the volume and mass of water it could contain.

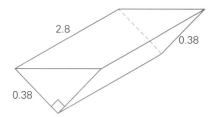

Figure 16.28 Water trough

36   A solid object is made from a hemisphere of radius 0.1 m on top of a cone of height 0.2 m, as shown in Figure 16.29. If it is made from material of density 2000 kg/m³, find its mass.

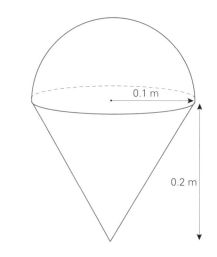

Figure 16.29

37   50 kg of plastic is made into 1000 spheres. If the density of the plastic is 900 kg/m³ find the radius of each sphere, in mm.

38   The density of curtain material is 0.2 kg/m². Find the mass of a curtain which is 2.3 m by 1.9 m.

39   The density of copper is 8900 kg/m³. Wire of diameter 0.5 mm is made from 2 kg of the copper. What is the length of the wire, in km?

Applications of geometry

Introduction

In this chapter we continue showing how to apply geometry to practical tasks.

When preparing to make an object, you often need a scale diagram of the object. Here we show how to connect the diagram and the real object. We also show how to construct the diagrams.

17.1 Similarity

Two figures (or diagrams) are **similar** if they have the same shape (but not necessarily the same size). For example, a scale diagram of a room is similar to the real room. A map of a town is similar to the real town.

Scales

In a scale diagram of a building plot, there is a constant ratio between the diagram and the real plot. See Figure 17.1. If the diagram is 0.5 m by 0.3 m, and the plot is 50 m by 30 m, then the scale is 0.5:50, i.e. 1:100.

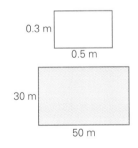

Figure 17.1

In general, if objects A and B are similar, then there is a constant ratio between the lengths of A and the lengths of B. See Figure 17.2.

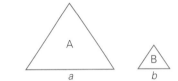

Figure 17.2

$$\text{length in A} : \text{length in B} = a{:}b$$

In terms of fractions, this is

$$\frac{\text{length in A}}{\text{length in B}} = \frac{a}{b}$$

Hence length in A = length in B $\times \dfrac{a}{b}$

length in B = length in A $\times \dfrac{b}{a}$

To convert lengths in B to lengths in A, multiply by $\dfrac{a}{b}$.

To convert lengths in A to lengths in B, multiply by $\dfrac{b}{a}$. (This is the same as dividing by $\dfrac{a}{b}$.)

EXAMPLE 17.1

A diagram of a building is in the scale 1:50. On the diagram the height of the house is 0.8 m. What is the actual height of the house?

Solution

Multiply 0.8 by the ratio $\frac{50}{1}$, obtaining 40.

The building is 40 m high

SELF TEST 17.1

A map is in the scale 1:10 000. On the map, a pond is 27 mm long. How long is the real pond? Give your answer in m.

270 m

EXAMPLE 17.2

The building in Example 17.1 above is 54 m wide. How wide is the building on the diagram?

Solution
Divide 54 by the ratio $\frac{50}{1}$, obtaining 1.08.

The diagram of the building is 1.08 m wide

SELF TEST 17.2

The distance between two towns is 6 km. How far apart are they on the map of Self Test 17.1? Give your answer in mm.

600 mm

EXAMPLE 17.3

A building site is 60 m long. A scale diagram of the site is 300 mm long. What is the scale of the diagram?

Solution
First convert the mm to m. 300 mm is equal to 0.3 m.
The scale is the ratio of the diagram length to the real length.

$$0.3{:}60 = 3{:}600 = 1{:}200$$

The scale of the diagram is 1:200

SELF TEST 17.3

Two villages are 8 km apart. On a map, they are shown as 16 mm apart. What is the scale of the map?

1:500 000

Similar figures

A geometrical diagram may contain similar shapes. In Figure 17.3 the triangles ABC and DEF are similar. It follows that the sides of ABC are in a constant ratio to the sides of DEF. Hence

$$\frac{AB}{DE} = \frac{BC}{EF} = \frac{CA}{FD}$$

For example, if we know AB, DE and EF, we can find BC.

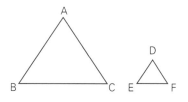

Figure 17.3

Note The order of the letters is important, just as it was for congruent triangles (Chapter 15).

EXAMPLE 17.4

Figure 17.4 shows a roof truss. Distances are in m. Find the height of the king post AB.

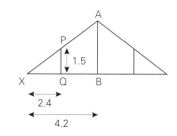

Figure 17.4

Solution
The triangles XAB and XPQ are similar.

Hence $\dfrac{AB}{PQ} = \dfrac{BX}{QX}$ hence $AB = PQ \times \dfrac{BX}{QX}$

From the figures given

$$AB = 1.5 \times \frac{4.2}{2.4} = 2.625$$

The height of the post is 2.625 m

SELF TEST 17.4

The two triangles shown in Figure 17.5 are similar. Find the length x.

8.125

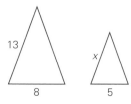

Figure 17.5

Ratios of areas and volumes

In Figure 17.6, the two squares are similar, in the ratio 1:3. Notice that 9 of the smaller square would fit into the larger square. Hence the ratio of the areas is 1:9. This is the *square* of the length ratio.

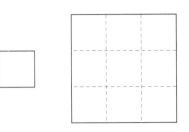

Figure 17.6

> If two figures are similar in the ratio *a:b*, their areas are in the ratio $a^2:b^2$.

In Figure 17.7, the two cubes are similar, in the ratio 1:3. Notice that 27 of the small cubes would make up the larger cube. Hence the ratio of the volumes is 1:27. This is the *cube* of the length ratio.

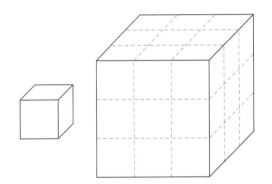

Figure 17.7

> If two figures are similar in the ratio *a:b*, their volumes are in the ratio $a^3:b^3$.

Note Remember to be careful when changing units in problems of similarity. The number of mm² in a m² is 1000², i.e. 1 000 000. It is not 1000.

EXAMPLE 17.5

A building site has length 20 m. A scale diagram of the site has length 0.5 m. If the area of the site on the diagram is 0.2 m², find the actual area of the site.

Solution
The scale of the diagram is 0.5:20, which is 1:40. Hence the areas are in the ratio $1^2:40^2$

ratio of areas is 1:1600

Multiply 0.2 by this ratio, obtaining 320.

The area of the site is 320 m²

SELF TEST 17.5

A scale drawing of a house is 0.8 m high, and the house itself is 10.4 m high. Find the scale of the drawing. If the front of the house in the drawing has area 1.4 m², find the area of the front of the real house.

1:13, 236.6 m²

EXAMPLE 17.6

Two spanners are made out of the same metal. They are similar, in the ratio 4:5. The larger one has a mass of 0.4 kg. What is the mass of the smaller one?

Solution
The spanners are made out of the same material, hence the ratio of their masses is the same as the ratio of their volumes. This is the cube of the length ratio.

ratio of volumes is $4^3:5^3$, i.e. 64:125

Multiply 0.4 by $\frac{64}{125}$, obtaining 0.2048.

The mass of the smaller spanner is 0.2048 kg

SELF TEST 17.6

A model of a building is in the ratio 1:20. The volume of the model is 0.4 m³. Find the volume of the real building.

3200 m³

17.2 Pythagoras' Theorem

Pythagoras' Theorem is the most famous theorem in Mathematics. Suppose the triangle ABC has a right-angle at B. (See Figure 17.8.) Then

$$AB^2 + BC^2 = AC^2$$

The longest side, AC, is the **hypotenuse**.

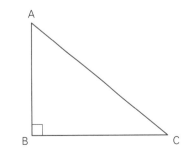

Figure 17.8 Pythagoras' Theorem

Essential mathematics for technicians

> In words, Pythagoras' Theorem is:
> The square on the hypotenuse is equal to the sum of the squares on the other two sides.

Hence if we know two sides of a right angled triangle, we can find the third side.

EXAMPLE 17.7

Three pieces of wood are nailed together to make a right-angled triangle. The shorter two pieces are 300 mm and 400 mm in length, as in Figure 17.9. What is the length of the third side?

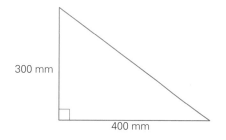

Figure 17.9

Solution

Here the hypotenuse is the longer side. Let its length be x mm. Then

$$300^2 + 400^2 = x^2$$
So $\qquad x^2 = 90\,000 + 160\,000 = 250\,000$
Hence $\qquad x = \sqrt{250\,000} = 500$

The longest side has length 500 mm

Note A triangle with sides in the ratio 3:4:5 is always right-angled. If you make a triangle with sides in this ratio, you can use it to check that an angle is 90°.

SELF TEST 17.7

The triangle ABC is such that AB = 5 m, AC = 12 m and $\hat{A} = 90°$. Find BC.

13 m

EXAMPLE 17.8

In triangle ABC, $\hat{B} = 90°$. AB = 7 m and AC = 25 m. Find BC.

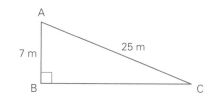

Figure 17.10

Solution

Note that AC is the hypotenuse. Use Pythagoras' theorem.

$$7^2 + BC^2 = 25^2$$
So $\qquad BC^2 = 25^2 - 7^2 = 625 - 49 = 576$
The square root of 576 is 24.

$$\mathbf{BC = 24\ m}$$

SELF TEST 17.8

In triangle LMN, $\hat{L} = 90°$, MN = 26 mm, LM = 10 mm. Find LN.

24 mm

EXAMPLE 17.9

The front wall of a shed is 3 m high, and the back wall is 2.5 m. The length of the sloping roof is 3.2 m. Find the distance between the walls of the shed.

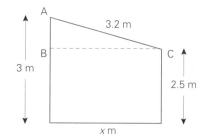

Figure 17.11 Side view of shed

Solution

Figure 17.11 is a side view of the shed. Let the walls be x m apart. The triangle ABC is right-angled at B, with AC = 3.2 m, AB = 0.5 m and BC = x m. Use Pythagoras' Theorem.

$$3.2^2 = 0.5^2 + x^2$$
So $\qquad x^2 = 3.2^2 - 0.5^2 = 9.99$
$$x = 3.16....$$

The walls are 3.16 m apart

SELF TEST 17.9

A ladder of length 2.8 m leans against a wall, reaching 2.5 m up the wall. How far is the foot of the ladder from the wall?

1.26 m

Isosceles triangles

Pythagoras' Theorem holds for right-angled triangles, not for general triangles. But an isosceles triangle can be cut down the middle into two right-angled triangles. See Figure 17.12.

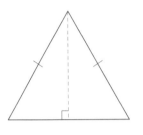

Figure 17.12

EXAMPLE 17.10

An aerial of height 6.8 m is secured vertically by two equal guy ropes on opposite sides of the aerial, as in Figure 17.13. If the ends of the ropes are 5.6 m apart, find the lengths of the ropes.

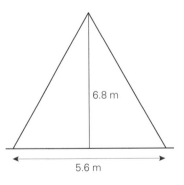

6.8 m

5.6 m

Figure 17.13

Solution
The top of the aerial and the two ends of the guy ropes form an isoceles triangle. The aerial itself cuts the triangle into two right-angled triangles. The shorter sides of these triangles are 6.8 m and half of 5.6 m, i.e. 2.8 m. Let the length of each rope be x m. By Pythagoras' Theorem

$$x^2 = 6.8^2 + 2.8^2 = 54.08$$
$$x = \sqrt{54.08} = 7.35....$$

The length of each rope is 7.35 m

SELF TEST 17.10

Triangle ABC is such that AB = AC = 55 mm, and BC = 42 mm. Find the distance of A from BC.

50.8 mm

17.3 Measuring circles

Arcs

Remember in Chapter 15 we learnt that an arc is a part of a circle. In Figure 17.14, an arc of length a, from a circle of radius r, subtends $\theta°$ at the centre of the circle. The length of the arc is a proportion of the circumference of the circle, in the ratio $\theta:360$.

As a formula this can be written

$$a = 2\pi r \times \frac{\theta}{360}$$

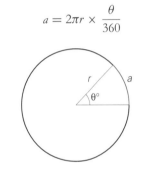

Figure 17.14   Arc of a circle

EXAMPLE 17.11

A soup tin of radius 35 mm has a label which subtends 79° at the centre of the tin. What is the width of the label?

Chicken Soup

Figure 17.15

Solution
Let the width be w mm.

$$w = 2\pi r \times \frac{\theta}{360}$$

$$w = 2\pi \times 35 \times \frac{79}{360} = 48.25....$$

The label has width 48.3 mm

SELF TEST 17.11

Find the arc lengths of the sectors of Figure 17.16.

$$a = 8.03, b = 20.8$$

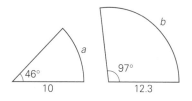

Figure 17.16

EXAMPLE 17.12

An arc of length 12 mm is taken from a circle of radius 17 mm, as in Figure 17.17. What angle does the arc subtend at the centre of the circle?

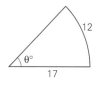

Figure 17.17

Solution

Use the formula for arc length, putting $a = 12$ and $r = 17$.

$$12 = 2\pi \times 17 \times \frac{\theta}{360}$$

$$\theta = \frac{12 \times 360}{2\pi \times 17} = 40.44....$$

The angle subtended is 40.4°

SELF TEST 17.12

An arc of length 1.8 m is part of a circle of radius 2.3 m. Find the angle subtended by the arc at the centre of the circle.

44.8°

EXAMPLE 17.13

A rope is wrapped tightly round three pipes of radius 56 mm, as shown in Figure 17.18. Find the length of the rope.

Solution

The straight portions of the rope are perpendicular to the radii of the circles. Hence each straight portion is equal to twice the radius, 2 × 56, i.e. 112 mm.

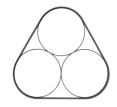

Figure 17.18

Each curved portion of the rope goes round a third of a circle. Put together, the three curved portions go round a complete circle of radius 56 mm. Hence the curved length is 2 × π × 56 mm, i.e. 351.9 mm. Add the lengths together

Total length = 3 × 112 + 351.9 = 687.85.....

The total length is 687.9 mm

SELF TEST 17.13

Three pulleys of radii 28 mm have their centres on the vertices of an equilateral triangle of side 70 mm. A belt passes tightly round the pulleys. Find the length of the belt.

386 mm

Pythagoras and circles

A radius and a tangent of a circle are at right angles, as in Figure 17.19. Hence we often use Pythagoras' Theorem when solving problems about circles.

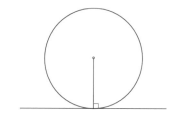

Figure 17.19

EXAMPLE 17.14

A cylindrical rod is held between two surfaces as shown in Figure 17.20. The radius of the rod is 35 mm, and its centre C is 58 mm from the join A of the surfaces. Find the distance from A to the point B where the cylinder touches one of the surfaces.

Solution

The radius CB is at right angles to the tangent AB. Hence Pythagoras' Theorem applies.

$$58^2 = 35^2 + AB^2$$

So
$$AB^2 = 58^2 - 35^2 = 2139$$
$$AB = \sqrt{2139} = 46.24....$$

The distance is 46.2 mm

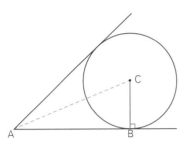

Figure 17.20

SELF TEST 17.14

A sphere of radius 127 mm rests on a horizontal table. The bottom of the sphere is 206 mm from point A on the table. Find the distance of the top of the sphere from point A.

327 mm

EXAMPLE 17.15

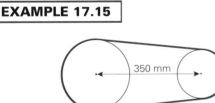

Figure 17.21

Figure 17.21 shows a belt passing over two pulleys. The centres of the pulleys are 350 mm apart, and the pulleys have radii 80 mm and 50 mm. Find the length of each straight section of belt.

Solution

The straight section is AB. This is a tangent to both circles. Hence ABC_1D is a rectangle.

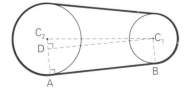

Figure 17.22

In the triangle C_1DC_2, $C_1C_2 = 350$ and $C_2D = 80 - 50$, i.e. 30. Use Pythagoras' Theorem

$$C_1D^2 = 350^2 - 30^2 = 121\,600$$
$$C_1D = \sqrt{121\,600} = 348.71....$$

Each straight section has length 348.7 mm

SELF TEST 17.15

A tight belt passes round two pulleys of radii 125 mm and 245 mm, which are just touching. Find the length of a straight section of the belt.

350 mm

17.4 Constructions

When you draw an accurate diagram, you are **constructing** geometrical shapes. The basic instruments for constructing shapes are as follows.

- Ruler for constructing straight lines
- Compasses for drawing circles
- Protractor for constructing angles
- Set square for angles of 90°, 30°, 60° and for drawing parallel lines

Construction of angles

Some angles can be constructed with a ruler and compasses. In the following you want to construct an angle at A.

To construct 90°

Put the point of the compasses at A. Draw short arcs at B and C. Widen the compasses and put the point of the compasses at B. Draw an arc above A. With the same radius put the point of the compasses at C, draw an arc cutting the other arc at D. Then DA makes 90° with BC. See Figure 17.23.

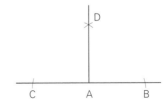

Figure 17.23

To construct 60°

Put the point of the compasses at A. Draw a long arc cutting the line at B. With the same radius put the point of the compasses at B, cut the first arc at C. Then $\hat{CAB} = 60°$. See Figure 17.24.

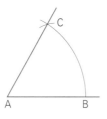

Figure 17.24

Bisecting angles

If you want to cut in half the angle at A. Put the point of the compasses at A, cut the lines at B and C. Put the point of the compasses at C, make a short arc between the lines. With the same radius put the point of the compasses at B, cut the arc above at D. Then DA will bisect the angle at A. See Figure 17.25.

By bisecting angles, you can construct angles of 30°, 15°, 45° and so on. But for most other angles, such as 20°, you have to use a protractor.

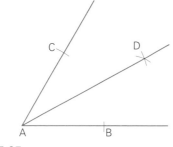

Figure 17.25

EXAMPLE 17.16

Use ruler and compasses to construct an angle of 135°.

Solution

Note that $135° = 90° + 45°$. Draw a straight line, BAC, through A. By the methods above, construct an angle $\hat{DAB}$ of 90°. Then find the point E such that EA bisects this angle, so that $\hat{EAC} = 45°$. Then $\hat{EAB}$ is 135°. See Figure 17.26.

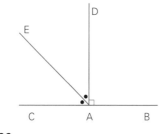

Figure 17.26

SELF TEST 17.16

Use ruler and compasses to construct an angle of 120°.

Constructions of triangles

We can construct a triangle accurately in the following four cases.

- SSS.
  When we know the three sides.
- SAS.
  When we know two sides and the angle between them.
- ASA.
  When we know two angles and one side.
- RHS.
  When we know a right angle, the hypotenuse and one other side.

Note These four cases follow the conditions for congruence of Section 15.2. If you can construct a triangle with certain values for the sides and angles, then any two triangles with those sides and angles must be identical.

EXAMPLE 17.17

The triangle ABC has AB = 63 mm, BC = 58 mm, AC = 55 mm. Construct the triangle and measure $\hat{A}$.

Note It is a good idea to draw a simple sketch of the required construction first. See figure 17.27.

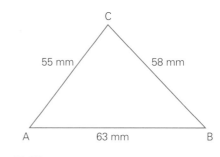

Figure 17.27

Solution

First draw a line of length 63 mm. This is AB. Separate compasses to 58 mm, put the point on B, and draw an arc. Separate compasses to 55 mm, put the point on A, and draw an arc. The arcs cross at C. Join C to A and to B. See Figure 17.28.

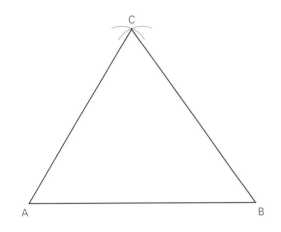

Figure 17.28

Measure Â with a protractor. You should get about 58°.

$$\hat{A} = 58°$$

SELF TEST 17.17

Construct ABC, in which AB = 73 mm, BC = 89 mm, CA = 99 mm. Find Â.

60°

EXAMPLE 17.18

The triangle ABC has AB = 78 mm, B̂ = 42°, BC = 68 mm. Construct the triangle and measure AC.

Solution
Draw a sketch first.

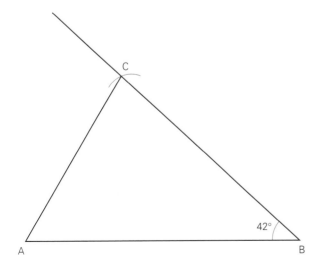

Figure 17.29

Draw a line of length 78 mm. Use a protractor to construct a line making 42° with AB. Measure out 68 mm along this line, to reach C. Join AC. See Figure 17.29.
Measure AC with a ruler. You should get about 53 mm.

The length of AC is 53 mm

SELF TEST 17.18

Construct ABC, in which AB = 113 mm, Â = 67°, CA = 129 mm. Find BC.

134 mm

EXAMPLE 17.19

In triangle ABC, Â = 63°, B̂ = 66° and AC = 73 mm. Construct ABC, and measure BC.

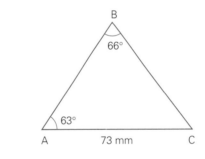

Figure 17.30

Solution
We are given Â, B̂ and AC, see Figure 17.30. By subtracting from 180°, Ĉ is 51°. Now we have ASA. Draw a line of length 73 mm. This is AC. At A use a protractor to draw a line making 63° with AC, and at C use a protractor to draw a line making 51° with AC. These lines cross at B.

Measure BC with a ruler. You should get about 71 mm.

The length of BC is 71 mm

SELF TEST 17.19

Construct ABC, in which Â = 46°, B̂ = 79°, CA = 125 mm. Find AB.

104 mm

EXAMPLE 17.20

In triangle ABC, $\hat{A} = 90°$, BC = 108 mm and AB = 83 mm.
Construct ABC and measure $\hat{B}$.

Solution

Draw a line of 83 mm. This is AB. At A construct a line
perpendicular to AB. Separate compasses to 108 mm, put
the point at B and draw an arc. The arc and the line cross at
C. See Figure 17.31.

Measure $\hat{B}$ with a protractor. You should get about 40°.

$\hat{B}$ is 40°

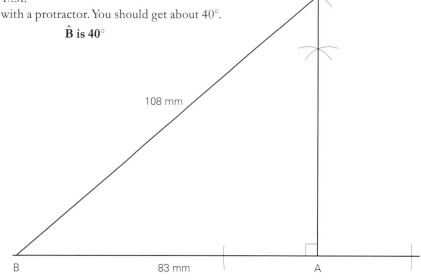

Figure 17.31

SELF TEST 17.20

Construct ABC, in which $\hat{A} = 90°$, BC = 121 mm, CA = 94 mm.
Find $\hat{C}$.

39°

■ CHECK YOUR UNDERSTANDING

● Similar figures have the same shape, but not necessarily the
same size. If two figures are similar, there is a constant ratio
between the lengths in the figures.
● If two figures are similar in the ratio $a:b$, their areas are in
the ratio $a^2:b^2$, and their volumes are in the ratio $a^3:b^3$.
● Suppose ABC is a triangle right-angled at A. The longest
side, BC, is the hypotenuse. Pythagoras' Theorem states that

$$AB^2 + AC^2 = BC^2.$$

This theorem has many uses in finding lengths.
● Suppose an arc from a circle of radius r, subtends an angle
of $\theta°$ at the centre of the circle. The length of the arc, a, is

$$a = 2\pi r \times \frac{\theta}{360}$$

● The basic instruments for construction are ruler,
compasses, protractor and set square. With ruler and
compasses you can construct angles of 90° and 60°. You can
bisect an angle to find angles of 45°, 30° and 15°.
● You can construct a triangle if you know any of the
following:
  i) All three sides,
 ii) Two sides and the angle between them,
iii) Two angles and a side,
 iv) A right angle, the hypotenuse and another side.

REVISION EXERCISES AND QUESTIONS

17.1 Similarity

1   A drawing of a room is in the scale 1:20.

 a) The length of the drawing is 350 mm. What is the
    length of the room?

 b) The width of the room is 3 m. What is the width of the
    drawing?

2 A map of a city is in the scale 1:50 000.

   a) On the map, two buildings are 25 mm apart. How far apart are the real buildings?

   b) Two parks are 7 km apart. How far apart are they on the map?

3 On a map of a country, two towns are 45 mm apart. The real towns are 90 km apart. What is the scale of the map?

4 In Figure 17.32, the triangles ABC and PQR are similar. They are not drawn to scale.

   a) If AB = 8 cm, BC = 9 cm, PQ = 12 cm find QR.

   b) If AB = $\frac{1}{2}$ cm, AC = $\frac{3}{4}$ cm, PR = 20 cm find PQ.

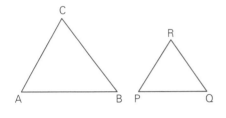

Figure 17.32

5 In Figure 17.33, BC and DE are both perpendicular to AE. The diagram is not to scale.

   a) If AE = 12 m, AC = 3 m, BC = 2 m find DE.

   b) If BC = 6 m, DE = 8 m, AB = 15 m find BD.

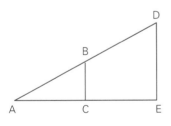

Figure 17.33

6 Two rectangles are similar, with sides in the ratio 2:3. The area of the smaller rectangle is 16 m². What is the area of the larger rectangle?

7 The triangles ABC and PQR are similar.

   a) If AB = 5 m, PQ = 7 m, and the area of △ABC is 10 m² find the area of △PQR.

   b) If AB = 8 m. The area of △ABC is 8 m², and the area of △PQR is 18 m² find PQ.

8 A diagram of a building is in the scale 1:20.

   a) The diagram of the front of the building has area 0.4 m². What is the area of the front of the building?

   b) The roof of the building has area 40 m². What is the area of the roof on the diagram?

9 Two drills are similar in shape and material. Their lengths are 40 mm and 30 mm. The shorter drill has mass 5 g. What is the mass of the longer drill?

17.2 Pythagoras' Theorem

10 In triangle ABC, $\hat{B} = 90°$. If AB = 8 m and BC = 15 m find AC.

11 In triangle PQR, $\hat{P} = 90°$. If QR = 20 mm and PQ = 16 mm find PR.

12 Point A is 60 m from the base of a 80 m high tree. How far is A from the top of the tree?

13 A 58 m mast is secured by a rope of length 68 m. How far is the base of the rope from the base of the mast?

14 A rectangular television screen is 16 inches wide, and 13 inches high. What is the length of the diagonal of the screen?

15 The diagonal of a square is 0.56 m. What is the side of the square?

16 An equilateral triangle has side 442 mm. What is the height of the triangle?

17 A plank of length 3.4 m leans against a wall. The base of the plank is 2.9 m from the base of the wall. How high up the wall does the plank reach?

18 A ship travels 50 km north, then 80 km east. How far is it from the starting place?

19 Point A is on the ground. From point A, it is 55 m to the top of a 43 m high tree. How far is it from A to the base of the tree?

20 Find the area of the triangle in Figure 17.34.

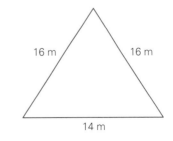

Figure 17.34

21 A bell tent is 4.7 m wide, and the sloping sides of the tent are of length 5.3 m. What is the height of the tent? (See Figure 17.35.)

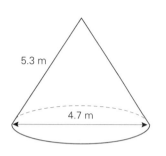

Figure 17.35   Bell tent

22 A cylindrical bar has radius 31 mm. A depth of 3 mm is shaved off, as shown in Figure 17.36. Calculate the width of the flat section.

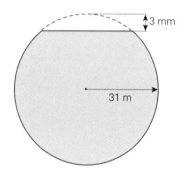

Figure 17.36

23 A horizontal cylindrical drain has radius 38 mm. Water lies in the drain, to a depth of 12 mm. Calculate the width of the water in the drain.

17.3 Measuring circles

24 An arc subtends 66° at the centre of a circle of radius 26 mm. Find the length of the arc.

25 A runner runs 48 m along a circular running track, turning through an angle of 63°. What is the radius of the track?

26 An arc of length 56 mm is taken from a circle of radius 86 mm. Find the angle of the arc.

27 Calculate the angle subtended by an arc of length 23 m at the centre of a circle of radius 52 m.

28 A ball of radius 0.2 m is rolled up against a wall (Figure 17.37). How far is the centre of the ball from the base of the wall?

Figure 17.37

29 In the diagram of Figure 17.38, a cylinder rests against two surfaces. Distances are in mm. Find the distance labelled x.

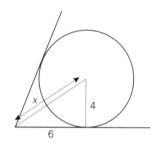

Figure 17.38

30 A belt passes tightly over two pulleys whose centres are 150 mm apart. The radii of the pulleys are 67 mm and 43 mm. Find the length of a straight section of the belt.

17.4 Constructions

31 With ruler and compasses, construct angles of
a) 15°   b) 75°   c) 150°   d) 210°.

32 In each of the following, construct the triangle ABC and measure the angle or side.
a) AB = 34 mm, BC = 38 mm, CA = 48 mm. Find $\hat{B}$.
b) AB = 41 mm, AC = 57 mm, $\hat{A}$ = 31°. Find BC and $\hat{B}$.
c) $\hat{A}$ = 72°, $\hat{C}$ = 58°, AB = 64 mm. Find AC.
d) $\hat{A}$ = 90°, BC = 87 mm, AB = 50 mm. Find $\hat{B}$.

Trigonometry

18

Introduction

The **trigonometric functions** link the angles and the sides of a triangle. Given a side and two angles of a triangle, we can find the other sides. Given the sides of a triangle, we can find the angles.

Trigonometry is very useful in surveying, navigation, construction and many other purposes.

Consider a tall building. You can measure the distance to its base, and the angle to the horizontal of a line to its top. (The angle of elevation). You can then use trigonometry to find the height of the building, without having to climb to the top.

The three functions which connect the ratios of the sides with θ are as follows

$$\text{sine } \theta = \frac{\text{OPP}}{\text{HYP}} \qquad \text{cosine } \theta = \frac{\text{ADJ}}{\text{HYP}} \qquad \text{tangent } \theta = \frac{\text{OPP}}{\text{ADJ}}$$

These are the **trigonometric ratios**.

18.1 The trigonometric functions

Figure 18.1 shows a right-angled triangle, with an acute angle of θ. The three sides of the triangle are as follows

- The longest side is the **hypotenuse** (HYP)
- The side next to θ is the **adjacent side** (ADJ)
- The side farthest from θ is the **opposite side** (OPP)

Sine

The sine function, usually written as sin, is the ratio of the opposite side to the hypotenuse.

In Figure 18.2, $\sin \theta = \dfrac{\text{AB}}{\text{BC}}$.

Or $\qquad\qquad \text{AB} = \text{BC} \times \sin \theta$

Hence if we know θ and BC, then we can find AB. The value of $\sin \theta$ can be found either from a calculator or from tables. Suppose we want to find $\sin 23.53°$.

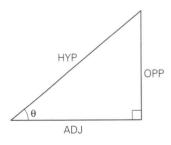

Figure 18.1

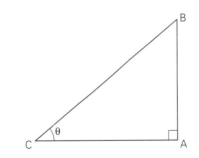

Figure 18.2

159

Calculator

The method depends on the make of calculator. Two possible orders are

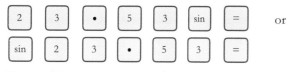

or

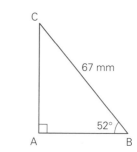

Figure 18.4

The result is 0.3992.

Tables

Look at your Natural Sines tables. If your tables are in minutes, you will need to convert 0.53° to minutes (32′). Look down to the 23 row. Look across to the 0.5 column. The figure is 0.3987. Look across to the 3 column in the difference table. This is 5. So add 0.0005 to 0.3987, obtaining 0.3992, as before.

EXAMPLE 18.1

An aerial is held vertical by two guy ropes of length 50 m. The ropes make 25° with the ground. Find the height of the aerial.

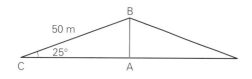

Figure 18.3

Solution

Label the figure with A, B, C as shown. The hypotenuse BC is the length of the guy rope, 50 m. The opposite side AB is the height of the aerial. The angle is 25°. From tables or a calculator, find that sin 25° = 0.4226.

$$\sin 25° = \frac{AB}{BC}$$

So $AB = 50 \times \sin 25° = 50 \times 0.4226 = 21.13$

The height of the aerial is 21.1 m

SELF TEST 18.1

In the triangle of Figure 18.4, $\hat{A} = 90°$, BC = 67 mm and $\hat{B} = 52°$. Find AC.

52.8 mm

Finding the angle

In Example 18.1 you were given the angle of 25° and found the ratio sin 25° to be 0.4226. The **inverse** function goes in the other direction, to find the angle from the ratio. It is written $\sin^{-1}$ or arcsin.

$$\sin^{-1} 0.4226 = 25°$$

Calculators or tables can be used to find $\sin^{-1}$.

To find $\sin^{-1} 0.7543$

Calculator

Two possible sequences are

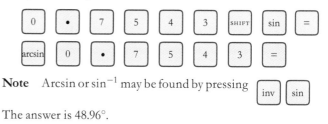

Note   Arcsin or $\sin^{-1}$ may be found by pressing [inv] [sin]

The answer is 48.96°.

Tables

Use the sine tables, but go in the other direction. In the tables, the number closest to, but less than 0.7543 is 0.7536, corresponding to 48.9°. We need an extra 0.0007 to reach 0.7543. In the differences table, there is 7 under the 6 column. Hence the answer is 48.96°, as above.

EXAMPLE 18.2

The guy ropes of Example 18.1 are lengthened to 80 m. Find the new angle that the ropes makes with the ground.

Solution

The height of the aerial is 21.13 m. If the new angle is θ, then

$$\sin \theta = \frac{21.13}{80} = 0.2641$$

$$\theta = \sin^{-1} 0.2641 = 15.31°$$

The new angle is 15.31°

In triangle PQR, $\hat{Q} = 90°$, PR = 12 m, QP = 7 m. Find $\hat{R}$.

35.69°

Cosine

In Figure 18.5, $\cos\theta = \dfrac{AC}{BC}$.

Or $AC = BC \times \cos\theta$

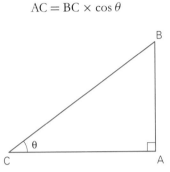

Figure 18.5

Hence if we know BC and θ, then we can find AC. Use a calculator or tables to find $\cos\theta$. There is one important difference in the use of tables.

Cos is a *decreasing* function. Hence we *subtract* the difference term instead of adding it.

For example, to find $\cos 62.34°$. In the 62 row and the 3 column, find 0.4648. In the difference column for 4, find 6. Subtract 0.0006 from 0.4648, obtaining 0.4642.

The roof of a shed is 3 m long, and slopes at 20°. What is the depth of the shed from back to front?

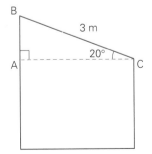

Figure 18.6   Side view of shed

Solution

Here BC = 3 and $\theta = 20°$. The depth across the shed is AC.

$$\cos 20° = \frac{AC}{BC}$$

So $AC = 3 \times \cos 20° = 3 \times 0.9397 = 2.8191$

The depth is 2.82 m

In triangle ABC, $\hat{A} = 90°$, $\hat{B} = 41.23°$ and BC = 34 mm. Find AB.

25.6 mm

Finding the angle

The inverse function $\cos^{-1}$ or arccos is defined similarly to $\sin^{-1}$.

$$\cos 53° = 0.6018.$$

Hence $53° = \cos^{-1} 0.6018$

Use of tables

When using tables to find $\cos^{-1}$, find the value which is *larger than* the ratio. Find the entry in the difference table which we *subtract* to find the ratio.

To find $\cos^{-1} 0.6$, look in the tables to find the value above 0.6. This is 0.6004, under 53.1°. In the differences, 0.0004 is under 3. Hence $\cos^{-1} 0.6 = 53.13°$.

A plank of length 2.5 m is laid against the wall of a house. The foot of the plank is 2.1 m from the wall. Find the angle between the plank and the ground.

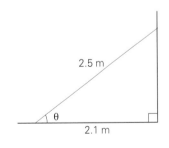

Figure 18.7

Solution

Let the angle be θ. In Figure 18.7, the length of the plank is HYP, and the distance along the ground is ADJ. Hence

$$\cos\theta = \frac{2.1}{2.5} = 0.84$$

$$\theta = \cos^{-1} 0.84 = 32.86°$$

The angle between the plank and the ground is 32.9°

SELF TEST 18.4

In triangle ABC, $\hat{A} = 90°$, BC = 8 m and CA = 5.7 m. Find $\hat{C}$.

44.56°

Tangent

In Figure 18.8, $\tan \theta = \dfrac{AB}{AC}$.

Or $AB = AC \times \tan \theta$

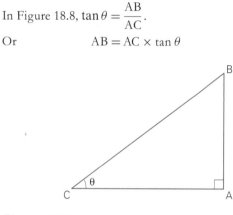

Figure 18.8

Tan is an increasing function. Hence tables can be used in exactly the same way as for sin. But if the angle θ is close to 90°, the tables are unreliable.

EXAMPLE 18.5

The slope of a staircase is 42°. The tread (the horizontal part of each stair) is 250 mm. Find the riser (the vertical part of the stair).

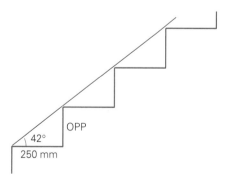

Figure 18.9   Staircase

Solution
Compare Figure 18.9 with Figure 18.1. The tread is the ADJ and the riser is the OPP. The tan ratio connects these two.

$$\tan \theta = \frac{OPP}{ADJ}$$

$$\tan 42° = \frac{OPP}{250}$$

Hence $OPP = 250 \times \tan 42°$.
By tables or a calculator find that $\tan 42° = 0.9004$.

$$OPP = 250 \times 0.9004 = 225.1$$

The riser is 225 mm

SELF TEST 18.5

In triangle LMN, $\hat{L} = 90°$, $\hat{M} = 29°$ and LM = 2.5 m. Find LN.

1.39 m

Finding the angle

Tan^{-1} or arctan is defined similarly to $\sin^{-1}$.

$$\tan 35° = 0.7002$$

Hence $35° = \tan^{-1} 0.7002$

EXAMPLE 18.6

The slope of a drain pipe is 1:40. Find the angle of slope.

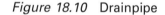

Figure 18.10   Drainpipe

Solution
The drain falls 1 m for every 40 m of horizontal distance. Comparing Figure 18.10 with Figure 18.1, OPP = 1 and ADJ = 40. Hence

$$\tan \theta = \frac{1}{40}$$

Hence

$$\theta = \tan^{-1} \frac{1}{40}$$

$$= 1.4321$$

The angle of slope is 1.43°

SELF TEST 18.6

In triangle XYZ, $\hat{X} = 90°$, XY = 2.34, XZ = 1.98. Find $\hat{Z}$.

49.76°

18.2 Solution of right-angled triangles

If you have a right-angled triangle in which you know another angle and one side, then you can find the other sides. If you know two sides, then you can find the angles. This is called **solving** the triangle. You must be sure to use the correct ratio.

Label the sides of the triangle you are trying to solve as HYP, OPP and ADJ. Mark the angle you know or want to know as θ.

● HYP is the longest side, opposite the right angle
● OPP is opposite the angle θ
● ADJ is next to the angle θ

If you are finding a side, you will know one side, and want to find another. If you are finding an angle, you will know two sides. In both cases, you deal with two sides.

● If they are OPP and HYP, use sin.
● If they are ADJ and HYP, use cos.
● If they are OPP and ADJ, use tan.

EXAMPLE 18.7

Find the side labelled x in Figure 18.11

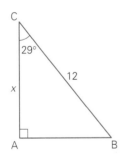

Figure 18.11

Solution
Compare the triangle with Figure 18.1. The HYP, opposite the right angle, is 12. The ADJ, next to the angle of 29°, is x.

The ratio connecting ADJ and HYP is cos. Use the cos ratio.

$$\cos 29° = \frac{x}{12}$$

$$x = 12 \times \cos 29° = 10.50$$

The value of x is 10.5

SELF TEST 18.7

In triangle ABC, $\hat{A} = 90°$, BA = 33 m, $\hat{B} = 65.2°$. Find AC.

71.4 m

EXAMPLE 18.8

Find the angle labelled θ in Figure 18.12.

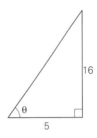

Figure 18.12

Solution
Compare the triangle with Figure 18.1. The ADJ is 5 and the OPP is 16. Use the tan ratio.

$$\tan \theta = \frac{16}{5} = 3.2$$

$$\theta = \tan^{-1} 3.2 = 72.6°$$

The value of θ is 72.6°

SELF TEST 18.8

From a point X on the ground, it is 58 m to the top, point Y, of a 32 m high tree. Find the angle between XY and the horizontal.

33.5°

Dividing by the ratio

In the examples so far, the unknown side was always the numerator of the fraction. If it is the denominator of the fraction, then we divide by the ratio. If you are using the cos ratio

$$\cos \theta = \frac{AB}{x}$$

So

$$x \times \cos \theta = AB$$

Hence

$$x = \frac{AB}{\cos \theta}$$

EXAMPLE 18.9

A kite is flying 13.7 m high. The string makes 47.2° with the horizontal. How long is the string?

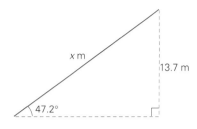

Figure 18.13

Solution
Let the length of the string be x m. In Figure 18.13, the HYP is x and the OPP is 13.7. Use the sin ratio

$$\sin 47.2° = \frac{13.7}{x}$$

$$x = \frac{13.7}{\sin 47.2°} = \frac{13.7}{0.7337} = 18.67$$

The length of the string is 18.7 m

 SELF TEST 18.9

In triangle PQR, $\hat{P} = 90°$, PQ = 7.2 m, $\hat{Q} = 76.3°$. Find QR.

30.4 m

18.3 Uses of trigonometry

Note The theory necessary to understand how some of the following equations are arrived at is beyond the scope of this book. However it is useful to see how frequently trigonometry is required in all aspects of science and engineering.

The sine bar

You can use a sine bar to measure angles accurately. A sine bar has rollers at each end. See Figure 18.14. The distance between the centres of the rollers is d say. If the difference in height between the rollers is h, then the bar is at an angle θ to the horizontal, where $\sin \theta = \dfrac{h}{d}$.

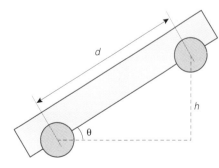

Figure 18.14   Sine bar

EXAMPLE 18.10

A 200 mm sine bar is to check an angle of 12.45°. Find the required difference in height between the centres of the rollers.

Solution
Here $d = 200$. Hence $\sin 12.45° = \dfrac{h}{200}$

So $\qquad h = 200 \times \sin 12.45° = 43.12$

The difference should be 43.12 mm

SELF TEST 18.10

A sine bar of length 300 mm is to check an angle of 21.37°. Find the required difference in height of the rollers.

109.3 mm

Taper balls

Suppose a pipe has non-constant diameter, i.e. is tapering. You can use taper balls to find the angle of taper, the angle θ between the sides of the pipe. Balls of different diameter are placed inside the pipe, as in Figure 18.15. The distance d between the centres of the balls is found. Then if the difference in radii is h,

$$\sin \tfrac{1}{2}\theta = \frac{h}{d}$$

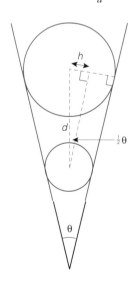

Figure 18.15   Taper balls

EXAMPLE 18.11

Two balls of diameters 38 mm and 26 mm are placed in a tapering pipe. The difference between the tops of the balls is 68 mm. Find the angle of taper.

Solution
The balls have radii 19 mm and 13 mm.
The distance between the centres is $68 - 19 + 13$ mm, i.e. 62 mm.
The difference between the radii is 6 mm.

Hence $\sin\frac{1}{2}\theta = \dfrac{6}{62}$

$\frac{1}{2}\theta = 5.553°$

Hence $\theta = 11.11°$

The angle of taper is 11.1°

SELF TEST 18.11

Two balls of radii 30 mm and 24 mm were placed in a pipe. The distance between the tops of the balls was 83 m. Find the angle of taper of the pipe.

8.94°

Illuminance

The trigonometric function cosine is used in lighting.

In Figure 18.16, a lamp of luminosity I candela is above a horizontal surface. The illuminance, E lux, at point A is given by

$$E = \frac{I}{h^2}\cos\theta$$

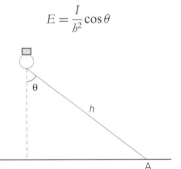

Figure 18.16 Illuminance

EXAMPLE 18.12

A lamp of luminosity 1000 candela is 2 m above point X on a horizontal surface. Find the illuminance at a point on the surface which is 3 m from X.

Solution
See Figure 18.17. Find the distance h by Pythagoras' theorem.

$$h^2 = 2^2 + 3^2 = 4 + 9 = 13$$

So $h = \sqrt{13}$

Hence $\cos\theta = \dfrac{2}{\sqrt{13}}$

Apply the formula $E = \dfrac{I}{h^2} \times \cos\theta$

$$E = \frac{1000}{13} \times \frac{2}{\sqrt{13}} = 42.67$$

The illuminance is 42.7 lux

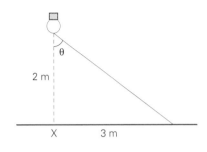

Figure 18.17

SELF TEST 18.12

In the situation of Example 18.12, calculate the illuminance at a point on the surface which is 1.7 m from X.

111 lux

Phase angle

The trigonometric function cosine is used in the theory of alternating current.

Suppose a circuit has resistance R Ω and impedance Z Ω. The **phase angle** θ is given by

$$\cos\theta = \frac{R}{Z}$$

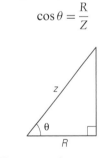

Figure 18.18 Phase angle

EXAMPLE 18.13

A circuit has resistance 10 Ω and impedance 17 Ω. Calculate the phase angle.

Solution
By the formula above

$$\cos\theta = \tfrac{10}{17}. \text{ Hence } \theta = 53.97°$$

The phase angle is 54°

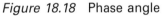

SELF TEST 18.13

A circuit of phase angle 23° has impedance 31 Ω. Find its resistance.

28.5 Ω

18.4 Sine rule and cosine rule

All the triangles considered above were right-angled triangles. There are two rules in trigonometry that we can use with *all* triangles. These rules are the **sine rule** and the **cosine rule**.

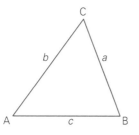

Figure 18.19

In the triangle shown in Figure 18.19, side a is opposite angle $\hat{A}$, side b is opposite angle $\hat{B}$, and side c is opposite angle $\hat{C}$.

The sine rule

The **sine rule** is as follows.

$$\frac{a}{\sin \hat{A}} = \frac{b}{\sin \hat{B}} = \frac{c}{\sin \hat{C}}$$

The sine rule for finding sides

Suppose you know one side of a triangle and two of the angles (ASA). Use the rule to find the other sides.

EXAMPLE 18.14

Find the side labelled x in the triangle shown in Figure 18.20.

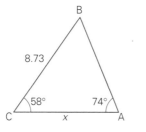

Figure 18.20

Solution

The angles are 74° and 58°. Subtract from 180° to find the third angle.

$$180 - 74 - 58 = 48$$

Use the sine rule, with $a = 8.73$, $b = x$, $\hat{A} = 74°$ and $\hat{B} = 48°$.

$$\frac{8.73}{\sin 74°} = \frac{x}{\sin 48°}$$

So

$$x = \frac{8.73 \times \sin 48°}{\sin 74°} = 6.749$$

The value of x is 6.75

SELF TEST 18.14

In triangle ABC, $\hat{A} = 78°$, $\hat{B} = 39°$, AC = 47 mm. Find BC.

73.1 mm

The sine rule for angles

Turn the sin rule upside down.

$$\frac{\sin \hat{A}}{a} = \frac{\sin \hat{B}}{b} = \frac{\sin \hat{C}}{c}$$

Use this version of the sine rule to find angles, when you know two sides and an angle not included (ASS).

EXAMPLE 18.15

Find the angle θ of Figure 18.21.

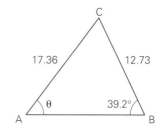

Figure 18.21

Solution

Here $\hat{A} = \theta$, $a = 12.73$, $b = 17.36$, $\hat{B} = 39.2°$. Apply the sine rule.

$$\frac{\sin \theta}{12.73} = \frac{\sin 39.2°}{17.36}$$

So

$$\sin \theta = \frac{12.73 \times \sin 39.2°}{17.36} = 0.4635$$

$$\theta = \sin^{-1} 0.4635 = 27.61°$$

The angle is 27.6°

In triangle PQR, PQ = 7.83 mm, QR = 9.564 mm, $\hat{P}$ = 64.5°. Find $\hat{Q}$.

67.9°

The ambiguous case

Sometimes the sine rule gives two possible values for an angle. Consider Figure 18.22. In both cases $\hat{A} = 30°$, $b = 10$ and $a = 9$. But there are two possible values for $\hat{B}$, θ_1 and θ_2. Note that they are connected by

$$\theta_2 = 180° - \theta_1$$

The sine rule gives the acute value of θ. Subtract from 180° to find the obtuse value.

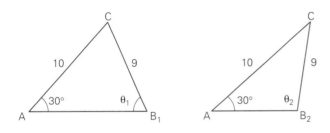

Figure 18.22

EXAMPLE 18.16

Find the possible values of θ in Figure 18.23.

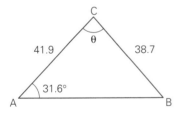

Figure 18.23

Solution
Here $a = 38.7$, $b = 41.9$ and $\hat{A} = 31.6°$. Apply the sine rule.

$$\frac{\sin 31.6°}{38.7} = \frac{\sin \hat{B}}{41.9}$$

So

$$\sin \hat{B} = \frac{41.9 \times \sin 31.6°}{38.7} = 0.5673$$

Hence the **acute value of $\hat{B}$** is $\sin^{-1} 0.5673$, i.e. **34.6°**. The obtuse value is obtained by subtracting from 180°.
    The **obtuse value of $\hat{B}$** is $180° - 34.6°$, i.e. **145.4°**.

The third angle of the triangle is θ. Subtract $\hat{A}$ and $\hat{B}$ from 180°.

$$\text{Either } \theta = 180 - 31.6 - 34.6 = 113.8°$$
$$\text{or} \quad \theta = 180 - 31.6 - 145.4 = 3.0°$$

The possible values of θ are 113.8° and 3.0°

In triangle ABC, $\hat{A} = 47°$, AB = 12.5 mm, BC = 11.8 mm. Find the possible values of $\hat{B}$.

82.2° or 3.8°

The cosine rule

With the same labelling of sides and angles as in Figure 18.19, the cosine rule is

$$a^2 = b^2 + c^2 - 2bc \cos \hat{A}$$

Alternatively,
$$b^2 = c^2 + a^2 - 2ca \cos \hat{B}$$
or
$$c^2 = a^2 + b^2 - 2ab \cos \hat{C}$$

The cosine rule for finding sides

You can use the cosine rule to find a side, when you know the other sides and the angle enclosed (SAS).

EXAMPLE 18.17

Find the side labelled x in Figure 18.24.

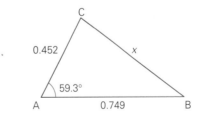

Figure 18.24

Solution
Here $a = x$, $b = 0.452$, $c = 0.749$ and $\hat{A} = 59.3°$. Apply the rule
$$a^2 = b^2 + c^2 - 2bc \cos \hat{A}$$
So $x^2 = 0.452^2 + 0.749^2 - 2 \times 0.452 \times 0.749 \times \cos 59.3°$
$$= 0.4196$$
Hence
$$x = \sqrt{0.4196} = 0.6478$$

The value of x is 0.648

SELF TEST 18.17

In triangle PQR, $\hat{P} = 58.2°$, PQ $= 17$ m, PR $= 23$ m. Find QR.

20.1 m

The cosine rule for angles

If we make cos $\hat{A}$ the subject of the cosine rule, we obtain

$$\cos \hat{A} = \frac{b^2 + c^2 - a^2}{2bc}$$

Hence we can find the angles of a triangle, when we know the three sides (SSS).

EXAMPLE 18.18

Find the angle labelled θ in Figure 18.25.

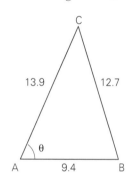

Figure 18.25

Solution
Here $\hat{A} = \theta$, $a = 12.7$, $b = 13.9$ and $c = 9.4$. Apply the formula.

$$\cos \hat{A} = \frac{b^2 + c^2 - a^2}{2bc}$$

So $\cos \theta = \dfrac{13.9^2 + 9.4^2 - 12.7^2}{2 \times 13.9 \times 9.4} = \dfrac{120.28}{261.32} = 0.4603$

Hence $\theta = \cos^{-1} 0.4603 = 62.59°$

The value of θ is 62.6°

SELF TEST 18.18

The three sides of a triangle are 9.1 m, 11.3 m and 14.4 m. Find the largest angle of the triangle. (Hint: the largest angle is opposite the largest side.)

89.1°

Solution of triangles

If you know sufficient information about the sides and angles of a triangle, use the sine rule or the cosine rule to find the other sides or angles. This is **solving** the triangle. Make sure you use the correct rule.

● With three sides (SSS) use the cosine rule to find the angles
● With two sides and an included angle (SAS) use the cosine rule to find the third side
● With two angles and a side (ASA) use the sine rule to find the other sides
● With two sides and an angle *not* included (ASS) use the sine rule to find the other angles. In this case, there may be two possible answers

Notes

1 In Section 17.4, we solved triangles by constructing them. It is much more accurate to solve them by trigonometry. You can check some of the constructions in Section 17.4 by the sine rule or the cosine rule.
2 The first three methods correspond to the conditions for congruence of Section 15.2, and to the methods of constructing triangles of Section 17.4. The fourth method, ASS, does not correspond to a condition for congruence, as there may be two different triangles.

EXAMPLE 18.19

Three holes, with centres A, B and C, are drilled in a steel plate, as shown in Figure 18.26. Distances are in mm. Find the angle $A\hat{C}B$.

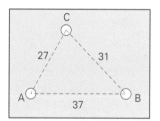

Figure 18.26

Solution
We know the three sides (SSS) of the triangle ABC. Hence use the cosine rule to find the angle.

$$\cos \hat{C} = \frac{27^2 + 31^2 - 37^2}{2 \times 27 \times 31} = 0.1918$$

Hence $\hat{C} = \cos^{-1} 0.1918 = 78.94°$

The angle $A\hat{C}B$ is 78.9°

EXAMPLE 18.20

An aerial of height 4.1 m is to be erected on a slope of 15°. It will be secured by two cables, each making 35° with the aerial, as shown in Figure 18.27. Find the length of the longer cable.

Solution

The aerial, the ground and the cable form a triangle. Label it as shown. The longer cable makes 55° with the horizontal, hence it makes 40° with the slope. So the angles of the triangle are 35°, 40° and 105°. We know the angles and one side, (ASA), hence use the sine rule to find the length of the cable.

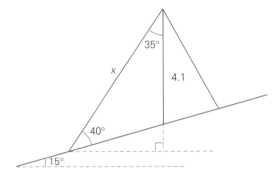

Figure 18.27

$$\frac{x}{\sin 105°} = \frac{4.1}{\sin 40°}$$

Hence

$$x = \frac{4.1 \times \sin 105°}{\sin 40°} = 6.161$$

The longer cable has length 6.16 m

EXAMPLE 18.21

Figure 18.28 shows a mechanism. It is a rotating crank AB of length 0.45 m and a connecting rod BC of length 3.17 m. The rod moves such that AC is always horizontal. When AB makes 20° with the horizontal, find the angle BC makes with the horizontal.

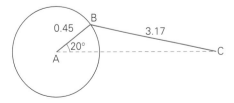

Figure 18.28

Solution

We know two sides of ABC and an angle not included. Use the sine rule to find the angle.

$$\frac{\sin \hat{C}}{0.45} = \frac{\sin 20°}{3.17}$$

Hence $\sin \hat{C} = \dfrac{0.45 \times \sin 20°}{3.17} = 0.04855$

Hence $\hat{C} = \sin^{-1} 0.04855 = 2.783°$

The rod makes 2.8° with the horizontal

Note   The acute value of $\hat{C}$ is 2.8°. The obtuse value is 177.2°. But 177.2° + 20° is greater than 180°. This use of the sine rule is not ambiguous.

EXAMPLE 18.22

A crane consists of a vertical mast AB of height 15.6 m, and a jib BC of length 18.3 m. Find the distance AC when the angle between the mast and the jib is 142°. See Figure 18.29.

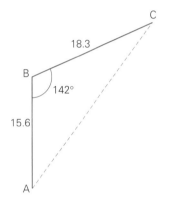

Figure 18.29   **Crane**

Solution

Here we know two sides and the angle between them. Use the cosine rule to find the third side.

$$AC^2 = 15.6^2 + 18.3^2 - 2 \times 15.6 \times 18.3 \times \cos 142°$$
$$= 1028$$

Hence AC = $\sqrt{1028} = 32.07$

The distance AC is 32.1 m

SELF TEST 18.19

In each of the following, find the side or angle indicated.
   a) $a = 7.4$, $b = 12.7$, $\hat{C} = 64.2°$. Find c.
   b) $a = 0.5$, $b = 0.7$, $c = 0.6$. Find $\hat{B}$.
   c) $a = 12$, $b = 17$, $\hat{B} = 63°$. Find $\hat{A}$.
   d) $a = 95$, $\hat{A} = 48°$, $\hat{B} = 81°$. Find b.

a) 11.6, b) 78.5°
c) 39.0°, d) 126

■ CHECK YOUR UNDERSTANDING

● Suppose a right-angled triangle contains an angle of θ. The three sides are as follows.

The longest side is the **hypotenuse**
The side next to θ is the **adjacent**
The side farthest from θ is the **opposite**.

● The three functions which connect the ratios of the sides with θ are as follows.

$$\sin\theta = \frac{\text{OPP}}{\text{HYP}} \qquad \cos\theta = \frac{\text{ADJ}}{\text{HYP}} \qquad \tan\theta = \frac{\text{OPP}}{\text{ADJ}}$$

● The inverse functions are defined as follows.

$$\theta = \sin^{-1}\left(\frac{\text{OPP}}{\text{HYP}}\right) = \cos^{-1}\left(\frac{\text{ADJ}}{\text{HYP}}\right) = \tan^{-1}\left(\frac{\text{OPP}}{\text{ADJ}}\right)$$

● Label a triangle so that angle $\hat{A}$ is opposite side a etc. The sine rule is below. Use this form when you know the angles and one side (ASA).

$$\frac{a}{\sin\hat{A}} = \frac{b}{\sin\hat{B}} = \frac{c}{\sin\hat{C}}$$

● The rule can also be written as below. Use this form when you know two sides and an angle not enclosed between them (ASS).

$$\frac{\sin\hat{A}}{a} = \frac{\sin\hat{B}}{b} = \frac{\sin\hat{C}}{c}$$

● The sine rule may be ambiguous. If you have found θ, $180° - \theta$ may be another value.
● The cosine rule is below. Use this form when you know two sides and the angle enclosed between them (SAS).

$$a^2 = b^2 + c^2 - 2bc\,\cos\hat{A}$$

● The rule can also be written as below. Use this form when you know all three sides (SSS).

$$\cos\hat{A} = \frac{b^2 + c^2 - a^2}{2bc}$$

REVISION EXERCISES AND QUESTIONS

18.1 The trigonometric functions

1 Find the sides x, y and z in the triangles of Figure 18.30.

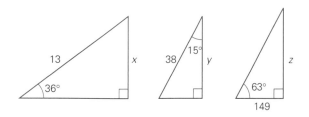

Figure 18.30

2 Find the angles P, Q and R in the triangles of Figure 18.31.

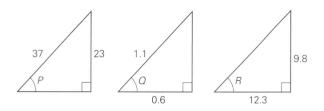

Figure 18.31

3 In triangle ABC, $\hat{A} = 90°$, BC = 17 m and $\hat{B} = 53°$. Find AB and AC.

4 In triangle PQR, $\hat{P} = 90°$, PR = 75 mm and $\hat{R} = 85°$. Find PQ.

5 In triangle ABC, $\hat{A} = 90°$, BC = 83 mm and BA = 71 mm. Find $\hat{B}$.

6 In triangle PQR, $\hat{P} = 90°$, PR = 127 mm and PQ = 152 mm. Find $\hat{Q}$.

18.2 Solution of right-angled triangles

7 Find the sides x, y and z in the triangles of Figure 18.32.

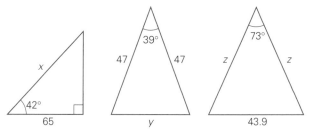

Figure 18.32

8 In triangle ABC, $\hat{A} = 90°$, $\hat{B} = 48°$ and AC = 66 mm. Find BC.

9 A cylinder of diameter 46 mm is to be sharpened to a point of angle 36°, as shown in Figure 18.33. Find the length of the sharpened section.

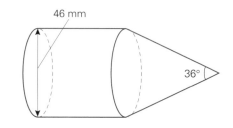

Figure 18.33

10 A flagpole is 6 m high. What is the length of its shadow when the elevation of the sun is 63°?

11 In Figure 18.34, a tapering slot has angle 44°. The depth of the slot is 10 mm, and the width at the top is 30 mm. Calculate the width at the bottom.

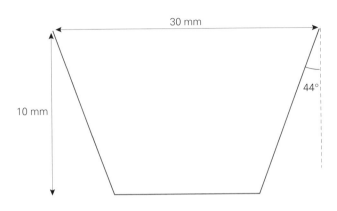

Figure 18.34

12 A tapering slot has depth 20 mm. The widths at top and bottom are 18 mm and 10 mm respectively. Calculate the angle of the slot.

13 A mast is 13 m high. It is secured by a guy rope at 23° to the mast. Find the length of the rope.

18.3 Uses of trigonometry

14 A sine bar has length 200 mm.

   a) To measure an angle of 27.43°, what is the required difference between the heights of the rollers?

   b) The difference in height of the rollers is 34.54 mm. What angle is measured?

15 Two taper balls have diameters 30 mm and 26 mm. They are inserted in a pipe.

   a) The difference in height between the tops of the balls is 87 mm. What is the angle of taper of the pipe?

   b) The angle of taper of the pipe is 6.4°. What is the difference in height of the tops of the balls?

16 A lamp of luminosity 2000 candelas is 2.5 m above a point X on a horizontal table. Point A is on the table, 1.59 m from X. Find the illuminance at A.

17 A circuit has impedance 120 Ω.

   a) If the resistance is 96 Ω, find the phase angle.

   b) If the phase angle is 39°, find the resistance.

18.4 Sine rule and cosine rule

18 Find the sides a and b in the triangles of Figure 18.35.

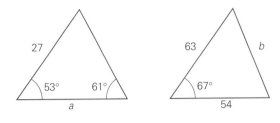

Figure 18.35

19 Find the angles A and B in the triangles of Figure 18.36.

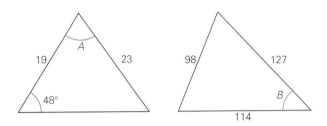

Figure 18.36

20 In triangle PQR, $\hat{P} = 67°$, PR = 29 mm and $\hat{R} = 55°$. Find PQ.

21 In triangle ABC, AB = 34 mm, AC = 39 mm and $\hat{A} = 39°$. Find $\hat{B}$.

22 In triangle ABC, AB = 58 mm, BC = 50 mm and $\hat{A} = 43°$. Find the possible values of $\hat{B}$.

23 In triangle LMN, LM = 8.6 mm, LN = 8.2 mm and MN = 7.2 mm. Find $\hat{N}$.

24 In triangle PQR, PQ = 154 mm, PR = 98 mm and $\hat{P} = 63°$. Find QR.

25 Three holes are drilled in a plate. The distances between the centres of the holes are 58.3 mm, 61.7 mm and 49.9 mm. Find the angles between the lines connecting the centres of the holes.

26 A roof is 10 m wide. The two sides of the roof slope at 12° and 15° to the horizontal. Find the lengths of the roof sections. Find the height of the ridge.

27 A mast of height 23 m stands on ground sloping at 11°. Two guy ropes, each at 28° to the mast, secure it to the ground. Calculate the lengths of the ropes.

28 From point A, town B is 23 km away on a bearing of 28°, and town C is 48 km away on a bearing of 97°. Find the distance between B and C.

Further areas and volumes

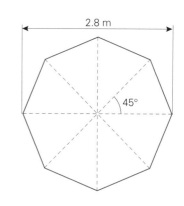

Introduction

In Chapter 16 we dealt with areas and volumes of shapes like rectangles, circles, cuboids, pyramids and so on. There are many other shapes which you may have to measure, such as ellipses, frustums of cones and frustums of pyramids.

Some shapes may not be regular at all. You may have to estimate their areas or volumes by some method of approximation.

19.1 Plane areas

Areas of triangles

The area of a triangle is half the base times the height (area $= \frac{1}{2}bh$). Two other useful formulae are below.

Using sine

In the triangle shown in Figure 19.1, the two sides a and b enclose the angle $\hat{C}$. The area of the triangle is

$$\frac{1}{2}ab\sin\hat{C} \qquad [1]$$

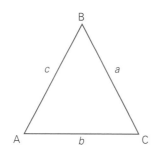

Figure 19.1

Using the sides of a triangle

Suppose the sides of the triangle are a, b and c. Let $s = \frac{1}{2}(a + b + c)$.

Then the area is given by the formula

$$\sqrt{(s(s - a)(s - b)(s - c))} \qquad [2]$$

EXAMPLE 19.1

A window is made in the shape of a regular octagon (8-sided shape). The distance between opposite vertices is 2.8 m. Find the area of the window.

Figure 19.2

Solution

Draw lines from the centre to the vertices. This divides the window into eight triangles. Each triangle has sides of length 1.4 m, enclosing an angle of $\frac{360°}{8}$ or $45°$. Use the formula [1] above to find the area of a triangle.

$$\text{Area of triangle} = \frac{1}{2}ab\sin\hat{C}$$

$$= \frac{1}{2} \times 1.4^2 \times \sin 45° = 0.6930$$

Multiply this by 8, obtaining 5.544

The area of the window is 5.54 m^2

SELF TEST 19.1

A regular figure has 20 sides. The distance between opposite vertices is 100 mm. Find the area of the figure.

7725 mm²

EXAMPLE 19.2

Figure 19.3 shows a triangle, with distances in mm. Find its area.

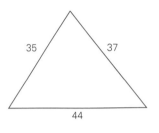

Figure 19.3

Solution
Apply the formula [2]. Area = $\sqrt{(s(s-a)(s-b)(s-c))}$

$$s = \tfrac{1}{2}(35 + 44 + 37) = 58$$
$$\text{Area} = \sqrt{(58(58-35)(58-44)(58-37))}$$
$$= \sqrt{(58 \times 23 \times 14 \times 21)}$$
$$= \sqrt{392\,196}$$
$$= 626.3$$

The area is 626 mm²

SELF TEST 19.2

A triangle has sides 12 m, 13 m, 17 m. Find its area.

77.8 m²

Areas of sectors and segments

In Figure 19.4 a sector of angle θ is taken from a circle of radius r.
The area of the sector is given by the formula

$$\frac{\pi r^2 \theta}{360}$$

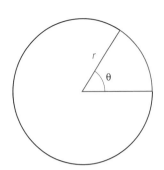

Figure 19.4

Figure 19.5 shows a segment cut off by a chord.
The area of the segment is given by the formula

$$\frac{1}{2}r^2\left(\frac{\pi\theta}{180} - \sin\theta\right)$$

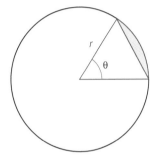

Figure 19.5

EXAMPLE 19.3

A sector of a circle of radius 1.3 m has angle 63°. Find its area.
Solution
Use the formula above, putting $r = 1.3$ and $\theta = 63$.

$$\text{Area of sector} = \frac{\pi r^2 \theta}{360}$$
$$= \frac{\pi 1.3^2 \times 63}{360}$$
$$= 0.9291$$

The area is 0.929 m²

SELF TEST 19.3

A sector of angle 28° is taken from a circle of radius 84 mm. Find its area.

1720 mm²

EXAMPLE 19.4

A chord of length 0.6 m cuts off a segment of a circle of radius 1.7 m. Find the area of the segment.

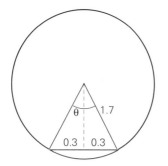

Figure 19.6

Solution
First find the angle. If θ is the angle subtended by the chord, then

$$\sin \tfrac{1}{2}\theta = \frac{0.3}{1.7}$$

This gives $\tfrac{1}{2}\theta = 10.16°$, and hence $\theta = 20.32°$. Use the formula above, putting $r = 1.7$ and $\theta = 20.32$.

$$\text{Area of segment} = \frac{1}{2}r^2\left(\frac{\pi\theta}{180} - \sin\theta\right)$$
$$= \frac{1}{2} \times 1.7^2\left(\frac{\pi \times 20.32}{180} - \sin 20.32\right)$$
$$= 0.0107$$

The area is 0.0107 m^2

SELF TEST 19.4

A chord of length 8 m cuts off a segment from a circle of radius 13 m. Find the area of the segment.

3.38 m^2

Ellipses

An **ellipse** is an oval shape, like a circle seen at an angle. The diameter of the ellipse is not constant. The greatest diameter is the **major axis**. The least diameter is the **minor axis**.

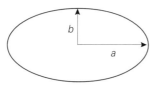

Figure 19.7   Ellipse

Let the greatest line from the centre be a, i.e. let a be half the major axis. Let the shortest distance from the centre be b, i.e. let b be half the minor axis. Then the area of the ellipse is given by the formula

$$\text{Area} = \pi ab$$

The approximate length of the perimeter is given by the formula

$$\text{Length} \simeq \pi(a + b)$$

Note A circle is a special ellipse, for which $a = b$. The formula for the area of an ellipse gives πaa, i.e. πa^2. This is the area of a circle with radius a. The formula for the perimeter of an ellipse gives $\pi(a + a)$, i.e. $2\pi a$. This is the perimeter of a circle. The formulae for the ellipse agree with the formulae for the circle.

EXAMPLE 19.5

Figure 19.8 shows a circle of radius 200 mm, drawn on graph paper with its centre at the origin. The circle is flattened to an ellipse, by halving its y coordinates. Find the area of the ellipse and the approximate perimeter of the ellipse.

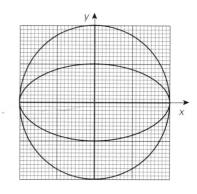

Figure 19.8

Solution
The major axis is 400 mm, and the minor axis is 200 mm. Hence $a = 200$ and $b = 100$. Apply the formulae for area and perimeter

$$\text{Area} = \pi ab$$
$$= \pi \times 200 \times 100 = 62\,831.8\ldots$$
$$\text{Perimeter} \simeq \pi(a + b)$$
$$\simeq \pi(200 + 100) = 942.4\ldots$$

The area is 62 800 mm^2

The perimeter is approximately 942 mm

SELF TEST 19.5

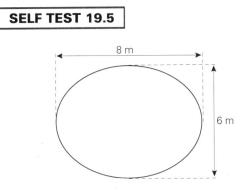

Figure 19.9

Find the area of the ellipse shown in Figure 19.9. Find the approximate value of its perimeter.

$$37.7 \text{ m}^2, 22 \text{ m}$$

19.2 Curved surface areas of solids

All the surface area of a sphere is curved. Cones and cylinders have flat surfaces and curved surfaces. The areas of the flat surfaces were given in Chapter 16. The curved surface areas of various solids are given below

Sphere

A sphere with radius r, as in Figure 19.10.

$$\text{Surface area} = 4\pi r^2$$

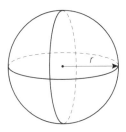

Figure 19.10 Area of a sphere

Cylinder

A cylinder with radius r and height h, as in Figure 19.11. The flat surfaces at each end are circles, each with area πr^2. The curved surface area is $2\pi rh$.

$$\text{Total surface area} = 2\pi rh + 2\pi r^2$$
$$= 2\pi r(r+h) \quad \text{(factorising by } 2\pi r\text{)}$$

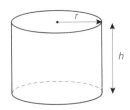

Figure 19.11 Area of a cylinder

Cone

A cone with radius r and height h, as in Figure 19.12. The slant height, l, up the side of the cone, is given by Pythagoras' Theorem.

$$l = \sqrt{(r^2 + h^2)}$$

The flat surface at the base is a circle with area πr^2. The curved surface area is πrl.

$$\text{Total surface area} = \pi r^2 + \pi rl$$
$$= \pi r(r+l) \quad \text{(factorising by } \pi r\text{)}$$

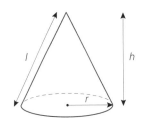

Figure 19.12 Area of a cone

EXAMPLE 19.6

An oil drum is a hollow cylinder with height 1.6 m and radius 0.34 m. It has a bottom and a lid. It is made from sheet metal of density 6 kg/m^2. Find its mass.

Solution
Find the surface area from the formula above, putting $r = 0.34$ and $h = 1.6$.

$$\text{Area} = 2\pi r(r+h)$$
$$= 2\pi \times 0.34\,(0.34 + 1.6)$$
$$= 4.144 \text{ m}^2$$

To obtain the mass from the area, multiply by 6, obtaining 24.9.

The mass is 24.9 kg

SELF TEST 19.6

Find the surface area of a solid cylinder with height 23 mm and radius 16 mm.

$$3920 \text{ mm}^2$$

EXAMPLE 19.7

Find the surface area of a sphere of radius 83 mm.

Solution
Use the formula above, putting $r = 83$.

$$\text{Area} = 4\pi r^2$$
$$= 4\pi \times 83^2$$
$$= 86\,570$$

The area is 86 600 mm^2

SELF TEST 19.7

Find the surface area of a sphere of radius 1.2 m.

18.1 m^2

EXAMPLE 19.8

A tent is made in the shape of a cone with height 2.8 m and radius 2.1 m. Find the curved surface area of the tent.

Solution
Use the formula above to find the slant height, l. Put $r = 2.1$ and $h = 2.8$.

$$l = \sqrt{(r^2 + h^2)}$$
$$= \sqrt{(2.1^2 + 2.8^2)}$$
$$= 3.5$$

Now use the formula $\pi r l$ for the area.

$$\text{Curved surface area} = \pi r l$$
$$= \pi \times 2.1 \times 3.5$$
$$= 23.09$$

The area is 23.1 m^2

SELF TEST 19.8

Find the total surface area of a solid cone of height 63 mm and radius 41 mm.

15 000 mm^2

19.3 Frustums

A **frustum** is a pyramid or cone with its top removed, as in Figures 19.13 and 19.14. Many food cartons are in the shape of a frustum of a cone. Let the height of the frustum be h, the area at the bottom be A and the area at the top be a.

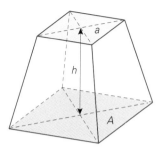

Figure 19.13 Frustum of a pyramid

Volume of a frustum

The volume is given by the formula
$$\text{Volume} = \tfrac{1}{3}h[A + \sqrt{(Aa)} + a]$$

If a frustum of a cone has radius R at the base and r at the top, as in Figure 19.14, the volume is
$$\tfrac{1}{3}h[\pi R^2 + \sqrt{(\pi R^2 \pi r^2)} + \pi r^2]$$

So   Volume of frustum of a cone $= \tfrac{1}{3}h(\pi R^2 + \pi Rr + \pi r^2)$
(factorising by π) $= \tfrac{1}{3}\pi h(R^2 + Rr + r^2)$

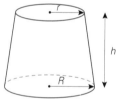

Figure 19.14 Frustum of a cone

Note   A cone is a special frustum, with its radius of the top equal to 0. Hence $r = 0$. The formula for the volume of a frustum becomes $\tfrac{1}{3}\pi h R^2$. This is the formula for the volume of a cone. The formula for a frustum agrees with the formula for a cone.

Surface area of a frustum

The slant height l of a frustum of a cone is given below. (See Figure 19.15.)
$$l = \sqrt{[h^2 + (R - r)^2]}$$

The curved surface area of the frustum is given by the formula
$$\pi l(R + r)$$

Hence the total surface area, including the circles at top and bottom, is
$$\pi l(R + r) + \pi R^2 + \pi r^2$$

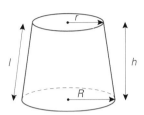

Figure 19.15   Surface area of a frustum of a cone

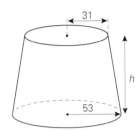

Figure 19.17

EXAMPLE 19.9

A wooden container is a frustum of a square pyramid, of depth 0.43 m. The top and the bottom are squares of side 1.2 m and 0.8 m respectively. Find its volume.

Solution
The area of top and bottom are 1.2^2 m^2 and 0.8^2 m^2 respectively. Use the formula, putting $h = 0.43$.

$$\text{Volume} = \tfrac{1}{3}h[A + \sqrt{(Aa)} + a]$$
$$= \tfrac{1}{3} \times 0.43[1.44 + \sqrt{(1.44 \times 0.64)} + 0.64]$$
$$= \tfrac{1}{3} \times 0.43(1.44 + 0.96 + 0.64)$$
$$= 0.4357$$

The volume is 0.436 m^3

SELF TEST 19.9

The frustum shown in Figure 19.16 has height 83 mm. The top and bottom are both rectangles, with sides 20 mm by 30 mm and 30 mm by 45 mm respectively. Find its volume.

78 900 mm^3

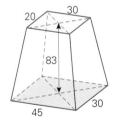

Figure 19.16

EXAMPLE 19.10

Figure 19.17 shows a food carton. It is a frustum of a cone, with bottom radius 53 mm and top radius 31 mm. It has volume 600 000 mm^3. Find the height of the carton.

Solution
Here the volume is 600 000, R = 53 and $r = 31$. Put these values into the formula.

$$\text{Volume} = \tfrac{1}{3}\pi h(R^2 + Rr + r^2)$$
$$600\,000 = \tfrac{1}{3}\pi h(53^2 + 53 \times 31 + 31^2)$$
$$= \tfrac{1}{3}\pi h(5413)$$

Hence
$$h = \frac{600\,000 \times 3}{\pi \times 5413}$$
$$= 105.8$$

The height of the carton is 106 mm

SELF TEST 19.10

A milk churn is a frustum of a cone with height 1.23 m. The radii of the base and the top are 0.18 m and 0.11 m respectively. Find its volume.

0.0828 m^3

EXAMPLE 19.11

Figure 19.18 shows a frustum of a solid cone with height 66 mm, base radius 48 mm and top radius 30 mm. Find its total surface area.

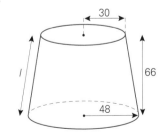

Figure 19.18

Solution

Find the slant height l. Apply the formula, with $h = 66$, $R = 48$ and $r = 30$.

$$l = \sqrt{[h^2 + (R - r)^2]}$$
$$= \sqrt{[66^2 + (48 - 30)^2]}$$
$$= \sqrt{(4356 + 324)}$$
$$= \sqrt{4680}$$
$$= 68.41$$

Total surface area $= \pi l(R + r) + \pi R^2 + \pi r^2$
$$= \pi 68.41(48 + 30) + \pi 48^2 + \pi 30^2$$
$$= \pi(5336 + 2304 + 900)$$
$$= \pi 8540$$

The total surface area is 26 830 mm^2

SELF TEST 19.11

Find the total surface area of the milk churn of Self Test 19.10.

1.26 m^2

19.4 Approximate areas and volumes

So far we have considered regular shapes, such as rectangles, circles, cylinders, cuboids and so on. The objects that you deal with may not be regular. Here we show various rules for finding the areas or volumes of irregular shapes.

Approximate areas

Consider the area shown in Figure 19.19. Three sides are straight lines, but the fourth is an unknown curve. Cut the area into n strips of equal width d. Three rules are as follows.

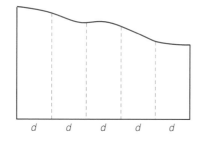

Figure 19.19

Mid-ordinate rule

Find the height of each strip at its midpoint, as in Figure 19.20. Let these heights be h_1, h_2, ..., h_n. The area is approximately

$$\text{Area} \simeq d(h_1 + h_2 + ... + h_n)$$

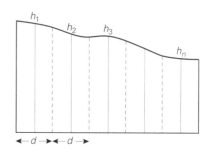

Figure 19.20   Mid-ordinate rule

Trapezium rule

For this rule and for the next rule, the heights of the area at the division points are $y_0, y_1, y_2, ..., y_n$, as in Figure 19.21.

Consider each strip to be a trapezium, area $= \frac{1}{2}h(a + b)$. Area under the curve

$$\simeq \frac{1}{2}d(y_0 + y_1) + \frac{1}{2}d(y_1 + y_2) .... \frac{1}{2}d(y_{n-1} + y_n)$$
$$\text{Area} \simeq \frac{1}{2}d[y_0 + y_n + 2(y_1 + y_2 + ... + y_{n-1})]$$

i.e., add the first and the last y values, then twice all the other y values. Then multiply by $\frac{1}{2}d$.

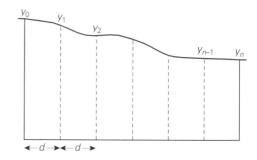

Figure 19.21   Trapezium and Simpson's rules

Simpson's rule

This gives an even better approximation to the area under the curve. For this rule, n must be even, i.e. there must be an even number of strips.

$$\text{Area} \simeq \frac{1}{3}d[y_0 + y_n + 4(y_1 + y_3 + ...) + 2(y_2 + y_4 + ...)]$$

i.e., add the first and the last y values, then 4 times the odd numbered values, then twice the even numbered values. Then multiply by $\frac{1}{3}d$.

Health warning!
Note the un-conventional labelling of ordinates; y_0, y_1, y_2 etc. and consequential un-conventional statement of Simpson's rule.

EXAMPLE 19.12

A river is 80 m wide. Its depth is measured at 10 m intervals. See Figure 19.22. The results are in the table below. Find the approximate area of its cross-section, using the trapezium rule and Simpson's rule.

Distance across (m)	0	10	20	30	40
Depth (m)	0	6.8	8.3	9.1	10.3
Distance across (m)	50	60	70	80	
Depth (m)	10.1	8.7	7.1	0	

Figure 19.22 **Cross-section of a river**

Distance across (m)	0	20	40	60	80
Length (m)	134	138	147	151	148
Distance across (m)	100	120	140	160	
Length (m)	144	138	129	126	

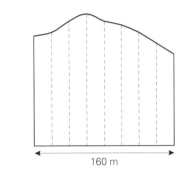

Figure 19.23

Find the approximate area of the field, using both the trapezium rule and Simpson's rule.

> **22 500 m², 22 490 m²**

EXAMPLE 19.13

An irregular piece of metal is shown in Figure 19.24. Find its approximate area, using the mid-ordinate rule. Distances are in mm.

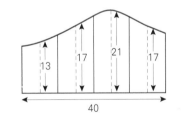

Figure 19.24

Solution

Here d is 10 and n is 8. The values of y are 0, 6.8, ..., 7.1, 0. Using the trapezium rule, add the first and the last values, and add all the other values.

First value + last value $= 0 + 0 = 0$
Add other values $= 6.8 + 8.3 + 9.1 + 10.3 + 10.1 + 8.7 + 7.1$
$\qquad\qquad\qquad = 60.4$

Now use the formula.

$$\text{Area} \simeq \tfrac{1}{2}d\,[\,y_0 + y_n + 2(y_1 + y_2 + ... + y_{n-1})]$$
$$\simeq \tfrac{1}{2} \times 10(0 + 2 \times 60.4) = 604$$

By the trapezium rule, the area is approximately 604 m²

For Simpson's rule, add the first and last values, the odd numbered values and the even numbered values

First value + last value $= 0 + 0 = 0$
Sum of odd numbered values $= 6.8 + 9.1 + 10.1 + 7.1 = 33.1$
Sum of even numbered values $= 8.3 + 10.3 + 8.7 = 27.3$

Now use the formula.

$$\text{Area} \simeq \tfrac{1}{3}d[\,y_0 + y_n + 4(y_1 + y_3 + ...) + 2(y_2 + y_4...)]$$

$$\text{Area} \simeq \tfrac{1}{3} \times 10(0 + 4 \times 33.1 + 2 \times 27.3) = 623.\dot{3}$$

By Simpson's rule, the area is approximately 623 m²

SELF TEST 19.12

Figure 19.23 is a diagram of a field. Three sides are bordered by straight lines, and the fourth is irregular. The length of the field is measured at 20 m intervals, as given in the table below.

Solution

The width of the object is 40 mm. Divide the width into 4 equal strips. Measure the height of the object at the middle of each strip, i.e. at 5, 15, 25 and 35. The heights are 13, 17, 21 and 17. Use the formula.

$$\text{Area} \simeq d(b_1 + b_2 ...)$$
$$\simeq 10 \times (13 + 17 + 21 + 17) = 680$$

The area is approximately 680 mm²

Health warning!
Note the un-conventional labelling of ordinates; A_0, A_1, A_2 etc. and consequential un-conventional statement of Simpson's rule.

SELF TEST 19.13

A flat object is 100 mm long. Its width is measured at intervals of 5 mm, 15 mm, ..., 95 mm, as below.

Distance along (mm)	5	15	25	35	45
Width (mm)	23	28	34	40	45
Distance along (mm)	55	65	75	85	95
Width (mm)	43	42	41	40	39

Use the mid-ordinate rule to estimate the area of the object.

3750 mm^2

Approximate volumes

The three rules above find the areas of irregular shapes. We can change the rules to find the volumes of irregular solids.

For areas, you cut the region into n strips of width d, and use the heights of the strips. For volumes, you cut the solid into n slices, and use the area of the slices. Each slice can be considered as a prism.

Mid-ordinate rule

See Figure 19.25. Find the area of each slice at its midpoint. Let these be A_1, A_2, ..., A_n. The volume is approximately

$$\text{Volume} \simeq d(A_1 + A_2 + ... + A_n)$$

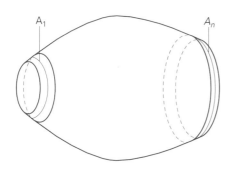

Figure 19.25

Trapezium rule and Simpson's rule

For these rules, the areas of the solid at the division points are $A_0, A_1, A_2, ..., A_n$.

Trapezium rule

$$\text{Volume} \simeq \tfrac{1}{2}d[A_0 + A_n + 2(A_1 + A_2 + ... + A_{n-1})]$$

i.e., add the first and the last areas, then twice all the other areas. Then multiply by $\tfrac{1}{2}d$.

Simpson's rule

If n is even, i.e. if there are an even number of slices,

$$\text{Volume} \simeq \tfrac{1}{3}d[A_0 + A_n + 4(A_1 + A_3 + ...) + 2(A_2 + A_4 + ...)]$$

i.e., add the first and the last areas, then 4 times the odd numbered areas, then twice the even numbered areas. Then multiply by $\tfrac{1}{3}d$.

EXAMPLE 19.14

The solid of Figure 19.26 has a circular cross-section. At 10 mm intervals from one end, the radius of cross-section is given in the table below. Use the trapezium rule and Simpson's rule to estimate the volume.

Distance (mm)	0	10	20	30	40	50	60
Radius (mm)	8.3	9.1	10.2	11.8	13.4	15.0	17.7

Figure 19.26

Solution

If the radius of cross-section is r, then the area of cross-section is πr^2. Hence the areas A_0, A_1 etc are $\pi 8.3^2$, $\pi 9.1^2$ etc. Find the sum of the first and last areas, and the sum of the other areas.

$$\text{First area} + \text{last area} = \pi 8.3^2 + \pi 17.7^2$$
$$= \pi 382.18$$
$$\text{Sum of odd numbered areas} = \pi 9.1^2 + \pi 11.8^7 + \pi 15^2$$
$$= \pi 447.05$$
$$\text{Sum of even numbered areas} = \pi 10.2^2 + \pi 13.4^2$$
$$= \pi 283.6$$
$$\text{Sum of odd and even numbered areas} = \pi(477.05 + 283.6)$$
$$= \pi 730.65$$

Now use the trapezium rule.

$$\text{Volume} \simeq \tfrac{1}{2} \times 10(\pi 382.18 + 2 \times \pi 730.65)$$
$$\simeq \pi 9217.4$$
$$\simeq 28\,957.3...$$

By the trapezium rule, the volume is approximately 28 960 mm^3

For Simpson's rule,

$$\text{Volume} \simeq \tfrac{1}{3} \times 10(\pi 382.18 + 4 \times \pi 447.05 + 2 \times \pi 283.6)$$
$$\simeq \pi 9125.3$$
$$\simeq 28\,667.8...$$

By Simpson's rule, the volume is approximately 28 670 mm³

Note In the calculations, we took out a common factor of π. This is much quicker than multiplying every term by π.

SELF TEST 19.14

An object has a square cross-section. The side of the square is measured at 5 mm intervals, as in the table below.

Distance (mm)	0	5	10	
Side of square (mm)	103	100	97	
Distance (mm)	15	20	25	30
Side of square (mm)	90	82	71	60

Use the trapezium rule and Simpson's rule to estimate its volume.

231 900 mm³, 231 700 mm³

EXAMPLE 19.15

Figure 19.27 shows a cone with curved sides. At a distance x mm from the point, the radius of cross-section is $0.8x^{1.3}$ mm. The cone is 60 mm long. Use the mid-ordinate rule with 6 intervals to estimate its volume.

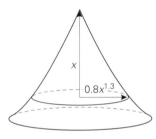

Figure 19.27

Solution
Evaluate the radius at x equal to 5, 15, 25, 35, 45 and 55. Then evaluate the cross-sectional areas at these points.

x	5	15	25
radius ($0.8\,x^{1.3}$)	6.48	27.04	52.53
area (πr^2)	42.0π	731.2π	2759.5π

x	35	45	55
radius ($0.8\,x^{1.3}$)	81.35	112.78	146.41
area (πr^2)	6618.5π	12 721.3π	21 435.0π

Use the formula for the mid-ordinate rule.

$$\text{Volume} \simeq 10 \times \pi(42.0 + 731.2 + 2759.5 + 6618.5 + 12\,721.3 + 21\,435.0)$$
$$\simeq 10 \times \pi \times 44\,307.5 = 1\,391\,961.1...$$

The volume is approximately 1 392 000 mm³

SELF TEST 19.15

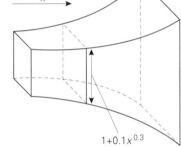

Figure 19.28

The object in Figure 19.28 is such that x m from one end, its cross-section is a square of side $(1 + 0.1x^{0.3})$ m. The object is 4 m long. Use the mid-ordinate rule with 4 intervals to estimate its volume.

5.00 m³

19.5 Pappus' theorems

These theorems enable us to find the volume and surface area of objects such as rings.

In Figure 19.29, a plane shape has been rotated in a circle. The centre of the shape is X, at a distance of R from the centre of the circle.

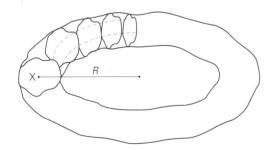

Figure 19.29

Volume

The volume of the solid generated is the distance moved by X, multiplied by the area of the shape.

$$\text{Volume} = \text{area of shape} \times 2\pi R$$

Area

The surface area of the solid generated is the distance moved by X, multiplied by the perimeter of the shape.

$$\text{Surface area} = \text{perimeter of shape} \times 2\pi R$$

EXAMPLE 19.16

A circular concrete wall is 1.8 m high. Its inner radius is 5.3 m, and its outer radius is 5.8 m. Find the volume of concrete. See Figure 19.30.

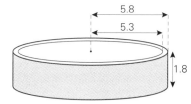

Figure 19.30

Solution

The plane shape is a rectangle, 1.8 high and 0.5 m wide. The area of the shape is 1.8×0.5, i.e. 0.9 m². The centre of the rectangle is halfway between the inner and the outer surfaces of the wall, hence it moves in a circle of radius $(5.3 + 0.25)$, 5.55 m. Use the theorem for volume.

$$\begin{aligned}\text{Volume} &= \text{area} \times 2\pi R \\ &= 0.9 \times 2\pi \times 5.55 \\ &= 31.384\ldots\end{aligned}$$

The volume of concrete is 31.4 m³

SELF TEST 19.16

The inner tube of a tyre occupies a shape formed by rotating a circle of radius 120 mm. The centre of this circle moves round a circle of radius 340 mm. Find the volume of the tyre.

9.66×10^7 mm³

EXAMPLE 19.17

Find the surface area of the inner tube of Self Test 19.16.

Solution

The perimeter of the shape is the circumference of the circle, $2\pi 120$ mm. Apply the theorem for surface area.

$$\begin{aligned}\text{Area} &= \text{perimeter} \times 2\pi R \\ &= 2\pi 120 \times 2\pi 340 \\ &= 1\,610\,719.4\ldots\end{aligned}$$

The area is 1 611 000 mm²

SELF TEST 19.17

Find the exposed surface area of the concrete wall of Example 19.16.

143 m²

19.6 Three-dimensional trigonometry and Pythagoras

You can use Pythagoras' theorem and the trig functions to find distances and angles in solid objects. It is difficult to understand three dimensional objects, so be certain to draw a clear diagram.

EXAMPLE 19.18

In Figure 19.31, VABCD is a pyramid, in which ABCD is a square of side 20 m. VA, VB, VC and VD are all equal to 15 m. Find the height of the pyramid. Find the area of VAB.

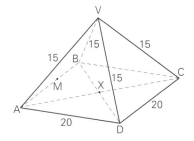

Figure 19.31

Solution

Let X be the centre of the base of the pyramid. Then VXA is a right-angled triangle. We know VA. To find AX use Pythagoras' theorem. AX is the hypotenuse of a triangle whose other sides are both 10 m.

$$AX = \sqrt{(10^2 + 10^2)} = \sqrt{200}$$

Now use Pythagoras' theorem in VXA, which is right-angled at X. The hypotenuse is VA.

$$VX = \sqrt{(VA^2 - AX^2)} = \sqrt{(225 - 200)} = 5$$

The height of the pyramid is 5 m

Let M be the midpoint of AB. Find VM by Pythagoras' theorem in VMX, which is right-angled at X. The hypotenuse is VM.

$$VM = \sqrt{(MX^2 + VX^2)} = \sqrt{(100 + 25)} = 11.18$$

Now use the formula for the area of a triangle.

$$\text{area} = \tfrac{1}{2} \times \text{base} \times \text{height}$$

$$\text{area} = \tfrac{1}{2} \times AB \times VM = \tfrac{1}{2} \times 20 \times 11.18 = 111.8$$

The area of VAB is 112 m^2

SELF TEST 19.18

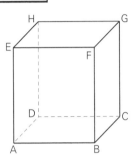

Figure 19.32

The cuboid ABCDEFGH in Figure 19.32 is such that AB = 3 m, AD = 4 m, AE = 6 m. Find the length AG.

7.81 m

Angle between line and plane

Figure 19.33 shows a line L above a plane Π. The line cuts the plane at A. From point B on the line, drop a perpendicular to C on the plane. The angle between L and Π is $\hat{CAB}$.

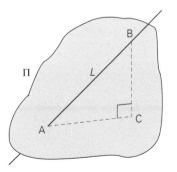

Figure 19.33　Angle between line and plane

Angle between planes

Figure 19.34 shows two planes Π$_1$ and Π$_2$ meeting in a line L. Take A on L. Let AB and AC lie in Π$_1$ and Π$_2$, perpendicular to L. The angle between Π$_1$ and Π$_2$ is $\hat{CAB}$.

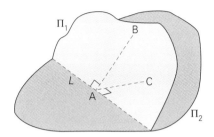

Figure 19.34　Angle between planes

EXAMPLE 19.19

The pyramid VABCD in Figure 19.35 has a square base ABCD of side 20 m, and has height 12 m. Find the angle between
  a) VA and ABCD　　　b) VAB and ABCD.

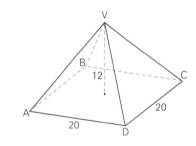

Figure 19.35

Solution

a) Refer to Figure 19.36. Let X be the centre of ABCD. V is directly above X, hence the angle needed is $\hat{VAX}$. VX is 12 m. Find AX by Pythagoras' theorem.

$$AX = \sqrt{(10^2 + 10^2)} = 14.14$$

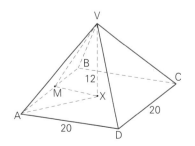

Figure 19.36

Now use trigonometry in triangle VAX. VX is the OPP and AX is the ADJ. Use the tan ratio.

$$\tan V\hat{A}X = \frac{12}{14.14}$$

$$V\hat{A}X = 40.32°$$

The angle between VA and ABCD is 40.3°

b) VAB and ABCD intersect in AB. Let M be the midpoint of AB. VM and XM are in VAB and ABCD respectively, and are perpendicular to AB. Hence the angle needed is VM̂X. VX is the OPP and MX is the ADJ. Use the tan ratio.

$$\tan V\hat{M}X = \frac{12}{10}$$

$$V\hat{M}X = 50.19°$$

The angle between VAB and ABCD is 50.2°

Note   AV is the shallowest line up the pyramid. MV is the steepest line.

SELF TEST 19.19

XPQRS is a pyramid, in which PQRS is a square of side 40 m. XP, XQ, XR and XS are all equal to 35 m. Find the angle between XP and PQRS. Find the angle between XPQ and PQRS.

36.1°, 45.9°

Area and volume calculations

EXAMPLE 19.20

A vertical chimney is a cylinder with radius 110 mm. It passes through a roof which slopes at 20° to the horizontal. Find the area of the hole in the roof through which the chimney passes.

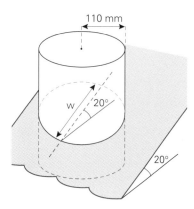

Figure 19.37   Chimney

Solution

The hole is an ellipse. The minor axis of the hole is the width of the chimney, 220 mm. The major axis, w mm, is found by trigonometry.

$$\cos 20° = \frac{220}{w}$$

$$w = \frac{220}{\cos 20°} = 234.12$$

The formula for the area of an ellipse is πab. Here $2a = 234.12$ and $2b = 220$.

Hence   Area $= \pi ab$

$$= \pi \times \frac{234.12}{2} \times \frac{220}{2}$$

$$= 40\,453.0...$$

The area is 40 450 mm²

SELF TEST 19.20

A solid cylinder has diameter 330 mm. It is cut by a plane which makes 30° with the axis of the cylinder. Find the area of the cut surface.

171 100 mm²

EXAMPLE 19.21

Figure 19.38 shows a steeple which is 30 m high. It is a pyramid, with a regular octagonal base of side 2.5 m. Find the area of the sloping sides of the steeple.

Figure 19.38   Steeple

Solution

Figure 19.39 shows the base of the pyramid. We need the distance from a side AB to the centre X of the octagon. The centre of AB is M.

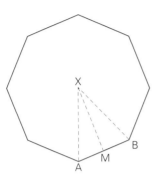

Figure 19.39

$$B\hat{X}A = 360° \div 8 = 45°$$

$$AM = \tfrac{1}{2} \times 2.5 = 1.25 \text{ m}$$

$$A\hat{X}M = \tfrac{1}{2} \times 45° = 22\tfrac{1}{2}°$$

$$\tan 22\tfrac{1}{2}° = AM \div XM$$

Hence $XM = 1.25 \div \tan 22\tfrac{1}{2}° = 3.018$ m

Now use Pythagoras' theorem. If H is the top of the steeple, then triangle HXM is right-angled at X. (See Figure 19.40.)

$$MH^2 = XH^2 + XM^2 = 30^2 + 3.018^2 = 909.1$$

$$MH = \sqrt{909.1} = 30.15 \text{ m}$$

Now use the formula for the area of a triangle.

$$\text{Area of } \triangle ABH = \tfrac{1}{2} \times 2.5 \times 30.15 = 37.69 \text{ m}^2$$

Finally multiply by 8, obtaining 301.52.

The area of the sloping faces is 301.5 m²

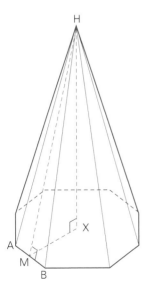

Figure 19.40

SELF TEST 19.21

The Great Pyramid in Egypt has a square base of side 230 m and a height of 147 m. Find the total surface area of the triangular faces.

85 850 m²

CHECK YOUR UNDERSTANDING

● If a triangle has two sides a and b enclosing an angle $\hat{C}$, then its area is $\tfrac{1}{2}ab \sin \hat{C}$.

● Suppose the sides of a triangle are a, b and c. Let $s = \tfrac{1}{2}(a + b + c)$. The area of the triangle is

$$\sqrt{(s(s - a)(s - b)(s - c))}$$

● If a sector of angle $\theta°$ is taken from a circle of radius r, then its area is $\dfrac{\pi r^2 \theta}{360}$. The area of the segment is $\tfrac{1}{2}r^2\left(\dfrac{\pi\theta}{180} - \sin\theta\right)$.

● If an ellipse has axes $2a$ and $2b$, then its area is πab. Its perimeter is approximately $\pi(a + b)$.

● If a sphere has radius r, then its surface area is $4\pi r^2$. If a cylinder has height h and radius r, then its curved surface area is $2\pi rh$. If a cone has height h and radius r, then its curved surface area is πrl, where $l = \sqrt{(r^2 + h^2)}$.

● If a frustum has height h, and areas A and a at top and bottom, then its volume is $\tfrac{1}{3}h[A + \sqrt{(Aa)} + a]$. In particular, if a frustum of a cone has radii R and r at top and bottom, then its volume is $\tfrac{1}{3}\pi h(R^2 + Rr + r^2)$

● To find the approximate area of a shape, divide it into strips of width d. If the heights at the middle of the strips are h_1, h_2, ..., h_n, then the mid-ordinate formula for area is

$$d(h_1 + h_2 + \ldots + h_n)$$

If the values of the heights at the edges of the strips are y_0, y_1, ..., y_n, then the trapezium rule for area is

$$\tfrac{1}{2}d[y_0 + y_n + 2(y_1 + y_2 + \ldots + y_{n-1})]$$

If n is even, then Simpson's rule for area is

$$\tfrac{1}{3}d[y_0 + y_n + 4(y_1 + y_3 + y_3 + \ldots) + 2(y_2 + y_4 + \ldots)]$$

● The volume of irregular solids can be found by these rules, by replacing the height by the area of cross-section.

● If a solid occupies the shape formed by rotating a plane shape, then its volume is the product of the distance moved by the centre of the shape and the area of the shape. The surface area of the solid is the product of the distance moved by the centre of the shape and the perimeter of the shape.

● Pythagoras' theorem and trigonometry can be used to find areas and volumes in three dimensional problems. It is essential to have a clear diagram.

19.1 Plane areas

1 Find the areas of the triangles in Figure 19.41 Lengths are in mm.

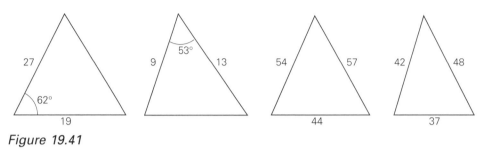

Figure 19.41

2 Find the areas of the sectors in Figure 19.42. Lengths are in m.

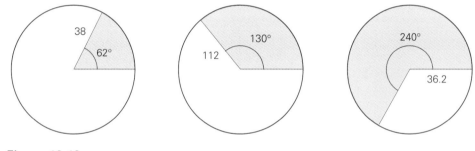

Figure 19.42

3 Find the areas of the segments in Figure 19.43. Lengths are in mm.

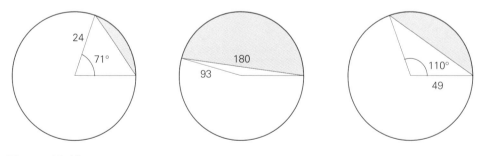

Figure 19.43

4 An arc AB of length 7.3 m is on a circle of radius 10.8 m. Find the angle subtended at the centre C, and hence find the area of the sector ABC.

5 A chord of length 78 mm cuts off a segment of a circle of radius 107 mm. Find the area of the segment.

6 The greatest width of an ellipse is 267 mm, and the least width is 188 mm. Find its area and its approximate perimeter.

7 The minor axis of an ellipse is 2.1 m. The area of the ellipse is 5.2 m². Find the major axis.

19.2 Curved surface areas

8 Find the curved surface areas of the following.
    a) A sphere with radius 2.3 m
    b) A sphere with diameter 46 mm
    c) A sphere with volume 87 000 mm^3
    d) A cylinder with height 76 mm and radius 23 mm
    e) A cylinder with height 1.2 m and diameter 0.3 m
    f) A cone with height 0.23 m and radius 0.17 m
    g) A cone with height 38 mm and base diameter 29 mm

9 A can is a cylinder with height 58 mm and base diameter 50 mm. It is made from metal of density 3.2 kg/m^2. Find the mass of the metal.

10 A hollow sphere of diameter 32 mm is made from thin plastic, of density 0.2 kg/m^2. Find the mass of the sphere.

11 A hemispherical dome is to be painted. Calculate how much paint will be required, if the dome has radius 28 m and a litre of the paint covers 30 m^2.

12 A heating pipe has diameter 56 mm. Calculate the curved surface area of 10 m of the pipe.

13 An inverted cone is to be lined with tin. Find the area of tin required, if the cone has diameter 110 mm and height 218 mm.

19.3 Frustums

14 Find the volumes and curved surface areas of the following frustums of cones.
    a) height 4 m, base radius 1.2 m, top radius 0.8 m
    b) height 166 mm, base radius 66 mm, top radius 27 mm

15 A frustum of a square based pyramid has height 2.3 m. The side of the top square is 0.7 m, and the side of the base square is 1.9 m. Find its volume.

16 A bucket is a frustum of a cone, with base radius 230 mm, top radius 350 mm and height 480 mm. Find its volume and the area of the curved side and the base.

17 A lampshade is a frustum of a cone, of height 0.15 m, base radius 0.12 m, top radius 0.09 m. Find the curved area of the shade.

18 A hole is dug in the ground, in the shape of a frustum of a pyramid. The depth of the hole is 1.8 m. The top is a square of side 0.9 m, and the base is a square of side 0.8 m. Find the volume of earth removed.

19 A funnel has the dimensions shown in Figure 19.44. Lengths are in mm. Find the volume of the funnel. Find its mass, if it is made from thin metal of density 2.8 kg/m^2.

20 A frustum is made by cutting off the top quarter of a cone. Find the ratio of the volume of the frustum to the volume of the original cone. Find the ratio of the curved surface area of the frustum to the curved surface area of the original cone.

19.4 Approximate areas and volumes

21 The depth of a stream, at 2 m intervals, is given in the table below. Use the trapezium rule or Simpson's rule to estimate the cross-sectional area of the stream.

Distance across (m)	0	2	4	6
Depth (m)	0	1.3	2.5	3.0
Distance across (m)	8	10	12	
Depth (m)	3.3	1.9	0	

22 A river is 60 m wide. The depth is measured as below. Use the mid-ordinate rule to estimate the area of cross-section.

Distance (m)	5	15	25
Depth (m)	2.6	3.4	4.8
Distance (m)	35	45	55
Depth (m)	4.1	2.5	1.4

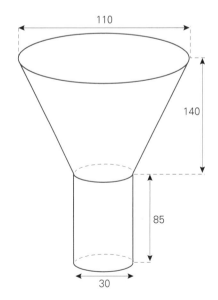

Figure 19.44 Funnel

23 Figure 19.45 is a scale diagram of a field. Distances are in m. Estimate the area of the field, by the mid-ordinate rule, the trapezium rule or Simpson's rule.

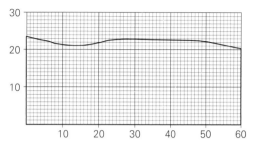

Figure 19.45

24 A tree trunk has a circular cross-section. The table below gives its diameter at 0.5 m intervals. Estimate the total volume of the trunk.

Distance (m)	0	0.5	1.0	1.5
Diameter (m)	1.2	1.1	1.1	1.0
Distance (m)	2.0	2.5	3.0	3.5
Diameter (m)	0.9	0.7	0.5	0.3

25 A trench is dug, of constant width 2 m. The table below gives its depth at 0.4 m intervals. Estimate the volume of earth removed for the trench.

Distance (m)	0	0.4	0.8	1.2	1.6
Depth (m)	0.8	0.9	1.0	1.2	1.2
Distance (m)	2.0	2.4	2.8	3.2	
Depth (m)	1.6	1.5	1.3	1.2	

26 A tower, 40 m high, has a circular cross-section. The table below gives the radius at different heights. Use the mid-ordinate rule to estimate the volume of the tower.

Height (m)	4	12	20	28	36
Radius (m)	21	18	16	15	14

19.5 Pappus' theorems

27 A circular concrete wall has internal radius 3.6 m. The thickness of the wall is 0.2 m and its height is 2.4 m. Find the volume of concrete.

28 A solid ring is formed by rotating a circle of radius 12 mm, so that its centre moves round a circle of radius 27 mm. Find the volume of the ring.

29 A solid ring is formed by rotating the ellipse of Figure 19.46, so that its centre moves round a circle of radius 1.6 m. Find the volume of material to make the ring.

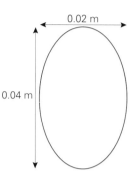

Figure 19.46

30 Find the exposed surface area of the wall of Question 27.

31 Find the surface area of the ring of Question 28.

32 Figure 19.47 shows a circular wall. The cross-section is a triangle, with base 0.2 m and sloping sides 0.7 m. The top of the wall is a circle of radius 20 m. Find the volume and exposed surface area of the wall.

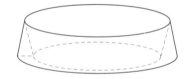

Figure 19.47

19.6 Three-dimensional trigonometry and Pythagoras

33 ABCDEFGH is a cuboid, with AB = EF = 1.2 m, AD = EH = 2.3 m, AE = 1.8 m. Find
a) AG,
b) the angle between AG and ABFE,
c) the angle between ABCD and ABGH.

34 VABCD is a pyramid, with a square base ABCD of side 16 m. V is 10 m above the centre of ABCD. Find
a) VA,
b) the angle between VA and ABCD,
c) the angle between VAB and ABCD.

35 Figure 19.48 shows the plan of a roof. (The view from above). The distances given are horizontal distances. The roof section ABLM slopes at 30° to the horizontal. Find
a) the height of the ridge LM above ABCD,
b) the length of AL,

c) the slope of CDML to the horizontal,
d) the slope of AL to the horizontal.

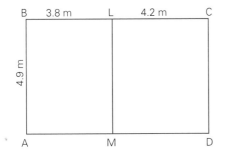

Figure 19.48

36 Find the areas of the roof sections of Question 35.

37 A roof slopes at 37° to the horizontal. A vertical cylindrical chimney of diameter 380 mm passes through the roof. Find the area of roof which has to be removed.

38 A steeple tapers to a point from a base which is a regular hexagon of side 2.8 m. The height of the steeple is 43 m. Find the total area of the sloping faces.

Further trigonometry

Introduction

In Chapter 18 we defined the trigonometric functions, sine, cosine and tangent (sin, cos and tan), in terms of a right-angled triangle. There are three other trigonometric functions, secant, cosecant and cotangent (sec, cosec and cot).

In Chapters 18 and 19 we solved problems of lengths and areas using the trigonometric functions. The functions have many other uses. In particular we can use the functions to describe electrical current. For this we need to define the functions for angles greater than 90°.

Figure 20.1 shows the screen of an oscilloscope. The screen shows two waves. These waves can be described in terms of the sine function.

20.1 Cosec, sec and cot

In Chapter 18 we defined the three functions sin, cos and tan. There are three other ratios of the sides of a right-angled triangle.

Look at Figure 20.2.

$$\operatorname{cosec}\theta = \frac{\text{HYP}}{\text{OPP}} \qquad \sec\theta = \frac{\text{HYP}}{\text{ADJ}} \qquad \cot\theta = \frac{\text{ADJ}}{\text{OPP}}$$

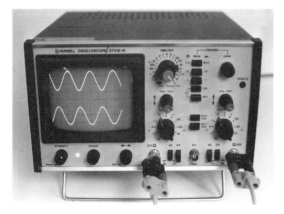

Figure 20.1 Oscilloscope

Note that cosec, sec and cot are the reciprocals of sin, cos and tan respectively.

$$\operatorname{cosec}\theta = \frac{1}{\sin\theta} \qquad \sec\theta = \frac{1}{\cos\theta} \qquad \cot\theta = \frac{1}{\tan\theta}$$

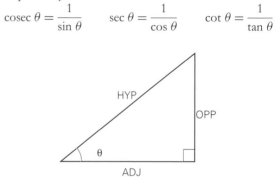

Figure 20.2

Finding cosec, sec and cot

A calculator does not have buttons for cosec, sec and cot. Books of 4-figure tables do not usually include these functions. Instead find the sin, cos or tan, and then take the reciprocal. There is a $\frac{1}{x}$ button on a calculator, and reciprocal tables are usually included in books of 4-figure tables.

EXAMPLE 20.1

Find cosec 25°.

Solution
Cosec is the reciprocal of sin. First find sin 25°, as 0.4226. Now take the reciprocal.

$$\operatorname{cosec}25° = \frac{1}{\sin 25°} = \frac{1}{0.4226} = 2.366$$

$$\mathbf{cosec\ 25° = 2.366}$$

SELF TEST 20.1

Find sec 43°.

1.367

Cosec^{-1}, sec^{-1}, cot^{-1}

The inverse functions of cosec, sec and cot are found from the inverse functions of sin, cos and tan respectively. Find the reciprocal of x, and then use sin, cos or tan.

Hence $\qquad$ $\text{cosec}^{-1}x = \sin^{-1}(\frac{1}{x})$

Similarly $\qquad$ $\sec^{-1}x = \cos^{-1}(\frac{1}{x})$

and $\qquad$ $\cot^{-1}x = \tan^{-1}(\frac{1}{x})$

EXAMPLE 20.2

Solve the equation $\sec x = 4$.

Solution
If $\sec x = 4$, then $\cos x = \frac{1}{4}$.
$$\cos^{-1}\tfrac{1}{4} = 75.52°$$

The solution is $x = 75.5°$

SELF TEST 20.2

Solve the equation $\cot y = 0.8$.

$$y = 51.3°$$

EXAMPLE 20.3

The formula below is used when measuring a screw thread. Find M when $D = 20$ mm, $p = 2.5$ mm and $\theta = 30°$.
$$M = D - \tfrac{5}{6}p\cot\theta + p \times \tfrac{1}{2}\sec\theta(\text{cosec }\theta + 1)$$

Solution
Put $D = 20$, $p = 2.5$ and $\theta = 30°$. Recall that cot, sec and cosec are the reciprocals of tan, cos and sin respectively.
$$\cot 30° = \tfrac{1}{\tan 30°} = 1.732$$
$$\sec 30° = \tfrac{1}{\cos 30°} = 1.155$$
$$\text{cosec }30° = \tfrac{1}{\sin 30°} = 2$$
Hence $M = 20 - \tfrac{5}{6} \times 2.5 \times 1.732 + 2.5 \times \tfrac{1}{2} \times 1.155(2+1)$
$$= 20.72$$

The value of M is 20.7 mm

SELF TEST 20.3

Use the formula above to evaluate M when $D = 15$ mm, $p = 3$ mm and $\theta = 35°$.

16.5 mm

20.2 Radians

Definition of radians

For ordinary purposes, we measure angles in degrees. There are 360° in a complete circle. For many scientific and mathematical purposes we measure angles in **radians**. There are 2π radians in a complete circle.

In Figure 20.3 an arc of length a is taken from a circle of radius r. The angle subtended is θ radians, where $\theta = \frac{a}{r}$.

For example, if the radius is 20 mm and the arc length is 5 mm, then the angle is $5 \div 20$, i.e. 0.25 radians.

The circumference of a circle of radius r is $2\pi r$. Hence there are $\frac{2\pi r}{r}$, i.e. 2π, radians in a complete circle.

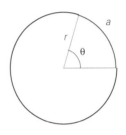

Figure 20.3

1 revolution $= 360° = 2\pi$ radians

Hence 180° is π radians and a right angle, 90°, is $\frac{1}{2}\pi$ radians.
- To convert radians to degrees, multiply by $\frac{180}{\pi}$.
- To convert degrees to radians, multiply by $\frac{\pi}{180}$.

Note If an angle is a simple multiple of π, we do not convert it to a decimal. Give an angle as $\frac{1}{3}\pi$ rather than as 1.047, as it is more accurate.

Table 20.1 Conversion chart for degrees and radians

Degrees	Radians
0°	0
30°	$\frac{1}{6}\pi$
45°	$\frac{1}{4}\pi$
60°	$\frac{1}{3}\pi$
90°	$\frac{1}{2}\pi$
180°	π
270°	$1\frac{1}{2}\pi$
360°	2π
720°	4π

EXAMPLE 20.4

Convert 15° to radians. Convert 1.2 radians to degrees.

Solution

$180° = \pi$ radians so multiply 15 by $\dfrac{\pi}{180}$, obtaining $\dfrac{\pi}{12}$.

15° is equivalent to $\dfrac{\pi}{12}$ radians

Multiply 1.2 by $\dfrac{180}{\pi}$, obtaining 68.75.

1.2 radians is equivalent to 68.75°

SELF TEST 20.4

Convert 174° to radians. Convert $\dfrac{\pi}{8}$ to degrees.

3.04 radians, $22\frac{1}{2}°$

Trigonometry using radians

You can measure angles in radians as well as in degrees. Hence you can find the trigonometric functions when the angle is in radians.

Using a calculator

Set the calculator to radian mode. You should see either R or rad appear. Now use the calculator in the same way as for degrees.

Using tables

Multiply by $\dfrac{180}{\pi}$, to convert the angle in radians to degrees. Then use the trig tables.

To find inverse trig functions from tables, find the angle in degrees, then multiply by $\dfrac{\pi}{180}$ to convert to radians.

EXAMPLE 20.5

a) Find sin 0.43, where the angle is measured in radians.
b) Find $\cos^{-1} 0.65$, giving your answer in radians.

Solution

a) If you have a scientific calculator, you can find sin 0.43 directly. If you are using tables, first convert to degrees, by multiplying by $\dfrac{180}{\pi}$.

$$0.43 \text{ radians} = 24.64°$$
$$\sin 0.43 \text{ radians} = \sin 24.64° = 0.4169$$

sin 0.43 = 0.417

b) If you have a scientific calculator, you can find $\cos^{-1}0.65$ directly in radians. If you are using tables, first find $\cos^{-1}0.65$ in degrees.

$$\cos^{-1}0.65 = 49.46°$$

To convert to radians, multiply by $\dfrac{\pi}{180}$, obtaining 0.8632.

$\cos^{-1}0.65 = 0.863$ radians

SELF TEST 20.5

a) Find cos 1.13, where the angle is measured in radians.
b) Find $\tan^{-1}2.3$, giving your answer in radians.

a) 0.427   b) 1.16 radians

Arcs

In Figure 20.4 a sector of a circle has an angle of θ radians. The length of the arc is the product of the radius and the angle.

$$l = r\theta$$

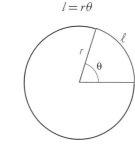

Figure 20.4

EXAMPLE 20.6

In Figure 20.5 a barrel of radius 450 mm has a panel which subtends 1.38 radians at the centre. What is the width of the panel?

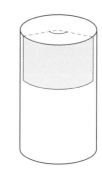

Figure 20.5 Barrel

Solution

Let the width be w mm. Use the formula.

$$w = r\theta$$
$$w = 450 \times 1.38 = 621$$

The panel has width 621 mm

SELF TEST 20.6

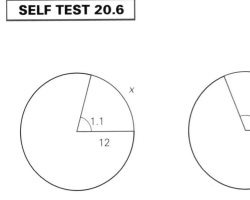

Figure 20.6

Find the arc lengths and angles in the sectors of Figure 20.6.
Lengths are in mm.

$$x = 13.2 \text{ mm}, \ y = 80.5 \text{ mm}, \ \alpha = 0.921, \ \beta = 2.11$$

EXAMPLE 20.7

Two pulleys of radii 50 mm and 80 mm have their centres
150 mm apart. A belt passes tightly round the pulleys, as
shown in Figure 20.7. Find the length of the belt.

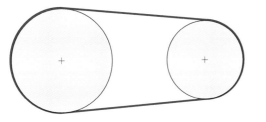

Figure 20.7

Solution

See Figure 20.8. There are two straight sections and two
curved sections. Find the length of the straight section AB
by the method of Example 17.15.

$$AB = DY = \sqrt{(XY^2 - DX^2)}$$
$$= \sqrt{(150^2 - 30^2)} = 147.0 \text{ mm}$$

For the length of the curved sections, we need the angles that
they subtend at the centre of the pulleys. For the smaller pulley,
it is 2θ, where θ is the angle between BY and XY.

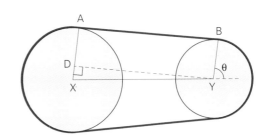

Figure 20.8

By corresponding angles, $\theta = D\hat{X}Y$.

$\cos D\hat{X}Y = \dfrac{30}{150}$. Hence $\theta = D\hat{X}Y = 1.369$ radians.

Length of shorter curved section $= 50 \times 2\theta = 136.9$ mm.

The rope goes round a complete circle. Hence the two angles
subtended must add up to 2π.

Angle subtended at centre of larger pulley
$$= 2\pi - 2\theta = 3.545$$

Length of longer curved section
$$= 80 \times 3.545 = 283.5 \text{ mm}$$

Total length $= 2 \times 147.0 + 136.9 + 283.5$
$$= 714.4$$

The length of the belt is 714.4 mm

SELF TEST 20.7

A belt passes tightly round two pulleys of radii 120 mm and
170 mm, whose centres are 350 mm apart. Find the length of
the belt.

1618 mm

Areas of sectors and segments

In Figure 20.9 a sector of θ radians is taken from a circle of radius r. The area of the sector is $\dfrac{\theta}{2\pi} \times \pi r^2$ or $\dfrac{\theta r^2}{2}$.

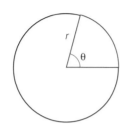

Figure 20.9

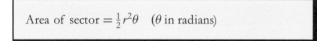

$$\text{Area of sector} = \tfrac{1}{2}r^2\theta \quad (\theta \text{ in radians})$$

In Figure 20.10 a chord cuts off a segment. The area of the segment is $\tfrac{1}{2}r^2(\dfrac{\pi\theta}{180} - \sin\theta)$ when θ is in degrees (See Section 19.1.) or $\tfrac{1}{2}r^2(\dfrac{\pi\theta}{\pi} - \sin\theta)$ when θ is in radians.

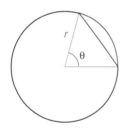

Figure 20.10

$$\text{Area of segment} = \tfrac{1}{2}r^2(\theta - \sin\theta) \quad (\theta \text{ in radians})$$

Note These formulae in terms of radians are simpler than the formulae in terms of degrees, and they do not require a value for π.

EXAMPLE 20.8

Find the areas of the sector and the segment shown in Figure 20.11. Distances are in mm.

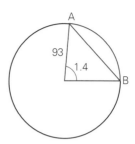

Figure 20.11

Solution
Apply the formulae.

$$\text{Area of sector} = \tfrac{1}{2}r^2\theta = \tfrac{1}{2} \times 93^2 \times 1.4 = 6054.3$$

The area of the sector is 6054 mm²

$$\text{Area of segment} = \tfrac{1}{2}r^2(\theta - \sin\theta) = \tfrac{1}{2} \times 93^2(1.4 - \sin 1.4)$$

$$= 1792.7...$$

The area of the segment is 1793 mm²

SELF TEST 20.8

A circle has radius 46 mm, and the chord AB subtends 0.68 radians at the centre X. Find the area of the sector ABX, and the area of the segment cut off by AB.

719.4 mm², 54.18 mm²

20.3 Angles greater than 90°

In Chapter 18 we defined the trigonometric function for acute angles, i.e. angles less than 90°. The definitions can be extended for angles greater than 90°. This is very useful for describing waves, such as sound waves, radio waves and so on.

Consider a pointer shown in Figure 20.12. It has length 1, and one end is at the origin. After it has rotated θ anti-clockwise from the x-axis, the y-coordinate of the end of the pointer is at $\sin\theta$. The definition of sine for angles greater than 90° follows this rule. For all angles, the y-coordinate of the end of the pointer is $\sin\theta$.

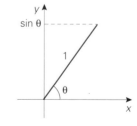

Figure 20.12

As the pointer rotates through a circle, θ goes from $0°$ to $360°$. The end of the pointer goes through the four quadrants.

First quadrant

In Figure 20.13 θ is at any angle between $0°$ to $90°$.

The y-coordinate goes from 0 to 1. Hence $\sin\theta$ increases from 0 to 1.

In particular, $\sin 0° = 0$ and $\sin 90° = 1$.

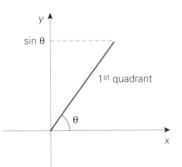

Figure 20.13

Second quadrant

In Figure 20.14, θ is at any angle between $90°$ to $180°$. The y-coordinate goes from 1 to 0. Hence $\sin\theta$ decreases from 1 to 0.

In particular, $\sin 90° = 1$ and $\sin 180° = 0$.

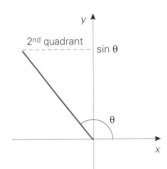

Figure 20.14

Third quadrant

In Figure 20.15, θ is any angle between $180°$ to $270°$. The y-coordinate becomes negative, going from 0 to -1. Hence $\sin\theta$ decreases from 0 to -1.

In particular, $\sin 180° = 0$ and $\sin 270° = -1$.

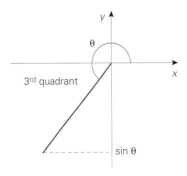

Figure 20.15

Fourth quadrant

In Figure 20.16, θ is any angle between $270°$ to $360°$. The y-coordinate is still negative, but rising from -1 to 0. Hence $\sin\theta$ increases from -1 to 0.

In particular, $\sin 270° = -1$ and $\sin 360° = 0$.

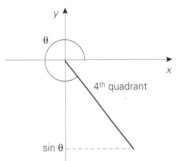

Figure 20.16

Graph

A graph of $\sin\theta$, as θ goes from $0°$ to $360°$, is shown in Figure 20.17. Notice how the value of $\sin\theta$ varies between -1 and 1 as indicated above. The curve is positive between $0°$ and $180°$ (quadrants 1 and 2) and is negative between $180°$ and $360°$ (quadrants 3 and 4).

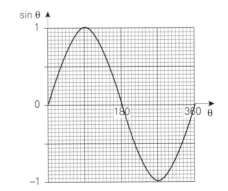

Figure 20.17 Sine θ

Beyond 360°

After 360° the pointer returns to its starting point. Hence for angles greater than 360°, the values of sin θ are repeated. The pattern of the graph of sin θ is also repeated, as shown in Figure 20.18.

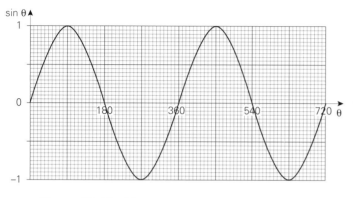

Figure 20.18   Sine θ

Cos

The definition of cos θ is similar. The x-coordinate of the end of the pointer is cos θ. See Figure 20.19.

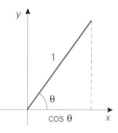

Figure 20.19

As θ goes between 0° and 180° the value of cos θ decreases from 1 to 0 and then to −1. Then it rises again to 1 as θ increases from 180° to 360°. As for sin θ, the values of cos θ are repeated after 360°. The graph of cos θ is shown in Fig. 20.20.

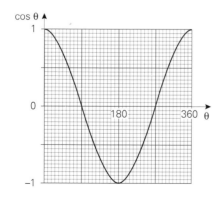

Figure 20.20   Cos θ

Calculation of sin, cos, tan

If you have a scientific calculator, you can find sin, cos and tan for all angles directly. If you are using tables, then you must first change the angle to an acute angle. The rules are as follows.

- For 90° $< \theta <$ 180°   subtract θ from 180°
- For 180° $< \theta <$ 270°   subtract 180° from θ
- For 270° $< \theta <$ 360°   subtract θ from 360°
- For 360° $< \theta$ subtract 360° from θ

The signs of sin, cos and tan are as follows.

- For 90° $< \theta <$ 180°   sin is +ve, cos and tan are −ve
- For 180° $< \theta <$ 270°   tan is +ve, sin and cos are −ve
- For 270° $< \theta <$ 360°   cos is +ve, sin and tan are −ve

These can be remembered by ASTC. (All Silly Tom Cats).

- In the first quadrant, $0° < \theta < 90°$ ALL are +ve.
- In the second quadrant, $90° < \theta < 180°$ SIN is +ve.
- In the third quadrant, $180° < \theta < 270°$ TAN is +ve.
- In the fourth quadrant, $270° < \theta < 360°$ COS is +ve.

EXAMPLE 20.9

Find
   a) sin 110°   b) cos 260°   c) tan 325°   d) sin 470°.

Solution

a) 110° is in the second quadrant. See Figure 20.21. Subtract 110° from 180°, obtaining 70°. In the second quadrant sin is +ve, hence sin 110° = sin 70°. Find that sin 70° = 0.9397.

sin 110° = 0.9397

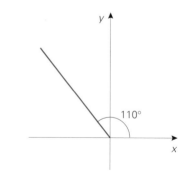

Figure 20.21

b) 260° is in the third quadrant. See Figure 20.22. Subtract 180° from 260°, obtaining 80°. In the third quadrant cos is −ve, hence cos 260° = −cos 80°. Find that cos 80° = 0.1736.

cos 260° = −0.1736

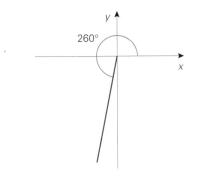

Figure 20.22

c) 325° is in the fourth quadrant. See Figure 20.23. Subtract 325° from 360°, obtaining 35°. In the fourth quadrant tan is −ve, hence tan 325° = −tan 35°. Find that tan 35° = 0.7002.

$$\textbf{tan } \textbf{325}° = -\textbf{0.7002}$$

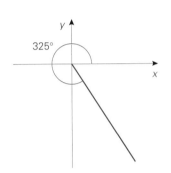

Figure 20.23

d) 470° is greater than 360°. Subtract 360° from 470°, obtaining 110°. Hence sin 470° = sin 110°. We have already found this in part a).

$$\textbf{sin } \textbf{470}° = \textbf{0.9397}$$

SELF TEST 20.9

Find
   a) sin 235°   b) cos 142°   c) tan 251°   d) cos 700°.

$$-0.8192, -0.7880, 2.904, 0.9397$$

Finding the angle

Sine

If x lies between −1 and 1, there are two angles θ for which $\sin \theta = x$. If x is positive, there is a solution in the first quadrant

and in the second quadrant. If x is negative, there is a solution in the third quadrant and in the fourth quadrant. (See Figure 20.24 and Figure 20.25.)

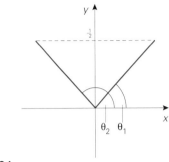

Figure 20.24

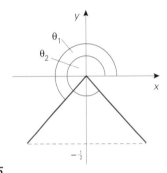

Figure 20.25

For example:
   to solve $\sin \theta = \frac{1}{2}$,
   there are the solutions $\theta = 30°$ and $\theta = 150°$,
   to solve $\sin \theta = -\frac{1}{2}$,
   there are the solutions $\theta = 210°$ and $\theta = 330°$.

In general, the solutions are found as follows. Let k be a positive number. Let θ_0 be the acute angle for which $\sin \theta_0 = k$.

   To solve $\sin \theta = k$. Take θ_0 and $(180° - \theta_0)$.
   To solve $\sin \theta = -k$. Take $(180° + \theta_0)$ and $(360° - \theta)$.

Cosine and tangent

Similar methods apply for cos and tan.
   Let θ_0 be the acute angle for which $\cos \theta_0 = k$.

   To solve $\cos \theta = k$. Take θ_0 and $(360° - \theta_0)$.
   To solve $\cos \theta = -k$. Take $(180° - \theta_0)$ and $(180° + \theta_0)$.

   Let θ_0 be the acute angle for which $\tan \theta_0 = k$.

   To solve $\tan \theta = k$. Take θ_0 and $(180° + \theta_0)$.
   To solve $\tan \theta = -k$. Take $(180° - \theta_0)$ and $(360° - \theta_0)$.

EXAMPLE 20.10

For each of the following equations, find two solutions between 0° and 360°.
   a) $\sin \theta = -0.6$ b) $\cos \theta = 0.35$ c) $\tan \theta = -1.7$

Solution

a) Apply the rule above. The value of θ for which $\sin\theta = +0.6$
    is

$$\theta_0 = \sin^{-1} 0.6 = 36.9°$$

Add 180°, obtaining 216.9°. Subtract from 360°, obtaining
323.1°.

$$\boldsymbol{\theta = 216.9° \text{ or } \theta = 323.1°}$$

b) Apply the rule above. The value of θ for which $\cos\theta = +0.35$
    is

$$\theta_0 = \cos^{-1} 0.35 = 69.5°$$

Subtract from 360°, obtaining 290.5°.

$$\boldsymbol{\theta = 69.5° \text{ or } \theta = 290.5°}$$

c) Apply the rule above. The value of θ for which $\tan\theta = +1.7$
    is

$$\theta_0 = \tan^{-1} 1.7 = 59.5°$$

Subtract from 180°, obtaining 120.5°. Subtract from 360°,
obtaining 300.5°.

$$\boldsymbol{\theta = 120.5° \text{ or } \theta = 300.5°}$$

SELF TEST 20.10

For each of the following equations, find two solutions
between 0° and 360°.

  a) $\sin\theta = 0.93$ b) $\cos\theta = -0.74$ c) $\tan\theta = 0.62$

  a) 68.4°, 111.6°   b) 137.7°, 222.3°   c) 31.8°, 211.8°

Angles in radians

If the angle is measured in radians, we can still use the
trigonometric functions. Replace 90° by $\frac{1}{2}\pi$, 180° by π and
360° by 2π. The graph for radians is in Figure 20.27.
For example for an angle of 2.7:

$$\tfrac{1}{2}\pi < 2.7 < \pi$$

so $\cos 2.7$ lies in the second quadrant.

So $\quad \cos 2.7 = -\cos(\pi - 2.7) = -\cos 0.4416 = -0.9041$

EXAMPLE 20.11

  a) Find $\tan 5.73$.
  b) Find two values of θ for which $\sin\theta = -0.43$.

Solution

a) 5.73 is between $1\frac{1}{2}\pi$ and 2π. It lies in the fourth quadrant.
    Subtract from 2π, obtaining 0.5532. The tan of this is 0.6175.
    In the fourth quadrant, tan is negative.

$$\boldsymbol{\tan 5.73 = -0.6175}$$

b) The angle x for which $\sin x = +0.43$ is 0.4445. Add this to π,
    and subtract from 2π.

$$\boldsymbol{\theta = 3.586 \text{ or } 5.839}$$

SELF TEST 20.11

Find $\sin 4.27$. Find two values of θ for which $\cos\theta = 0.324$.

−0.9037, 1.241 or 5.042

20.4 Graphs of trigonometric functions

In the previous section we considered a pointer OA rotating
about the origin O. After rotating through θ, The x-coordi-
nate of A is $\cos\theta$, and the y-coordinate of A is $\sin\theta$. If we plot
the graph of the y-coordinate against θ, we obtain the graph
of $y = \sin\theta$. Figure 20.26 shows the graph.

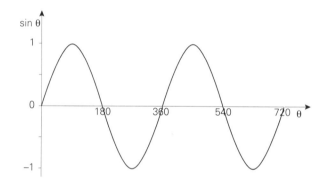

Figure 20.26

Note the wave form of the curve. Many curves are of this
form. In particular, the graph of alternating electrical current
has this form. Curves of this form are **sine curves**. The curve
is also called the **sine wave**.

Radians

If the angle θ is measured in radians, the graph has the same
shape. Figure 20.27 shows the sine curve with θ in radians.

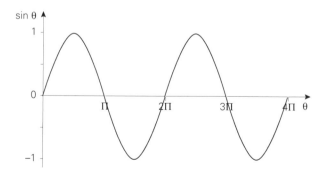

Figure 20.27

Amplitude

Consider the function $y = 2 \sin x$. Figure 20.28 shows the graph of this function. Notice that the greatest value of y is 2, and the least value -2.

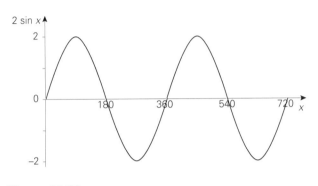

Figure 20.28

> The greatest height of the wave is called the **amplitude**. The wave of $y = k \sin x$, where k is positive, has amplitude k.

EXAMPLE 20.12

What is the amplitude of the wave of $y = \frac{1}{2} \sin x$? Sketch the graph of the wave.

Solution
Here $k = \frac{1}{2}$.

The amplitude is $\frac{1}{2}$

The graph of $y = \frac{1}{2} \sin x$ has greatest value $\frac{1}{2}$, and least value $-\frac{1}{2}$. Figure 20.29 shows the graph.

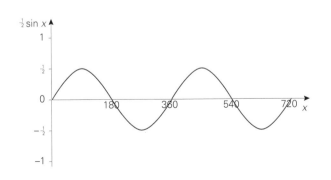

Figure 20.29

SELF TEST 20.12

Sketch the graph of $y = 3 \sin x$.

Period

The curve or wave $y = \sin x$ consists of a pattern, between $0°$ and $360°$, repeated. The pattern is a **cycle** of the wave. The **period** of the wave is the length of the cycle. Hence the **period** of this curve is $360°$.

Consider the wave of $y = \sin 2x$, shown in Figure 20.30. When x goes between $0°$ and $180°$, $2x$ goes between $0°$ and $360°$. Hence the graph of $y = \sin 2x$ repeats itself after every $180°$. Its period is $180°$.

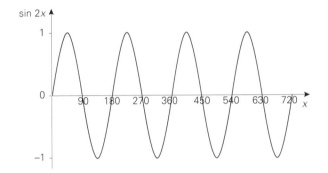

Figure 20.30

> The **period** of a wave is the length of its cycle.
>
> The period of $y = \sin kx$ is $\dfrac{360°}{k}$.

EXAMPLE 20.13

Find the period of $y = \sin \frac{1}{2}x$. Sketch its graph.

Solution
Here $k = \frac{1}{2}$. Hence the period is $\dfrac{360°}{\frac{1}{2}}$, i.e. $720°$.

The period is $720°$

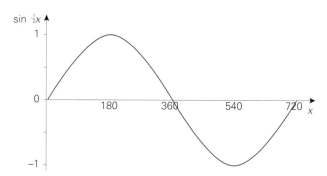

Figure 20.31

The wave of $y = \sin \frac{1}{2}x$ goes through a cycle every 720°. The amplitude of the curve goes between 1 and −1. Figure 20.31 shows its graph.

SELF TEST 20.13

Find the period of $y = \sin 3x$. Sketch its graph.

120°

Phase angle

Consider the wave $y = \sin(x + 30°)$. When $x = 0$, then $y = \sin 30°$. The graph for $y = \sin(x + 30°)$ starts 30° further on than the graph of $y = \sin x$. (See Figure 20.32.)

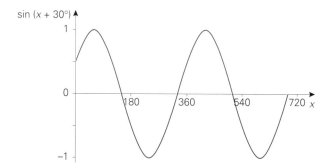

Figure 20.32

> The graph of $y = \sin(x + \varphi)$ has **phase angle** φ. If the phase angle is positive, the wave is **leading** the standard $\sin \theta$ wave. If the phase angle is negative, then it is **lagging** the standard $\sin \theta$ wave.

EXAMPLE 20.14

Sketch the graph of $y = \sin(x − 60°)$.

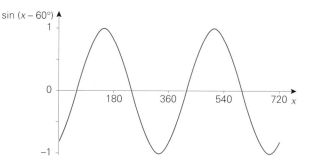

Figure 20.33

Solution

The phase angle is −60°. Shift the graph of $y = \sin x$ to the right, by 60°. Figure 20.33 shows the result. Note that this wave is lagging the standard $\sin \theta$ wave.

SELF TEST 20.14

Sketch the graph of $y = \sin(x + 45°)$.

The cos graph

Refer back to the cos graph of Figure 20.20. Note that it leads the sin graph by 90°. Hence

$$\cos x = \sin(x + 90°)$$

Alternating current

Sine waves are used in electricity. Alternating current can be delivered at 50 cycles per second.

EXAMPLE 20.15

At t seconds, the current through a circuit, I amps, is given by $I = 6 \sin 18\,000t$. Sketch a graph of I against t, for t from 0 to 0.05.

Solution

Note that $18\,000 = 50 \times 360$. Period $= 360 \div 18\,000 = \frac{1}{50}$ sec.

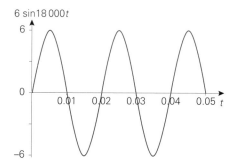

Figure 20.34

Hence there are 50 cycles per second. During the time of 0.05 seconds there will be 2.5 cycles. The amplitude is 6. The sketch is shown in Figure 20.34.

SELF TEST 20.15

Sketch the graph of $y = 3 \sin 10t$.

Sin²θ and cos²θ graphs

The graphs of $\sin^2\theta$ and $\cos^2\theta$ are shown in Figure 20.35. Note that

● Both graphs are positive. (Any square must be positive.)
● Both curves go through two complete cycles between $0°$ and $360°$. Hence they have period $180°$.

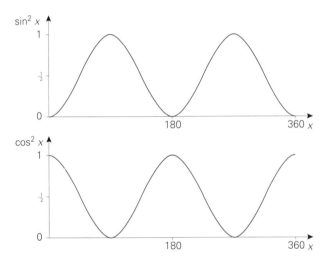

Figure 20.35

SELF TEST 20.16

Sketch the graph of $y = 2\cos^2 x$.

Sine curves with different frequencies

EXAMPLE 20.16

Plot the graph of $y = 2 \sin x + 3 \sin \frac{1}{2}x$, for values of x between $0°$ and $720°$.

Solution
Use a calculator or tables to fill in the table below.

x	0	60	120	180	240	300	
$2 \sin x$	0	1.7	1.7	0	−1.7	−1.7	
$3 \sin \frac{1}{2}x$	0	1.5	2.6	3	2.6	1.5	
y	0	3.2	4.3	3	0.9	−0.2	
x	360	420	480	540	600	660	720
$2 \sin x$	0	1.7	1.7	0	−1.7	−1.7	0
$3 \sin \frac{1}{2}x$	0	−1.5	−2.6	−3	−2.6	−1.5	0
y	0	0.2	−0.9	−3	−4.3	−3.2	0

The graph is plotted in Figure 20.36. It is not a sine curve, but it is periodic, with period $720°$.

SELF TEST 20.17

Plot the graph of $y = \sin \frac{1}{2}x + \sin \frac{1}{3}x$, for values of x between $0°$ and $1080°$.

CHECK YOUR UNDERSTANDING

● The functions cosec, sec and cot are defined by
$$\text{cosec}\,\theta = \frac{\text{HYP}}{\text{OPP}} \qquad \sec\theta = \frac{\text{HYP}}{\text{ADJ}} \qquad \cot\theta = \frac{\text{ADJ}}{\text{OPP}}$$

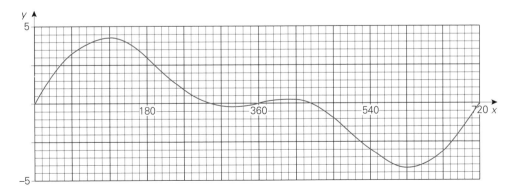

Figure 20.36

Note that cosec, sec and cot are the reciprocals of sin, cos and tan respectively. Use this to find cosec θ, or to solve cosec $\theta = x$

● If an arc of length a is taken from a circle of radius r, then the angle subtended by the arc is $\dfrac{a}{r}$ radians.

● To convert from radians to degrees, multiply by $\dfrac{180}{\pi}$.

   To convert from degrees to radians, multiply by $\dfrac{\pi}{180}$.

   Some commonly used angles are multiples of π. For example 90° is $\frac{1}{2}\pi$ radians.

● The trig functions can be defined for angles greater than 90°, as follows.

Second quadrant, 90°—180°.
   Subtract from 180°.   Sin is $+$, cos and tan $-$.
Third quadrant, 180°—270°.
   Subtract 180°.   Tan is $+$, cos and sin $-$.
Fourth quadrant, 270°—360°.
   Subtract from 360°.   Cos is $+$, sin and tan $-$.
Beyond 360°. Subtract 360, until the angle lies between 0° and 360°.

● The graphs of $\sin x$ and $\cos x$ have a wave form. The amplitude of a sine wave is its greatest value. The period of a sine wave is the length of a cycle. The phase angle of a sine wave is the angle by which the wave is ahead of the wave $y = \sin x$.

   The graph of $y = A \sin x$ has amplitude A.

   The graph of $y = \sin kx$ has period $\dfrac{360}{k}$.

   The graph of $y = \sin(x + \varphi)$ has phase angle φ.

REVISION EXERCISES AND QUESTIONS

20.1 Cosec, sec and cot

1   Find the following.
    a) sec 73°   b) cosec 27°   c) cot 41°
    d) cosec 81°   e) cot 17°   f) sec 44°

2   Find the following.
    a) $\sec^{-1} 2.4$ b) $\cot^{-1} 2.8$ c) $\csc^{-1} 5$
    d) $\cot^{-1} 0.4$ e) $\sec^{-1} 1.88$ f) $\csc^{-1} 2.3$

3   Use the formula of Example 20.3 to find M when $D = 30$ mm, $p = 2$ mm and $\theta = 25°$.

20.2 Radians

4   Convert the following angles from degrees to radians, giving your answers to three decimal places.
    a) 27°   b) 48°   c) 29.4°

5   Convert the following angles from degrees to radians, giving your answers as multiples of π.
    a) 120°   b) 15°   c) 720°

6   Convert the following angles from radians to degrees.
    a) 1.184   b) 0.671   c) 0.056
    d) $\frac{2}{3}\pi$ e) $\frac{3}{4}\pi$ f) 3π

7   Find the following. The angle is measured in radians.
    a) cos 0.562   b) sin 1.006   c) tan 0.102
    d) $\tan\frac{1}{3}\pi$ e) $\cos\frac{3}{8}\pi$ f) $\sin\frac{1}{4}\pi$

8   Find the following, giving your answers in radians.
    a) $\cos^{-1} 0.581$ b) $\sin^{-1} 0.956$ c) $\tan^{-1} 2.71$

9   Find the angle subtended by an arc of length 27 mm at the centre of a circle of radius 38 mm.

10 A sector of angle 0.85 radians is from a circle of radius 4.1 m. Find the length of the arc and the area of the sector.

11 A chord subtends 0.43 radians at the centre of a circle of radius 2.65 m. Find the length of the chord and the area of the segment cut off by the chord.

12 A belt passes tightly round two pulleys of radii 90 mm and 110 mm, whose centres are 300 mm apart. Find the length of the belt.

20.3 Angles greater than 90°

13 Find the following.
    a) sin 135°   b) cos 173°   c) tan 103°
    d) sin 201°   e) cos 255°   f) tan 225°
    g) sin 285°   h) cos 300°   i) tan 355°

14 For each of the following equations, find two solutions between 0° and 360°.
    a) $\sin x = 0.45$ b) $\sin x = -0.89$ c) $\cos x = 0.66$
    d) $\cos x = -0.44$ e) $\tan x = 2.7$ f) $\tan x = -0.78$

20.4 Graphs of trigonometric functions

15 Sketch the graphs of the following.
    a) $y = 5 \sin x$ b) $y = -1\frac{1}{2}\sin x$ c) $y = \sin 3x$
    d) $y = \sin\frac{1}{3}x$ e) $y = \sin(x + 10°)$ f) $y = \sin(x - 50°)$
    g) $y = 2 \sin(x + 120°)$ h) $y = 2\frac{1}{2}\sin(x - 40°)$

16 For each of the functions of Question 15, give the amplitude, the period and the phase angle.

17 Sketch the graphs of the following.
    a) $y = 3 \sin^2 x$ b) $y = \sin x + \sin\frac{1}{3}x$
    c) $y = 2 \sin 2x + 3 \sin 3x$

Statistics

Introduction

Suppose you have measured the lengths of 40 components. Your results are below, given correct to the nearest 0.01 mm.

9.55 9.60 9.59 9.56 9.57 9.62 9.58 9.55 9.56 9.61

9.56 9.58 9.58 9.56 9.54 9.60 9.61 9.57 9.55 9.55

9.63 9.60 9.58 9.59 9.60 9.57 9.55 9.57 9.59 9.57

9.57 9.58 9.63 9.64 9.58 9.57 9.59 9.56 9.63 9.55

When you see a great number of figures like those above, it is hard to understand what they can tell you. If you present your results to other people, they will also find them difficult to understand. Hence it is important to present figures in a clear way. Statistics helps you to do this.

There are many ways to present the figures above in a clear way. We could

● Sort them into a frequency table.
● Draw a diagram illustrating the figures.
● Calculate an average and measure the spread of the figures.

This chapter shows you how do do these things.

21.1 Frequencies

Suppose you have collected a great amount of numbers. Before you can make them meaningful you need to sort them in some way. Make a **frequency table**.

Suppose the numbers are the ages of employees of a firm, as below.

19 18 34 28 24 18 38 49 22 30 20 25 34 40 50

37 20 16 23 28 22 17 38 21 20 53 33 36 27 15

Divide the data (the numbers you have collected) into four groups, 15–24, 25–34, 35–44 and 45–54. There are 14 employees in the age range 15 to 24, 8 in the range 25 to 34, 5 in the range 35 to 44, and 3 in the range 45 to 54. The table below shows these facts.

Age (completed years)	15–24	25–34	35–44	45–54
Frequency	14	8	5	3

Note

1 Do not have too many groups. If you have 40 groups, one for each year, then the information is not easier to understand.

2 Do not have too few groups. If you have only two groups, 15–34 and 35–54, then too much information is lost.

3 It is easy to miscount. It often helps to make a tally sheet. For each item, make a tally stroke / on the sheet. After four items, cross the strokes as $\cancel{////}$. Figure 21.1 is a tally sheet for the ages.

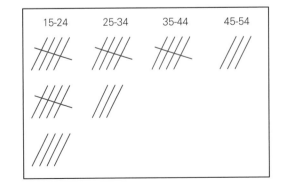

Figure 21.1 Tally sheet

EXAMPLE 21.1

The marks for a test were as below. Represent them in a frequency table.

2 9 13 10 17 15 16 16 17 14 19 20 13 8 16

12 17 16 4 15 15 19 12 15 8 18 13 16 15 14

Solution

Have groups of 0–4, 5–9, 10–14, 15–20. Set up a tally sheet for the groups. Cross off the marks, and make tallies as in Figure 21.2.

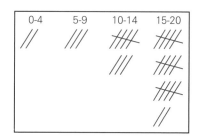

Figure 21.2

There are 2 in the 0–4 group, 3 in the 5–9 group and so on. The frequency table is shown below.

Mark	0–4	5–9	10–14	15–20
Frequency	2	3	8	17

SELF TEST 21.1

The length of service, in completed years, of the employees of a factory are as below. Construct a frequency table to show the data.

9 1 8 4 7 2 3 6 8 3

1 1 2 5 6 2 3 1 8 3

Discrete and continuous data

Some quantities must be whole numbers. The number of days in a month, or the number of people in a class, is a whole number. This is a **discrete** quantity. The time to complete a race is measured in fractions of a second. It is a **continuous** quantity.

A discrete quantity takes values which are separated from each other. Usually the values are whole numbers. Examples of discrete quantities are

● The number of cars in a car park. There cannot be $3\frac{1}{2}$ cars.
● The number of goals scored in a football match. The score cannot be 3.2 to 0.
● The number of employees in a factory. There cannot be $8\frac{2}{3}$ employees.

A continuous quantity takes any value within a given range. Examples of continuous quantities are

● The voltage of a car battery. The voltage could be 12.294 V.
● The temperature of a freezer. The temperature could be −9.36°C.
● The mass of a potato. The potato could have mass 0.1881 kg.

Class boundaries

The class boundaries are the numbers at the ends of the groups of a frequency table. If the data is continuous, the end of one interval is the beginning of the next. If the data is discrete, there is a gap between intervals. Below are frequency tables for exam marks (discrete) and masses (continuous).

Mark	0–19	20–39	40–59	60–79	80–100
Frequency	6	28	63	39	17

Mass (kg)	10–20	20–30	30–40	40–50	50–60
Frequency	8	13	26	25	10

In the second table 20 kg occurs at the end of the first interval and at the beginning of the second interval. This does not matter. It is unlikely that the object has mass of *exactly* 20 kg.

Rounding data

You cannot measure a continuous quantity exactly. The values are rounded. This changes the class boundaries. If the second table is rounded, it might change to

Mass (nearest kg)	10–19	20–29	30–39	40–49	50–60
Frequency	7	15	25	25	10

EXAMPLE 21.2

Below are the diameters of 30 ball bearings, in mm rounded to two decimal places. Put the data into a frequency table.

6.70 6.79 6.67 6.69 6.75 6.59 6.60 6.75 6.82 6.66

6.69 6.58 6.64 6.61 6.70 6.64 6.70 6.82 6.77 6.73

6.81 6.75 6.63 6.70 6.57 6.79 6.81 6.65 6.64 6.67

Solution

The values range from 6.58 to 6.82. Take groups 6.55–6.59, 6.60–6.64 etc. The table is shown below.

Diameter (mm)	6.55–6.59	6.60–6.64	6.65–6.69
Frequency	3	6	6
Diameter (mm)	6.70–6.74	6.75–6.79	6.80–6.84
Frequency	5	6	4

SELF TEST 21.2

A race had 40 entrants. Their times, in seconds to one decimal place, are given below. Put the information into a frequency table.

12.3 12.8 13.2 10.9 12.5 12.3 13.4 13.4 13.9 13.6

11.9 10.8 12.7 13.4 13.0 12.9 11.6 11.8 11.3 12.1

11.7 11.6 12.4 10.8 12.4 11.5 11.6 13.0 12.5 10.9

11.0 12.1 12.6 11.6 13.8 13.0 13.1 12.4 11.3 13.0

21.2 Illustrating data

Many people understand information better from a diagram than from a frequency table. There are many sorts of statistical diagram, such as pictograms, bar charts and pie charts.

Pictogram

In a pictogram, each picture represents a certain number of data.

EXAMPLE 21.3

The pictogram of Figure 21.3 shows the Blue Army. Each figure represents 10 000 men. How many men are in the Blue Army?

Figure 21.3 Pictogram for the Blue Army

The Green Army has 45 000 men. Construct a pictogram to show this.

Solution

There are three and a half figures. Multiply $3\frac{1}{2}$ by 10 000, obtaining 35 000.

The Blue Army has 35 000 men

Divide 45 000 by 10 000, giving $4\frac{1}{2}$. Draw four and a half men, as in Figure 21.4.

Figure 21.4 Pictogram for the Green Army

SELF TEST 21.3

Figure 21.5

The production of the Wananchiwagon company is shown in the pictogram of Figure 21.5, where each symbol represents 1000 cars. How many cars were produced? Draw a pictogram for a company which produced 5500 cars.

2500 cars

Bar chart

In a bar chart, the lengths of the bars give the sizes of the groups.

EXAMPLE 21.4

The table below gives the colour of the cars in a car park. Construct a bar chart to illustrate the data.

Colour	black	white	red	other
Frequency	25	58	15	82

Solution

Draw and label axes. Draw a bar of length 25 for black, of length 58 for white, and so on. The result is Figure 21.6.

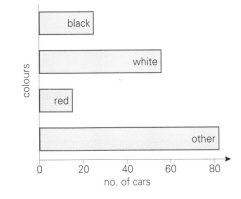

Figure 21.6 Colours of cars in a car park

SELF TEST 21.4

The table below gives the weekly sales of an electronics shop. Construct a bar chart to illustrate the data.

Item	radio	television	CD player	computer
Frequency	16	31	14	19

Pie chart

In a pie chart, the angles of the sectors give the sizes of the groups.

For a pie chart, find the total of the frequencies. For each group, the angle of its sector is its fraction of the whole circle. Take the frequency of the group, divide by the total frequency, then multiply by 360°.

EXAMPLE 21.5

Construct a pie chart to illustrate the data in Example 21.4.

Solution
The total frequency is 180. Divide each frequency by 180, then multiply by 360 (i.e. multiply by 2). The angles are calculated as follows.

Angle for black $\frac{25}{180} \times 360° = 50°$

Angle for white $\frac{58}{180} \times 360° = 116°$

Angle for red $\frac{15}{180} \times 360° = 30°$

Angle for other $\frac{82}{180} \times 360° = 164°$

Note   The sum of the four angles is 360°. This checks the arithmetic.

Construct the pie chart with these angles. The result is Figure 21.7.

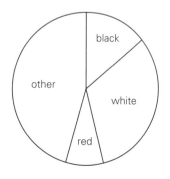

Figure 21.7   Pie chart showing colours of cars

SELF TEST 21.5

Construct a pie chart for the data of Self Test 21.4.

Histogram

A histogram is a bar chart in which all the data is numerical. Fit the bars to a numerical scale along the horizontal axis. The bars join up.

EXAMPLE 21.6

The masses of 150 children are given in the table below. Draw a histogram for the data.

Mass (kg)	45–50	50–55	55–60	60–65	65–70
Frequency	28	34	48	29	11

Solution
Put the mass along the x-axis, and the frequency up the y-axis. Measure out bars, with lengths corresponding to the frequencies. The result is Figure 21.8.

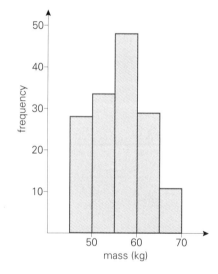

Figure 21.8   Histogram showing the masses of 150 children

SELF TEST 21.6

The heights of 113 people are given in the table below. Draw a histogram for the data.

Height (m)	1.2–1.4	1.4–1.6	1.6–1.8	1.8–2.0
Frequency	13	29	39	32

Histograms with unequal intervals

In the histograms considered so far, the data is divided into equal intervals. If the intervals are not equal, we adjust the heights of the bars, so that the size of a group is represented by the *area* of its bar.

Decide upon the standard width of interval. If an interval is twice the standard width, then halve the height of its bar. If an interval is half the standard width, then double the height of its bar.

EXAMPLE 21.7

The table below gives the lifetimes of 100 electric cells. Draw a histogram to show the data.

Lifetime (hours)	6–8	8–9	9–10	10–11	11–12	12–15
Frequency	16	11	19	21	24	9

Solution

The most common width is 1 hour. This is the standard width. The first interval has width 2 hours, hence halve the height of its bar, to 8. The last interval has width 3 hours, hence divide the height of its bar by 3. The histogram is shown in Figure 21.9. Note that the vertical axis is labelled 'Frequency per 1 hour interval'.

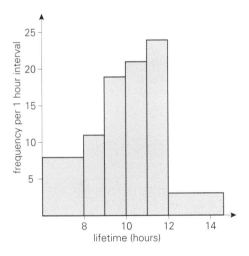

Figure 21.9　Lifetime of electric cells

SELF TEST 21.7

The table below gives the midday temperatures over 80 days. Draw a histogram to show the data.

Temperature (°C)	10–20	20–25	25–30	30–35
Frequency	23	18	28	11

21.3 Averages

If you have a collection of numbers, an **average** indicates where the centre is. There are three commonly used averages.

Mean

To find the mean of n numbers, add them up and divide by n.

Consider the ten numbers, 20, 30, 50, 50, 60, 70, 70, 70, 80 and 90. To find their mean, add them up and divide by 10.
$$\text{Mean} = \tfrac{1}{10}(20+30+50+50+60+70+70+70+80+90)$$
$$= 59$$

Median

To find the median of a set of numbers, arrange them in order and find the middle number.

The numbers above are in order. There are ten numbers, hence the median is halfway between the 5th number, which is 60, and the 6th number, which is 70. Halfway between 60 and 70 is 65.

For an odd number of terms, the median is the middle term. If there were eleven terms, the median would be the 6th term.

Mode

The mode of a set of numbers is the most frequent.

In the list of numbers above, 70 occurs most frequently. Hence the mode is 70.

SELF TEST 21.8

Find the mean, median and mode of the following data.

12 13 13 14 14 14 14 15 16 18 19 21 25

16, 14, 14

Σ notation

If x_1, x_2, x_3, up to x_n represent the values taken by the variable x, then Σx_i represents the sum of the values of the variable. For example, if x takes the values 3, 5, 6, 7 and 10, then
$$\Sigma x_i = 3+5+6+7+10 = 31.$$
The letter Σ is pronounced *sigma*. It is used in statistical expressions. For example, above we saw that the mean of n values is found by adding the values and dividing by n. Hence if the variable x takes n values, then the mean of x, written $\bar{x}$, is given by
$$\text{Mean of } x = \bar{x} = \tfrac{1}{n}\Sigma x_i$$

Averages from frequency tables

If data is presented in a frequency table, you cannot find the mean exactly. Assume that the data in each interval is spread evenly about the centre of the interval.

EXAMPLE 21.8

The frequency table below gives the mass of 100 tiles. Estimate the mean mass.

Mass (g)	95–100	100–105	105–110	110–115
Frequency	12	48	31	9

Solution

We do not know the exact mass of each tile. There are 12 tiles between 95 g and 100 g. Assume that these tiles are evenly spread about the middle of the interval, 97.5 g.

Similarly assume that the 48 tiles between 100 g and 105 g are spread about 102.5 g. The total mass is approximately
$12 \times 97.5 + 48 \times 102.5 + 31 \times 107.5 + 9 \times 112.5 = 10\,435$ g.
There are 100 tiles so divide by 100 to obtain the mean mass.
The mean mass of the tiles is approximately 104.35 g

SELF TEST 21.9

The frequency table below gives the time that 60 workers took to complete a task. Estimate the mean time needed to complete the task.

Time (min)	10–12	12–14	14–16	16–18	18–20
Frequency	3	8	19	18	12

15.93 min

Use of Σ

Let the mid-interval values be represented by x_i, and let the frequencies be represented by f_i. In terms of the Σ notation, the mean is

$$\text{mean} = \frac{\Sigma(f_i \times x_i)}{\Sigma f_i}$$

i.e., multiply each mid-interval value by its frequency, then add them together. Divide by the sum of the frequencies.

Mode from frequency table

The mode of data can be approximated from a histogram of a frequency table.

1 Take the highest bar. (The mode lies within this bar.)

2 Take the bar on the right and join the left corners of this bar and the highest bar.

3 Take the bar on the left and join the right corners of this bar and the highest bar.

The approximate value of the mode is where these lines meet, as shown in Figure 21.10.

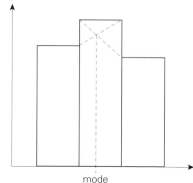

Figure 21.10   Finding the mode

EXAMPLE 21.9

Estimate the mode for the masses of Example 21.6.
Solution
The histogram of Figure 21.8 is copied in Figure 21.11. The highest bar is in the 55–60 interval. Join its corners with the next bars. The lines cross at 57.
The mode is approximately 57

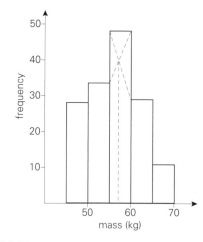

Figure 21.11

SELF TEST 21.10

Estimate the mode for the heights of Self Test 21.6.

1.72 cm

21.4 Cumulative frequency and measures of spread

The mean, median and mode do not tell everything about a set of numbers. We may also want to know how widely spread the numbers are. A figure that tells us this is a **measure of spread**. Examples of the use of a measure of spread are

● Machine production. Suppose a machine produces ball bearings. We want the bearings to be almost identical in size. Hence we want the measure of spread of the diameters to be as small as possible.
● Temperature. Suppose the temperature in a country is measured every month for a year. A measure of spread of the temperature tells us how much the climate changes over the year.

Examples of measure of spread are the **range**, the **interquartile range** and the **variance**.

Cumulative frequency

If we have a large amount of data, it would take a long time to arrange them in order. Also, if the data are in a frequency table, then they cannot be arranged in order. We need a way to find the median for a frequency table. The cumulative frequency gives us a way of doing this.

The **cumulative frequency** at a value is the number of data less than that value. For example, suppose an exam is taken by 10 000 candidates. The graph of Figure 21.12 gives the cumulative frequencies of the marks, i.e. the number of candidates who scored less than each mark.

We see from the graph that the cumulative frequency of the marks at 30% is 4000. Hence 4000 candidates scored less than 30%.

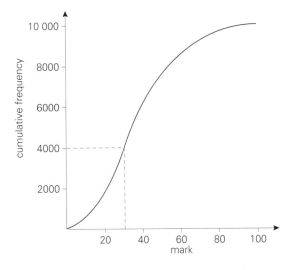

Figure 21.12 Cumulative frequency graph

We evaluate cumulative frequencies by making running totals of the frequencies. A **cumulative frequency graph** is drawn by plotting the cumulative frequencies against the right-hand ends of the intervals. Example 21.10 shows the procedure.

EXAMPLE 21.10

The frequency table below gives the diameters of 1000 ball bearings. Find the cumulative frequencies and draw a cumulative frequency graph.

Diameter (mm)	10.0–10.1	10.1–10.2	10.2–10.3
Frequency	53	259	394
Diameter (mm)	10.3–10.4	10.4–10.5	
Frequency	217	77	

Solution
There are 53 ball bearings under 10.1 mm. Adding 53 and 259, there are 312 under 10.2 mm. Find the other cumulative frequencies similarly.

The cumulative frequencies are 53, 312, 706, 923, 1000
Now plot the graph. The first point is at (10.1, 53), the second at (10.2, 312) and so on. Join the points up by a smooth curve, as shown in Figure 21.13.

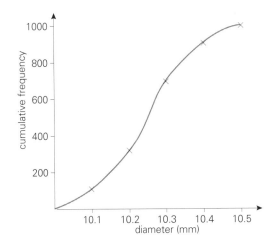

Figure 21.13

Note The points are plotted at the *ends* of the intervals, not in the middles.

The table below gives the times taken by 240 workers to perform a task. Find the cumulative frequencies and draw a cumulative frequency curve.

Time (secs)	40–45	45–50	50–55	55–60	60–65	65–70
Frequency	29	48	47	58	31	27

Range

The range of a set of numbers is the difference between the highest and the lowest. Consider the 12 numbers below

34 35 36 37 37 39 41 42 45 48 51 63

The highest is 63 and the lowest is 34. Hence the range is 63–34, i.e. 29.

Advantages

The range is easy to calculate.

Disadvantages

Abnormally large or small values can distort the range. For the numbers above, the large value of 63 distorts the range.

Quartiles

The median of a set of numbers is the number halfway along when they are arranged in ascending order. The **lower quartile** is the number a quarter along. The **upper quartile** is the number three quarters along. The **interquartile range** is the difference between the upper and lower quartiles.

The numbers between the quartiles are in the middle half of the data. The interquartile range gives the spread of this middle half. If the interquartile range is large, then the middle half vary by a large amount. If it is small, the numbers are close together.

Advantages

The interquartile range is not affected by extreme values, as they are in the top quarter or the bottom quarter.

Disadvantages

The interquartile range takes longer to calculate than the range.

Use of cumulative frequency curve

You can use the cumulative frequency curve to find the median and the quartiles. The median is the value at which the cumulative frequency is $\frac{1}{2}$ the total. The lower and upper quartiles are the values at which the cumulative frequencies are $\frac{1}{4}$ and $\frac{3}{4}$ of the total.

The **deciles** are the values which separate the data into tenths. The third decile, for example, is the value at which the cumulative frequency is $\frac{3}{10}$ of the total. Similarly the **percentiles** are the values which separate the data into hundredths. The 23rd percentile, for example, is the value at which the cumulative frequency is 23% of the total.

EXAMPLE 21.11

For the data of Example 21.10 above, find the median and the interquartile range. Find the fourth decile.

Solution

At the median, the cumulative frequency is $\frac{1}{2}$ the total, i.e. 500. Go across from 500 to the curve, and read off the diameter. In Figure 21.14 the cumulative frequency of 500 is reached at 10.25.

The median is 10.25 mm

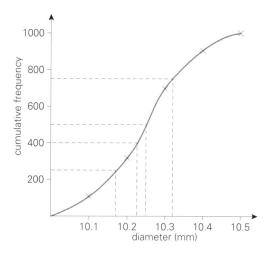

Figure 21.14

Similarly, at the quartiles the cumulative frequencies are 250 and 750. These correspond to 10.17 and 10.32 respectively. The difference between these is 0.15.

The interquartile range is 0.15 mm

The fourth decile corresponds to a cumulative frequency of $\frac{4}{10} \times 1000$, i.e. 400. this is reached at a diameter of 10.23.

The fourth decile is 10.23 mm

SELF TEST 21.12

Find the median, the interquartile range and the second decile for the data in Self Test 21.11.

55s, 11s, 47s

Variance and standard deviation

The variance and the standard deviation are the most important measures of spread. They measure the difference between the values and the mean.

Let a set of data be $x_1, x_2, ..., x_n$. Let the mean be $\bar{x}$. The **variance** is given by the formula

$$\frac{1}{n}\Sigma(x_i - \bar{x})^2$$

An equivalent form is

$$\frac{1}{n}\Sigma x_i^2 - \bar{x}^2$$

This second form is usually more convenient.

> Variance is the mean of the squares minus the square of the mean.
>
> $$\frac{1}{n}\Sigma x_i^2 - \bar{x}^2$$

The **standard deviation** is the square root of the variance.

> Standard deviation is the square root of the variance.
>
> $$\sqrt{\left(\frac{1}{n}\Sigma x_i^2 - \bar{x}^2\right)}$$

Note   Most scientific calculators have a facility to evaluate variance and standard deviation. Usually this is in the SD mode.

EXAMPLE 21.14

Find the variance and the standard deviation for the numbers below.

12.6 13.7 14.1 15.0 15.6 15.9 16.1 16.2

Solution

There are eight numbers here. First find the mean.

$$\text{mean} = \bar{x} = \frac{1}{n}\Sigma x_i = \frac{1}{8}(12.6 + 13.7 + ... + 16.2) = 14.9$$

Now use the second form of the variance. Find the sum of the squares.

$$\begin{aligned}\text{sum of squares} &= \Sigma x_i^2 \\ &= 12.6^2 + 13.7^2 + ... + 16.2^2 \\ &= 1788.08\end{aligned}$$

Now use the formula.

$$\begin{aligned}\text{Variance} &= \frac{1}{n}\Sigma x_i^2 - \bar{x}^2 \\ &= \frac{1}{8} \times 1788.08 - 14.9^2 = 1.5\end{aligned}$$

This is the variance. Take the square root to find the standard deviation, 1.225.

$$\text{Standard deviation} = \sqrt{\text{variance}} = \sqrt{1.5} = 1.225$$

The variance is 1.5 and the standard deviation is 1.225

SELF TEST 21.13

Find the variance and standard deviation for the list of numbers below.

1.05 1.06 1.05 1.10 1.07 1.08 1.09

0.000327, 0.0181

21.5 Correlation

Suppose data consists of pairs of values. We might have found the height and the weight of several people. When we plot the pairs, we obtain a **scatter graph**. A possible scatter graph of height and weight is in Figure 21.15.

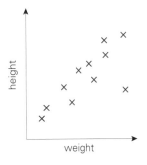

Figure 21.15 Scatter graph of height and weight

If the points lie roughly on a straight line, the quantities are **correlated**. If the straight line has a positive gradient, the correlation is **positive**. If the line has a negative gradient, the correlation is **negative**. The heights and weights above are positively correlated.

Figure 21.16 Scatter graph of age and price of cars

The price and ages of cars (Figure 21.16) are negatively correlated.

In Chapter 13 we drew lines of best fit by eye, and then found the equation of the line. Here we use a formula to calculate the equation of the line.

Suppose the data values are (x_1, y_1), (x_2, y_2), ..., (x_n, y_n). A scatter graph of the points is shown in Figure 21.17. A line is drawn through the points. The vertical distances from the points to the line are d_1, d_2, ..., d_n. The **method of least squares** makes the sum of the squares of these distances as small as possible. i.e.

$$d_1^2 + d_2^2 + ... + d_n^2 \text{ has its least value}$$

If the line is $y = ax + b$, then a is the gradient and b is where the line crosses the x-axis.

$$a = \frac{\frac{1}{n}\Sigma x_i y_i - \bar{x}\bar{y}}{\frac{1}{n}\Sigma x_i^2 - \bar{x}^2} \qquad b = \bar{y} - a\bar{x}$$

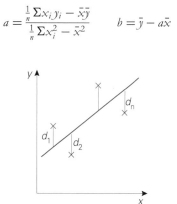

Figure 21.17 Method of least squares

Notes

1 The denominator of the expression for a is the variance of x.

2 Many scientific calculators have a facility for evaluating a and b. (Usually in LR mode). If you evaluate a and b on paper, make a table for the values as shown in the next example.

3 To calculate a and b, you need n, Σx_i, Σy_i, Σx_i^2 and $\Sigma x_i y_i$. Set up a table to find these expressions. Example 21.13 shows the method.

EXAMPLE 21.13

The table below gives the temperature of a jar of liquid at various times. Find the best fit line giving the temperature in terms of time.

Time (minutes)	0	5	10	15	20	25	30
Temperature °C	89	77	66	55	45	34	26

Solution

Let x be the time, and y the temperature. Set up a table as below.

x	0	5	10	15	20	25	30	$\Sigma x = 105$
y	89	77	66	55	45	34	26	$\Sigma y = 392$
x^2	0	25	100	225	400	625	900	$\Sigma x^2 = 2275$
xy	0	385	660	825	900	850	780	$\Sigma xy = 4400$

Use the formulae above. The value of n is 7, giving $\bar{x} = 105 \div 7 = 15$ and $\bar{y} = 392 \div 7 = 56$.

$$a = \frac{\frac{1}{n}\Sigma x_i y_i - \bar{x}\bar{y}}{\frac{1}{n}\Sigma x_i^2 - \bar{x}^2} = \frac{\frac{1}{7} \times 4400 - 15 \times 56}{\frac{1}{7} \times 2275 - 15^2}$$

$$= \frac{-211.43}{100}$$

$$= -2.1143$$

$$b = \bar{y} - a\bar{x}$$

$$= 56 - (-2.1143) \times 15 = 87.71$$

Hence the line is $y = -2.11x + 87.7$. Figure 21.18 shows the line.

At time x minutes, the temperature is $(-2.11x + 87.7)°C$

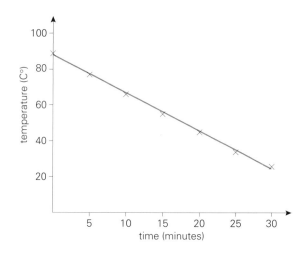

Figure 21.18

SELF TEST 21.14

From the data below find the line giving y in terms of x.

x	1	2	3	4	5	6	7	8
y	21	38	41	49	57	71	78	84

$$y = 8.80x + 15.3$$

■ CHECK YOUR UNDERSTANDING

● Data is easier to understand if it is organised into a frequency table.

● Statistical diagrams give a picture of data. Bar charts, pie charts, pictograms and histograms are types of statistical diagram.

● When drawing a histogram, if the intervals of a frequency table are not equal, then adjust the heights of the bars.

● The mean of n numbers is found by adding them together and dividing by n. The median is found by arranging the numbers in order and taking the middle number. The mode is the most frequent number.

● If data is in a frequency table, the approximate value of the mean is found by assuming that the data is evenly spread within each interval.

● The range of a set of numbers is the difference between the highest and the lowest number. The upper and lower quartiles are the numbers which cut off the top and bottom quarters of the set. The interquartile range is the difference between the quartiles.

● The variance of a set of numbers is the mean of the squares of the differences from the square of the mean. It can be found from either of the following formulae

$$\frac{1}{n}\Sigma(x_i - \bar{x})^2$$

or

$$\frac{1}{n}\Sigma x_i^2 - \bar{x}^2$$

where $\bar{x}$ is the mean of the numbers.

● If the quantities x and y are connected, the method of least squares gives a linear equation for y in terms of x. It is

$$y = ax + b,$$

where

$$a = \frac{\frac{1}{n}\Sigma x_i y_i - \bar{x}\bar{y}}{\frac{1}{n}\Sigma x_i^2 - \bar{x}^2}$$

and

$$b = \bar{y} - a\bar{x}$$

REVISION EXERCISES AND QUESTIONS

21.1 Frequencies

1 Below are the temperatures, in °C of 40 places in a country. Construct a frequency table.

18 12 19 24 16 29 30 31 25 26

24 26 20 18 29 26 29 20 21 31

18 26 28 23 24 28 25 20 30 17

28 23 22 28 31 30 24 22 28 23

2 A type of electrical component is sold as having a capacitance of 40 μF. The table below gives the capacitance, to the nearest 1 μF, of a batch of 30. Arrange the data in a frequency table.

45 42 41 40 39 38 43 40 42 44 39 40 38 41 45

43 42 40 37 41 39 44 43 41 40 43 37 40 45 44

3 The diameters of 30 washers, in mm to the nearest 0.1 mm, were measured. The results are below. Construct a frequency table.

15.5 15.3 15.2 15.8 15.0 15.3 15.5 15.6 15.5 15.4

15.7 15.3 15.0 15.6 15.5 15.4 15.6 15.4 15.7 15.4

15.6 15.7 15.6 15.5 15.8 15.6 15.4 15.3 15.2 15.5

21.2 Illustrating data

4 The daily production of a bakery is shown in Figure 21.19, where each symbol represents 100 loaves. How many loaves were produced? Draw a pictogram to show a production of 350 loaves.

Figure 21.19

5 In a housing estate there are 50 one-bedroom dwellings, 89 two-bedroom dwellings, and 61 three-bedroom dwellings. Construct a pie chart to illustrate this data.

6 The staff of a firm is divided into categories as shown below. Construct a pie chart and a bar chart to illustrate the information.

Managerial	Clerical	Skilled manual	Unskilled manual
12	43	81	104

7 A certain electrical component is sold as having a resistance of 100 Ω. The frequency table below gives the resistance of 50 components. Construct a histogram to illustrate the data.

Resistance (Ω)	96–98	98–100	100–102	102–104	104–106
Frequency	4	10	15	12	9

8 The frequency table below gives the internal diameters of 80 pipes. Construct a histogram to illustrate the data.

Diameter (mm)	29.5–30.0	30.0–30.5	30.5–31
Frequency	6	20	28
Diameter (mm)	31–31.5	31.5–32	
Frequency	19	7	

9 The monthly salaries of the employees of a company are in the table below. Construct a histogram to illustrate the data.

Salaries (100#)	6–10	10–12	12–14	14–16	16–18	18–24
Frequency	22	56	63	41	21	33

10 The time taken to perform a task was found for 100 workers. The results are below. Construct a histogram to illustrate the data.

Time (minutes)	4–5	5–6	6–$6\frac{1}{2}$	$6\frac{1}{2}$–7
Frequency	8	12	11	12
Time (minutes)	7–8	8–9	9–10	10–15
Frequency	18	17	10	12

21.3 Averages

11 Find the mean and median of the following sets of data.

a) 17 18 20 21 23 25 26 26 28 30

b) 10.3 10.7 10.8 11.0 11.2 11.3 11.9 12.0 12.8

c) −0.5 −0.1 0.0 0.2 0.7 1.0 1.2 1.3

12 In 12 matches, a football team scored the following numbers of goals. Find the mean, median and mode number of goals.

0 0 0 0 0 1 1 1 2 2 3 5

13 The heights of 100 plants are given in the table below. Estimate the mean height.

Height (cm)	10–12	12–14	14–16	16–18	18–20
Frequency	7	22	39	29	3

14 The output per month of a copper mine is given below, for a period of 20 months. Estimate the mean monthly output.

Output (100 tonnes)	3–3.5	3.5–4	4–4.5	4.5–5
Frequency	2	11	5	2

15 From the histogram of Question 7, estimate the mode of the resistances.

16 From the histogram of Question 8, estimate the mode of the diameters.

21.4 Cumulative frequency and measures of spread

17 For each of the data sets below, find the range.

a) 34 36 38 41 44 44 47 48
   51 51 53 56 57 58 61 66

b) 105 105 106 108 109 110 111 113 117

c) 3.23 3.25 3.26 3.26 3.27 3.28 3.29 3.29 3.30 3.31

18 Find the variance and the standard deviation of the data sets of Question 17.

19 Two machines each produce ball bearings. For each machine, the diameters of a batch of 10 are measured. The results are below. For each machine, find the mean and the standard deviation. What is the difference between the machines?

Machine A:

5.34 5.35 5.35 5.36 5.36 5.36 5.36 5.37 5.37 5.39

Machine B:

5.26 5.27 5.29 5.31 5.31 5.32 5.35 5.38 5.42 5.45

20 For the data in Question 7, find the cumulative frequencies and construct a cumulative frequency curve. From your curve estimate the median and quartiles of the resistance.

21 For the data in Question 8, find the cumulative frequencies and construct a cumulative frequency curve. From your curve estimate the interquartile range of the diameters. Estimate the 30th percentile of the data.

21.5 Correlation

22 For the data sets below, find the line giving y in terms of x.

a)

x	1	2	3	4	5	6	7	8
y	103	152	182	205	221	251	276	277

b)

x	10	15	20	25	30	35	40
y	0.1	0.7	1.0	1.1	1.3	1.8	2.3

c)

x	−2	−1	0	1	2	3	4	5	6
y	53	52	49	41	46	39	31	33	21

23 The table below gives the resistance of an electrical component at different temperatures. Find the line giving resistance, $R\ \Omega$, in terms of temperature, $T°\mathrm{C}$.

Temperature (°C)	0	20	40	60	80	100
Resistance (Ω)		29.2	31.0	33.1	33.8	34.1	35.3

24 A gas was kept in a closed container, and its pressure at various temperatures was found. The results are below. Find the line giving pressure, $P\ \mathrm{N/m^2}$, in terms of temperature, $T°\mathrm{C}$.

At absolute zero the pressure of gas is zero. From your result estimate absolute zero.

Temperature (°C)	0	50	100	150	200	250
Pressure (N/m²)	1500	1780	2100	2330	2620	2910

Matrices and vectors

Introduction

We represent quantities like mass and temperature with a single number. A car might have a mass of 950 kg, or the temperature might be 23°C. For other quantities, we need more than one number. For the force acting on a girder, we need to know its direction as well as its size. The impedance of an electrical circuit might have three components, the resistance, the inductance and the capacitance.

Matrices, **vectors** and **complex numbers** consist of more than one ordinary number. They can be used to represent quantities like force and impedance.

22.1 Matrices

A **matrix** is a rectangular block of numbers. If the block has n rows and m columns, then it is a n by m matrix. The matrix below is a 2 by 3 matrix.

$$\begin{pmatrix} 5 & 6 & 7 \\ 9 & 0 & 1 \end{pmatrix}$$

Matrix arithmetic

Addition and subtraction

If matrices have the same number of rows and columns, then they can be added or subtracted. Add or subtract the corresponding terms.

Addition

$$\begin{pmatrix} 2 & 3 & 4 \\ 2 & -4 & 1 \end{pmatrix} + \begin{pmatrix} 8 & 1 & -7 \\ 4 & 6 & 8 \end{pmatrix} = \begin{pmatrix} 2+8 & 3+1 & 4-7 \\ 2+4 & -4+6 & 1+8 \end{pmatrix}$$
$$= \begin{pmatrix} 10 & 4 & -3 \\ 6 & 2 & 9 \end{pmatrix}$$

Subtraction

$$\begin{pmatrix} 2 & 3 & 4 \\ 2 & -4 & 1 \end{pmatrix} - \begin{pmatrix} 8 & 1 & -7 \\ 4 & 6 & 8 \end{pmatrix} = \begin{pmatrix} -6 & 2 & 11 \\ -2 & -10 & -7 \end{pmatrix}$$

Note

1 Both of these matrices being added and subtracted are 2 by 3. You cannot add or subtract a 2 by 3 matrix and a 2 by 4 matrix. The expression below does not make sense.

$$\begin{pmatrix} 1 & 2 & 1 \\ 0 & 1 & 3 \end{pmatrix} + \begin{pmatrix} 5 & 2 & 3 & 2 \\ 1 & 0 & 1 & 4 \end{pmatrix}$$

2 Adding or subtracting two n by m matrices results in a n by m matrix.

Multiplication

To multiply a matrix by an ordinary number, multiply every term of the matrix by the number.

$$3 \times \begin{pmatrix} 2 & 4 \\ 1 & -2 \end{pmatrix} = \begin{pmatrix} 3 \times 2 & 3 \times 4 \\ 3 \times 1 & 3 \times -2 \end{pmatrix} = \begin{pmatrix} 6 & 12 \\ 3 & -6 \end{pmatrix}$$

Multiplying two matrices is more complicated. To find the product **AB**, the number of columns of **A** must be equal to the number of rows of **B**. So if **A** is n by m, and **B** is p by q, then $m = p$. (And the resulting matrix will be $n \times q$.)

Each row of **A** is put alongside each column of **B**, then the corresponding terms are multiplied and added.

Consider

$$\begin{pmatrix} 2 & 3 & 5 \\ 1 & 5 & 2 \end{pmatrix} \times \begin{pmatrix} 4 & 1 \\ 1 & 3 \\ 1 & 2 \end{pmatrix}$$

The top row of A contains 2, 3, 5. The left column of B contains 4, 1, 1. Multiply corresponding terms and add.

$$2 \times 4 + 3 \times 1 + 5 \times 1 = 16.$$

This gives the top left term of **A** × **B**. Similarly, the top right term of **A** × **B** comes from the top row of **A** and the right column of **B**.

$$2 \times 1 + 3 \times 3 + 5 \times 2 = 21$$

The bottom row is found similarly, from the bottom row of **A** multipliying the columns of **B**. The complete product is

$$\begin{pmatrix} 2 & 3 & 5 \\ 1 & 5 & 2 \end{pmatrix} \times \begin{pmatrix} 4 & 1 \\ 1 & 3 \\ 1 & 2 \end{pmatrix} = \begin{pmatrix} 2\times4+3\times1+5\times1 & 2\times1+3\times3+5\times2 \\ 1\times4+5\times1+2\times1 & 1\times1+5\times3+2\times2 \end{pmatrix}$$

$$= \begin{pmatrix} 16 & 21 \\ 11 & 20 \end{pmatrix}$$

The product **AB** is a 2 by 2 matrix. The product **BA** is different. It is a 3 by 3 matrix.

$$\begin{pmatrix} 4 & 1 \\ 1 & 3 \\ 1 & 2 \end{pmatrix} \times \begin{pmatrix} 2 & 3 & 5 \\ 1 & 5 & 2 \end{pmatrix} = \begin{pmatrix} 4\times2+1\times1 & 4\times3+1\times5 & 4\times5+1\times2 \\ 1\times2+3\times1 & 1\times3+3\times5 & 1\times5+3\times2 \\ 1\times2+2\times1 & 1\times3+2\times5 & 1\times5+2\times2 \end{pmatrix}$$

$$= \begin{pmatrix} 9 & 17 & 22 \\ 5 & 18 & 11 \\ 4 & 13 & 9 \end{pmatrix}$$

Note

1 Multiplying row x by column y results in the element for row x, column y.
2 Multiplying a n by m matrix by a m by q matrix results in a n by q matrix.

EXAMPLE 22.1

Let $\mathbf{C} = \begin{pmatrix} 2 & 3 \\ 3 & -1 \end{pmatrix}$ and $\mathbf{D} = \begin{pmatrix} 1 & -1 \\ 1 & 3 \end{pmatrix}$. Find $\mathbf{C} + \mathbf{D}$ and $\mathbf{CD}$.

Solution
For the sum, add the corresponding terms.

$$\mathbf{C} + \mathbf{D} = \begin{pmatrix} 2 & 3 \\ 3 & -1 \end{pmatrix} + \begin{pmatrix} 1 & -1 \\ 1 & 3 \end{pmatrix}$$

$$= \begin{pmatrix} 2+1 & 3-1 \\ 3+1 & -1+3 \end{pmatrix}$$

$$= \begin{pmatrix} 3 & 2 \\ 4 & 2 \end{pmatrix}$$

For the product, multiply each row of **C** with each column of **D**.

$$\mathbf{CD} = \begin{pmatrix} 2 & 3 \\ 3 & -1 \end{pmatrix}\begin{pmatrix} 1 & -1 \\ 1 & 3 \end{pmatrix} = \begin{pmatrix} 2\times1+3\times1 & 2\times-1+3\times3 \\ 3\times1+-1\times1 & 3\times-1+-1\times3 \end{pmatrix}$$

$$= \begin{pmatrix} 5 & 7 \\ 2 & -6 \end{pmatrix}$$

$$\mathbf{C} + \mathbf{D} = \begin{pmatrix} 3 & 2 \\ 4 & 2 \end{pmatrix} \qquad \mathbf{CD} = \begin{pmatrix} 5 & 7 \\ 2 & -6 \end{pmatrix}$$

SELF TEST 22.1

Let $\mathbf{P} = \begin{pmatrix} 4 & -7 \\ 2 & 1 \end{pmatrix}$ and $\mathbf{Q} = \begin{pmatrix} 2 & 3 \\ -2 & 1 \end{pmatrix}$. Find $\mathbf{P} + \mathbf{Q}$ and $\mathbf{PQ}$.

$$\begin{pmatrix} 6 & -4 \\ 0 & 2 \end{pmatrix}, \quad \begin{pmatrix} 22 & 5 \\ 2 & 7 \end{pmatrix}$$

Division

Suppose you want to divide by a matrix. Remember that for an ordinary number like 2, dividing by 2 is the same as multiplying by $\frac{1}{2}$, i.e. by 2^{-1}. In order to divide by a matrix **A**, you multiply by $\mathbf{A}^{-1}$. This is the **inverse** of **A**.

To have an inverse, **A** must be square, i.e. **A** must be n by n for some n. If **A** is a 2 by 2 matrix, its inverse is given by:

If
$$\mathbf{A} = \begin{pmatrix} a & b \\ c & d \end{pmatrix},$$

then
$$\mathbf{A}^{-1} = \frac{1}{ad-bc}\begin{pmatrix} d & -b \\ -c & a \end{pmatrix}.$$

So interchange the top-left and the bottom-right, and multiply top-right and bottom-left by -1. Then divide all the terms by $ad - bc$.

The expression $ad - bc$ is called the **determinant** of the matrix. It is sometimes written using straight lines as below.

$$\text{determinant of } \begin{pmatrix} a & b \\ c & d \end{pmatrix} = \begin{vmatrix} a & b \\ c & d \end{vmatrix} = ad - bc.$$

If the determinant is zero, then the matrix has no inverse.

EXAMPLE 22.2

Find the inverse of the matrix $\mathbf{A} = \begin{pmatrix} 3 & -2 \\ 4 & 5 \end{pmatrix}$

Solution
The determinant of the matrix is $3 \times 5 - (-2) \times 4$, i.e. 23. This is not zero, hence the matrix has an inverse. Interchange the 3 and the 5. Multiply the -2 and the 4 by -1. Then divide by 23.

$$\begin{pmatrix} 3 & -2 \\ 4 & 5 \end{pmatrix}^{-1} = \frac{1}{23}\begin{pmatrix} 5 & 2 \\ -4 & 3 \end{pmatrix}$$

The inverse is $\begin{pmatrix} \frac{5}{23} & \frac{2}{23} \\ -\frac{4}{23} & \frac{3}{23} \end{pmatrix}$

SELF TEST 22.2

Find the inverse of the matrix $B = \begin{pmatrix} 5 & 1 \\ 3 & -1 \end{pmatrix}$

$$\begin{pmatrix} \frac{1}{8} & \frac{1}{8} \\ \frac{3}{8} & -\frac{5}{8} \end{pmatrix}$$

Solving equations

A set of simultaneous equations can be written as a single matrix equation. If the matrix has an inverse, it can be used to solve the equations.

EXAMPLE 22.3

Solve the following equations using matrices.

$$3x - 2y = 7$$
$$4x + 5y = 8$$

Solution
The coefficients of x and y form a matrix. Write the equations as a single matrix equation.

$$\begin{pmatrix} 3 & -2 \\ 4 & 5 \end{pmatrix}\begin{pmatrix} x \\ y \end{pmatrix} = \begin{pmatrix} 7 \\ 8 \end{pmatrix}$$

We need to divide both sides of the equation by $\begin{pmatrix} 3 & -2 \\ 4 & 5 \end{pmatrix}$,

i.e. we need to multiply by the inverse of $\begin{pmatrix} 3 & -2 \\ 4 & 5 \end{pmatrix}$.

This matrix is the same as that of Example 22.2. Example 22.2 gives the inverse matrix. Multiply both sides of the equation by the inverse matrix. Leave the factor of $\frac{1}{23}$ outside the matrix until the end of the calculation.

$$\begin{pmatrix} 3 & -2 \\ 4 & 5 \end{pmatrix}^{-1}\begin{pmatrix} 3 & -2 \\ 4 & 5 \end{pmatrix}\begin{pmatrix} x \\ y \end{pmatrix} = \frac{1}{23}\begin{pmatrix} 5 & 2 \\ -4 & 3 \end{pmatrix}\begin{pmatrix} 7 \\ 8 \end{pmatrix}$$

$$\begin{pmatrix} x \\ y \end{pmatrix} = \frac{1}{23}\begin{pmatrix} 5 \times 7 + 2 \times 8 \\ -4 \times 7 + 3 \times 8 \end{pmatrix}$$

$$= \frac{1}{23}\begin{pmatrix} 51 \\ -4 \end{pmatrix}$$

The solution is $x = \frac{51}{23}$ and $y = -\frac{4}{23}$

SELF TEST 22.3

Use matrices to solve these equations.

$$5x + y = 7$$
$$3x - y = 4$$

$$x = 1\tfrac{3}{8}, \quad y = \tfrac{1}{8}$$

Solution by determinants

You can use determinants to solve simultaneous equations. Given the following equations

$$ax + by = e$$
$$cx + dy = f$$

Then $\quad x = \dfrac{\begin{vmatrix} e & b \\ f & d \end{vmatrix}}{\Delta}\quad$ and $\quad y = \dfrac{\begin{vmatrix} a & e \\ c & f \end{vmatrix}}{\Delta}$

where Δ is the determinant $ad - bc$.

EXAMPLE 22.4

Use determinants to solve the equations of Example 22.3.

Solution
The equations are

$$3x - 2y = 7$$
$$4x + 5y = 8$$

Here $\Delta = 23$, as found in Example 22.3. The formula gives

$$x = \frac{\begin{vmatrix} 7 & -2 \\ 8 & 5 \end{vmatrix}}{23} = \frac{7 \times 5 - (-2) \times 8}{23} = \frac{51}{23}$$

$$y = \frac{\begin{vmatrix} 3 & 7 \\ 4 & 8 \end{vmatrix}}{23} = \frac{3 \times 8 - 7 \times 4}{23} = \frac{-4}{23}$$

The solution is $x = \frac{51}{23}$ and $y = -\frac{4}{23}$

Note The answers to Examples 22.2 and 22.4 are the same.

SELF TEST 22.4

Use determinants to solve the equations of Self Test 22.3 above.

$$x = 1\tfrac{3}{8}, \quad y = \tfrac{1}{8}$$

The determinant method of solving simultaneous equations is useful when the numbers involved are not integers.

EXAMPLE 22.5

A gear system is such that an effort of E N will overcome a resistance of R N. E and R are related by $E = aR + b$, where a and b are constant. An effort of 4.83 N will overcome 2.93 N, and 5.66 N will overcome 4.82 N. Find a and b.

Solution
Substitute the numbers into the formula, to obtain two simultaneous equations.

$$4.83 = 2.93a + b$$
$$5.66 = 4.82a + b$$

Rearrange as

$$2.93a + b = 4.83$$
$$4.82a + b = 5.66$$

Use the determinant method. $\Delta = 2.93 \times 1 - 1 \times 4.82 = -1.89$

$$a = \frac{\begin{vmatrix} 4.83 & 1 \\ 5.66 & 1 \end{vmatrix}}{-1.89} = \frac{4.83 \times 1 - 5.66 \times 1}{-1.89} = \frac{-0.83}{-1.89} = 0.4392$$

$$b = \frac{\begin{vmatrix} 2.93 & 4.83 \\ 4.82 & 5.66 \end{vmatrix}}{-1.89} = \frac{2.93 \times 5.66 - 4.83 \times 4.82}{-1.89} = \frac{-6.6968}{-1.89} = 3.543$$

$$a = 0.439 \text{ and } b = 3.54$$

SELF TEST 22.5

Use determinants to solve the simultaneous equations

$$1.293x + 4.975y = 20.43$$
$$2.094x + 0.892y = 11.32.$$

$$x = 4.112, \; y = 3.038$$

22.2 Vectors

A **vector** is a quantity which has size and direction. We sometimes use the word **magnitude** for size. Examples of vectors are

● Force. An architect wants to know the direction of the forces in a building, as well as their size.
● Velocity. When describing the journey of a car, you need to give the direction it is moving, as well as its speed.
● Electrical current. The direction of a current is important as well as its size.

A **scalar** is a quantity with magnitude only. Examples are

● Time. You cannot speak of 'two hours acting north'.
● Speed. The speed of a car tells us how fast it is going, not *where* it is going.
● Electrical charge. When charge accumulates on a body, it has no direction.

In books, vectors are shown in bold type, as **a**, **b** etc. In handwriting, underline the letter, as a͟, b͟ etc. On a diagram, we show a vector by a line with an arrow, as in Figure 22.1. The magnitude or size of the vector is written as |**a**|.

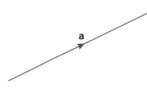

Figure 22.1   Vector **a**

Vectors do not have position. In Figure 22.2, all of the vectors labelled **a** are equal, as they all have the same size and direction.

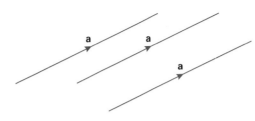

Figure 22.2

Arithmetic of vectors

When you multiply a vector by a scalar, multiply the length but do not change the direction. Figure 22.3 shows **a** and 2**a**, which is twice as long. Its magnitude has been doubled, i.e. |2**a**| = 2|**a**|.

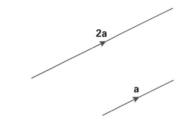

Figure 22.3

Add vectors **a** and **b** by putting the tail of **b** onto the head of **a**. (Or the tail of **a** onto the head of **b**). The third side of the triangle is **a** + **b**. This construction is a **triangle of vectors**. It can also be done by a parallelogram. **a** + **b** is the diagonal of the parallelogram with sides **a** and **b**. Figure 22.4 shows both constructions.

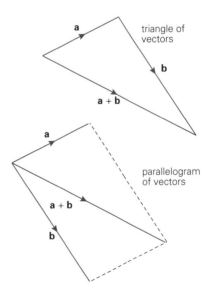

Figure 22.4

$\mathbf{a} + \mathbf{b}$ is the **resultant** of $\mathbf{a}$ and $\mathbf{b}$. If $\mathbf{a}$ and $\mathbf{b}$ represent forces, then their resultant is the single force equivalent to them.

To subtract $\mathbf{a}$ from $\mathbf{b}$, obtain $-\mathbf{a}$ by reversing the direction of $\mathbf{a}$. Then

$$\mathbf{b} - \mathbf{a} = \mathbf{b} + (-\mathbf{a})$$

Figure 22.5 shows the construction.

Figure 22.5

EXAMPLE 22.6

The vectors $\mathbf{a}$ and $\mathbf{b}$ have magnitudes 6 and 7 respectively, and directions north and north east respectively. Find $\mathbf{a} + \mathbf{b}$.

Solution

Figure 22.6 shows a sketch of the vectors. Complete the third side of the triangle as shown. By measurement or by the cosine rule, find the length of $\mathbf{a} + \mathbf{b}$.

cosine rule: $|\mathbf{a} + \mathbf{b}|^2 = |\mathbf{a}|^2 + |\mathbf{b}|^2 - 2|\mathbf{a}|\,|\mathbf{b}|\cos 135°$
$$= 6^2 + 7^2 - 2 \times 6 \times 7 \times \cos 135°$$

Hence $|\mathbf{a} + \mathbf{b}| = \sqrt{(36 + 49 - 84 \times \cos 135°)}$
$$= 12.02$$

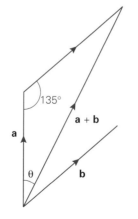

Figure 22.6

By measurement or by the cos rule, find the angle $\mathbf{a} + \mathbf{b}$ makes with the north direction.

$$\cos\theta = \frac{|\mathbf{a} + \mathbf{b}|^2 + |\mathbf{b}|^2 - |\mathbf{a}|^2}{2 \times |\mathbf{a} + \mathbf{b}| \times |\mathbf{b}|}$$
$$= \frac{12.02^2 + 6^2 - 7^2}{2 \times 12.02 \times 6} = 0.9112.$$

Hence $\theta = 24.3°$.

$\mathbf{a} + \mathbf{b}$ has magnitude 12, and acts on a bearing of 024°

SELF TEST 22.6

The vectors $\mathbf{a}$ and $\mathbf{b}$ have magnitudes 4 and 5 respectively. They act on bearings of 23° and 107° respectively. Find the magnitude and direction of $\mathbf{a} + \mathbf{b}$.

6.72, 70.7°

Components

A vector can be split into simple parts. The **component** of a vector is its part in a particular direction. If θ is the angle between the vector and the direction, then the component is $|\mathbf{a}|\cos\theta$. See Figure 22.7.

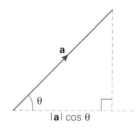

Figure 22.7 Component of a vector

Let $\mathbf{i}$ and $\mathbf{j}$ be vectors of magnitude 1 in the x and y directions respectively. Then $\mathbf{a}$ can be split into x and y components as

$$\mathbf{a} = a_1\mathbf{i} + a_2\mathbf{j}$$

where $a_1 = |\mathbf{a}|\cos\theta$ and $a_2 = |\mathbf{a}|\sin\theta$. See Figure 22.8.

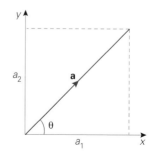

Figure 22.8 Components of a vector

The vector **a** can also be written in the form below, called a **column vector**.

$$\mathbf{a} = \begin{pmatrix} a_1 \\ a_2 \end{pmatrix}$$

This way is easier when writing vectors by hand. The **i** and **j** method is easier when typing or printing.

A column vector has n rows and 1 column. Hence it is a n by 1 matrix.

The magnitude of **a** can be found from the component form. Using Pythagoras' Theorem (see Figure 22.8)

$$|\mathbf{a}| = \sqrt{(a_1^2 + a_2^2)}$$

The angle θ that **a** makes with the x-axis can be found by trigonometry. Make sure you get the correct quadrant. The method is like that of Section 20.3.

$$\tan \theta = \frac{a_2}{a_1}$$

a_1 positive	a_2 positive	θ between 0° and 90°
a_1 negative	a_2 positive	θ between 90° and 180°
a_1 negative	a_2 negative	θ between 180° and 270°
a_1 positive	a_2 negative	θ between 270° and 360°

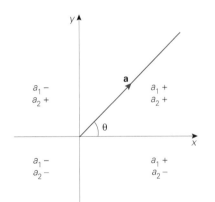

Figure 22.9

EXAMPLE 22.7

A vector **a** has magnitude 10 and makes 35° with the x-axis. Express **a** in terms of components and as a column vector.

Solution
See Figure 22.10. The **i** and **j** components are $10 \times \cos 35°$ and $10 \times \sin 35°$ respectively. These are 8.19 and 5.74.

$$\mathbf{a} = 8.19\mathbf{i} + 5.74\mathbf{j}$$

In column form, **a** has 8.19 on top and 5.74 below.

$$\mathbf{a} = \begin{pmatrix} 8.19 \\ 5.74 \end{pmatrix}$$

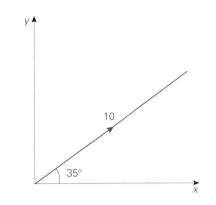

Figure 22.10

SELF TEST 22.7

The vector **a** has magnitude 53 and makes 125° with the positive x-axis. Find **a** in terms of components and as a column vector.

$$-30.4\mathbf{i} + 43.4\mathbf{j}, \begin{pmatrix} -30.4 \\ 43.4 \end{pmatrix}$$

EXAMPLE 22.8

The vector $\mathbf{a} = 3.28\mathbf{i} - 6.91\mathbf{j}$. Find the magnitude of **a** and the angle it makes with the x-axis.

Solution
The magnitude is found by from Pythagoras' Theorem.

$$|\mathbf{a}| = \sqrt{(a_1^2 + a_2^2)}$$
$$= \sqrt{(3.28^2 + 6.91^2)}$$
$$= \sqrt{58.51} = 7.65$$

Note that a_1 is positive and a_2 negative. Hence **a** is in the fourth quadrant. The angle θ is found from $\tan^{-1}\left(\dfrac{6.91}{3.28}\right)$.

$$\theta = 360° - \tan^{-1}\left(\frac{6.91}{3.28}\right)$$
$$= 360° - 64.6° = 295.4°$$

a has magnitude 7.65, and makes an angle of 295.4° with the x-axis

SELF TEST 22.8

The vector $\mathbf{a} = 0.654\mathbf{i} + 0.816\mathbf{j}$. Find the magnitude of **a** and the angle it makes with the x-axis.

1.05, 51.3°

Three dimensions

All the vectors so far have been in two dimensions. In three dimensions there is an extra coordinate axis, the z-axis. A unit vector along the z-axis is $\mathbf{k}$, as shown in Figure 22.11. A vector in three dimensions is written in either of the following forms

$$\mathbf{a} = a_1\mathbf{i} + a_2\mathbf{j} + a_3\mathbf{k} = \begin{pmatrix} a_1 \\ a_2 \\ a_3 \end{pmatrix}$$

The magnitude of the vector is given by Pythagoras' theorem.

$$|\mathbf{a}| = \sqrt{(a_1^2 + a_2^2 + a_3^2)}$$

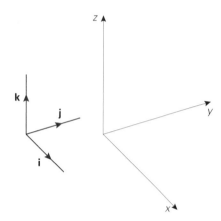

Figure 22.11

EXAMPLE 22.9

Find the magnitude of the vector $\mathbf{v} = 2\mathbf{i} + \mathbf{j} + 2\mathbf{k}$. Find the angle it makes with the x-axis.

Solution
Find the magnitude of $\mathbf{v}$ by Pythagoras' theorem.

$$|\mathbf{v}| = \sqrt{(2^2 + 1^2 + 2^2)} = \sqrt{9} = 3$$

v has magnitude 3

The x component of $\mathbf{v}$ is 2. If $\mathbf{v}$ makes θ with the x-axis,

$$|\mathbf{a}| \cos\theta = 2. \text{ Hence } \cos\theta = \tfrac{2}{3}$$

$$\theta = 48.2°$$

v makes 48.2° with the x-axis

SELF TEST 22.9

Find the magnitude of the vector $3\mathbf{i} - 2\mathbf{j} + \mathbf{k}$. Find the angle it makes with the z-axis.

3.74, 74.5°

22.3 Phasors

In Chapter 20, the graph of $y = \sin\theta$ was obtained by a rotating pointer. The vector corresponding to this pointer is a **phasor**. The length of the phasor is the amplitude of the wave, and the angle to the x-axis at which it starts is the phase angle.

EXAMPLE 22.10

Find the phasor for the curve $y = 4\sin(x - 20°)$.

Solution
The amplitude is 4, and the curve lags by 20°. (See Section 20.4) Hence the phasor is 20° below the x-axis at the start of the rotation. Figure 22.12 shows the phasor.

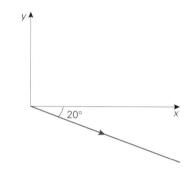

Figure 22.12

SELF TEST 22.10

Find the phasor for the curve $y = \tfrac{1}{2}\sin(x + 50°)$.

amplitude = $\tfrac{1}{2}$, 50° above x-axis

Adding sine waves

In electrical work we often need to combine two wave functions, i.e. to add two sine functions. If the waves have the same frequency, then their sum is another sine wave.

You can add two sine waves with the same frequency by combining their phasors. The phasors are added either by drawing or by using the cosine rule.

In Figure 22.13, the phasors $\mathbf{A}$ and $\mathbf{B}$ are shown. Their sum is $\mathbf{C}$. The curve obtained by combining the curves of $\mathbf{A}$ and $\mathbf{B}$ is generated by the single phasor $\mathbf{C}$.

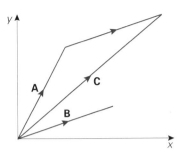

Figure 22.13

EXAMPLE 22.11

Use phasors to combine the graphs of $y = 3 \sin (\theta + 20°)$ and $y = 4 \sin (\theta + 70°)$.

Solution
The first graph has amplitude 3 and phase angle 20°. The second has amplitude 4 and phase angle 70°. Their phasors are shown in Figure 22.14.

The sum of the phasors is the third side of the triangle shown. By measurement, the length of this side is 6.4.
By the cosine rule $c^2 = a^2 + b^2 - 2ab \cos \gamma$

$$\mathbf{C}^2 = 3^2 + 4^2 - 2 \times 3 \times 4 \times \cos 130° = 40.43$$

Hence $\qquad \mathbf{C} = 6.36$

By measurement, $\mathbf{C}$ makes 49° with the x-axis. By using the cosine rule,

$$\cos \theta = \frac{6.36^2 + 4^2 - 3^2}{2 \times 6.36 \times 4} = 0.932.$$

Hence $\qquad \theta = 21.2°.$

Subtract 21.2° from 70°, to obtain an angle of 48.8°. Hence the new phasor has amplitude 6.36, and phase angle 48.8°. The sum of the two functions can now be written down.

The sum is $6.36 \sin (\theta + 48.8°)$

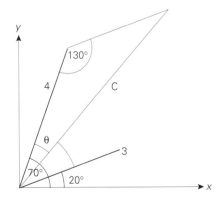

Figure 22.14

SELF TEST 22.11

Use phasors to combine the graphs of $y = 2 \sin (x + 20°)$ and $y = 3 \sin (x - 30°)$.

4.55 sin (x − 10.3°)

22.4 Complex numbers

The square of any ordinary number is positive.

$$(-1)^2 = 1^2 = 1$$

Hence the square root of a negative number does not exist as an ordinary number. So mathematicians have *invented* a special symbol, j, for the square root of −1.

$$j = \sqrt{-1}. \text{ Hence } j^2 = -1.$$

Note

In some books you will see i, rather than j, used for $\sqrt{-1}$. Technicians and engineers use j.

Now we can define the square root of other negative numbers. For example

$$\sqrt{(-4)} = \sqrt{4}\sqrt{(-1)} = 2j$$

A **complex number** is of the form $x + jy$, where x and y are real (ordinary) numbers. The **real** part is x, and the **imaginary** part is y.

In particular, if we put $x = 0$ and $y = 1$, then we obtain j itself. If we put $y = 0$, then we obtain the real number x.

Using complex numbers, we can now solve any quadratic equation. The next example shows the method.

EXAMPLE 22.12

Solve the equation $x^2 + 4x + 13 = 0$.

Solution
Use the formula for the solution of a quadratic equation.

$$x = \frac{-b \pm \sqrt{(b^2 - 4ac)}}{2a}$$

$$x = \frac{-4 \pm \sqrt{(4^2 - 4 \times 1 \times 13)}}{2 \times 1} = \frac{-4 \pm \sqrt{(-36)}}{2}$$

Now we find the square root of −36.

$$\sqrt{(-36)} = \sqrt{36}\sqrt{(-1)} = 6j$$

$$x = \frac{-4 \pm 6j}{2}$$

$$x = -2 + 3j \text{ or } x = -2 - 3j.$$

The solution is $x = -2 + 3j$ or $x = -2 - 3j$

SELF TEST 22.12

Solve the equation $x^2 - 2x + 2 = 0$.

> **1 + j, 1 - j**

Arithmetic of complex numbers

Complex numbers obey the same rules of arithmetic as ordinary numbers.

Addition and subtraction

When adding (or subtracting) complex numbers, add (or subtract) the real parts and add (or subtract) the imaginary parts.

$$(2 + 3j) + (4 + 7j) = 6 + 10j$$
$$(3 - 2j) - (1 + 2j) = 2 - 4j$$

Multiplication

When multiplying two complex numbers, multiply each term and simplify.

$$(2 + 3j) \times (4 + 7j) = 2 \times 4 + 2 \times 7j + 3j \times 4 + 3j \times 7j$$
$$= 8 + 26j + 21j^2$$

Remember that $j^2 = -1$.

So $(2 + 3j) \times (4 + 7j) = 8 + 26j - 21 = -13 + 26j$

SELF TEST 22.13

Let $z = 4 + 2j$ and $w = 7 - 3j$. Find $z + w$ and zw.

> **11 - j, 34 + 2j**

Division

If $z = x + jy$, then the **conjugate** of z is defined as
$$\bar{z} = x - jy$$
When z and $\bar{z}$ are multiplied, the result is real.
$$z\bar{z} = (x + jy)(x - jy)$$
$$= x^2 - j^2y^2$$
$$= x^2 + y^2$$

When one complex number is divided by another, simplify by multiplying the numerator and denominator of the fraction by the conjugate of the denominator. The next example illustrates this.

EXAMPLE 22.13

Evaluate $(3 + 4j) \div (2 + 3j)$.

Solution

Write the expression as a fraction.
$$(3 + 4j) \div (2 + 3j) = \frac{3 + 4j}{2 + 3j}$$

Multiply numerator and denominator by the conjugate of $2 + 3j$, i.e. by $2 - 3j$.
$$\frac{(3 + 4j)(2 - 3j)}{(2 + 3j)(2 - 3j)} = \frac{6 - 9j + 8j - 12j^2}{4 - 9j^2} = \frac{18 - j}{13}$$

The denominator is now real. Divide by 13.
$$(3 + 4j) \div (2 + 3j) = \tfrac{18}{13} - \tfrac{1}{13}j$$

SELF TEST 22.14

Evaluate $(3 - 2j) \div (4 - 3j)$.

> $\tfrac{18}{25} + \tfrac{1}{25}j$

Impedance

Complex numbers can be used to represent the impedance of an electrical circuit.

Suppose two impedances are Z_1 and Z_2. When they are connected in series, the total impedance Z is
$$Z = Z_1 + Z_2$$

When they are connected in parallel, the total impedance Z is given by
$$\frac{1}{Z} = \frac{1}{Z_1} + \frac{1}{Z_2}$$

To find Z, use the arithmetic of complex numbers.

EXAMPLE 22.14

Two impedances are given by $Z_1 = 1 + 3j$ and $Z_2 = 7 - j$. Find the total impedance when they are connected a) in series, b) in parallel.

Solution

a) When they are in series, add the impedances
$$Z_1 + Z_2 = 8 + 2j$$

The total impedance in series is 8 + 2j

b) Use the formula above.
$$\frac{1}{Z} = \frac{1}{1 + 3j} + \frac{1}{7 - j}$$

Multiply numerator and denominator of the first fraction by $1 - 3j$, and multiply numerator and denominator of the second fraction by $7 + j$.

So

$$\frac{1}{Z} = \frac{1-3j}{(1+3j)(1-3j)} + \frac{7+j}{(7-j)(7+j)}$$

$$= \frac{1-3j}{10} + \frac{7+j}{50}$$

$$= 0.1 - 0.3j + 0.14 + 0.02j$$

$$= 0.24 - 0.28j$$

Invert to find Z.

$$Z = \frac{1}{0.24-0.28j} = \frac{0.24+0.28j}{(0.24-0.28j)(0.24+0.28j)}$$

$$= \frac{0.24+0.28j}{0.24^2+0.28^2} = 1.765 + 2.059j$$

The total impedance in parallel is 1.765 + 2.059j

SELF TEST 22.15

Two impedances are $3 + 4j$ and $8 - 6j$. Find the total impedance if they are connected a) in series, b) in parallel.

a) 11 − 2j, b) 4 + 2j

■ CHECK YOUR UNDERSTANDING

● A matrix is a rectangular block of numbers. Matrices can be added if they have the same number of rows and the same number of columns. If the number of columns of A is equal to the number of rows of B, then the product AB can be formed.
● Matrices can be used to solve simultaneous equations. Determinants can also be used.
● A vector is a quantity with direction as well as magnitude. A scalar is a quantity with magnitude only.
● Add vectors by a vector triangle. Use drawing or trigonometry.
● Unit vectors parallel to the x and y axes are **i** and **j** respectively. The component of a vector **v** along the x-axis is $|\mathbf{v}| \cos \theta$, where $|\mathbf{v}|$ is the magnitude of **v** and θ is the angle it makes with the x-axis. The y component is defined similarly.
● If the x and y components of **v** are a and b respectively, then **v** can be written in either of the following forms.

$$\mathbf{v} = a\mathbf{i} + b\mathbf{j} \qquad \mathbf{v} = \begin{pmatrix} a \\ b \end{pmatrix}$$

● Sine graphs with the same frequency can be combined by adding phasors. The addition can be done either by drawing or by trigonometry.
● The imaginary number j is such that $j^2 = -1$. A complex number is of the form $x + jy$, where x and y are real. With complex numbers, any quadratic equation can be solved.

● Complex numbers obey the rules of arithmetic. To divide by $x + jy$, multiply top and bottom of the fraction by the conjugate, $x - jy$.
● Complex numbers can be used to represent impedance in electrical circuits.

REVISION EXERCISES AND QUESTIONS

22.1 Matrices

1 Let $\mathbf{A} = \begin{pmatrix} 1 & 4 \\ 2 & -1 \end{pmatrix}$ and $\mathbf{B} = \begin{pmatrix} 5 & 7 \\ 3 & 2 \end{pmatrix}$. Find $\mathbf{A} + \mathbf{B}$ and $\mathbf{AB}$.

2 Let $\mathbf{C} = \begin{pmatrix} 2 & 1 & 3 \\ -1 & 3 & 0 \end{pmatrix}$. With **A** as in Question 1, find **AC**.

Explain why **CA** and $\mathbf{A} + \mathbf{C}$ cannot be found.

3 Find the inverses of the matrices **A** and **B** of Question 1.

4 By inverse matrices or by determinants solve the following simultaneous equations.

   a) $3x + 2y = 20$ b) $5x + 2y = 27$ c) $2.1x + 4.7y = 31$
      $7x + 5y = 34$ $2x - 3y = 5$ $1.8x - 2.5y = 41$

22.2 Vectors

5 Vector **a** acts east and has magnitude 7. Vector **b** acts north east and has magnitude 8. Find the magnitude and direction of $\mathbf{a} + \mathbf{b}$.

6 Vector **a** acts north, and has magnitude 12. A vector **b**, acting south east, makes $\mathbf{a} + \mathbf{b}$ act east. What is the magnitude of **b**?

7 For the following vectors, find their magnitudes and the angles they make with the x-axis.

   a) $3\mathbf{i} + 4\mathbf{j}$ b) $-2\mathbf{i} + 3\mathbf{j}$ c) $\frac{1}{2}\mathbf{i} + \frac{2}{3}\mathbf{j}$

8 A vector **b** has magnitude 12 and makes $20°$ with the x-axis. Express **b** in component form. Write **b** as a column vector.

9 Let $\mathbf{a} = 3\mathbf{i} + 4\mathbf{j} - 5\mathbf{k}$. Find $|\mathbf{a}|$ and the angle **a** makes with the y-axis.

22.3 Phasors

10 Use phasors to write the following in the form $A \sin (x + a)$. Sketch the graph of the function.
    a) $\sin (x + 60°) + \sin x$
    b) $3 \sin (x + 40°) + 4 \sin (x + 10°)$
    c) $\frac{1}{2} \sin x + \frac{1}{3} \sin (x - 50°)$
    d) $2 \sin (x + 40°) + 3 \sin (x - 20°)$

22.4 Complex numbers

11   Write in terms of j.

  a) $\sqrt{-100}$ b) $\sqrt{-\frac{1}{4}}$ c) $\sqrt{-9} + \sqrt{-36}$

12   Solve the following equations.

  a) $x^2 + 49 = 0$

  b) $x^2 - 6x + 25 = 0$

  c) $x^2 + x + 1 = 0$

13   Let $z = 2 + 5j$ and $w = 7 - 4j$. Evaluate the following.

  a) $z + w$ b) $z - w$ c) zw

  d) $\bar{w}$ e) $z\bar{w}$ f) $\dfrac{z}{w}$

14   Let Z_1 and Z_2 be two impedances represented by $Z_1 = 6 + 8j$ and $Z_2 = 7 - j$. Find the total impedance if Z_1 and Z_2 are connected

  a) in series   b) in parallel.

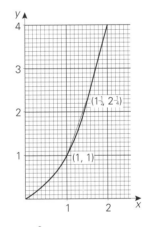

Differentiation 23

Introduction

Science and technology deal with things that change. If a metal rod is heated at one end, its temperature changes along its length. The electrical charge on a piece of equipment can change over time. **Calculus** is the branch of mathematics which deals with change.

There are two branches of calculus. The first finds the rate of change of a quantity. This is **differentiation**. The second finds the original quantity if we know the rate of change. This is **integration**. (Chapter 24 covers this topic).

23.1 Differentiation from first principles

A function of the form $y = mx + c$ has a straight line graph. It has a constant gradient of m. A curved graph has a changing gradient. Differentiation finds the gradient at any point. First we find the gradient of the function $y = x^2$.

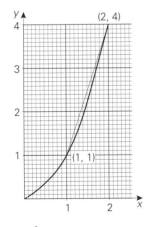

Figure 23.1 $y = x^2$

Figure 23.1 shows the graph of $y = x^2$. A chord goes from $(1, 1)$ to $(2, 4)$. The gradient of the chord is the y-change divided by the x-change.

$$\text{gradient} = \frac{4 - 1}{2 - 1} = 3$$

Figure 23.2 $y = x^2$

Now take the chord from $(1, 1)$ to $(1\frac{1}{2}, 2\frac{1}{4})$, as shown in Figure 23.2. This has gradient given by

$$\text{gradient} = \frac{2\frac{1}{4} - 1}{1\frac{1}{2} - 1} = 2\frac{1}{2}$$

Now take the chord from $(1, 1)$ to $(1.1, 1.21)$. This has gradient given by

$$\text{gradient} = \frac{1.21 - 1}{1.1 - 1} = 2.1$$

Continue this process, by taking shorter and shorter chords. As the chords get shorter, they become closer to the tangent at $(1, 1)$. The gradient of the chord approaches the gradient of the tangent. In this case it can be shown that the gradients approach 2. The tangent to $y = x^2$ at $(1, 1)$ has gradient 2.

227

In general, let (x, y) be on the curve $y = x^2$. Then the point is (x, x^2). Increase x by a small amount δx. Then y increases by a small amount δy. Find δy by finding the change in x^2.

$$\delta y = (x + \delta x)^2 - x^2$$
$$= x^2 + 2\delta x \times x + (\delta x)^2 - x^2$$
$$= 2\delta x \times x + (\delta x)^2$$

Consider the chord joining (x, y) to $(x + \delta x, y + \delta y)$. This has gradient given by

$$\text{gradient} = \frac{y\text{-change}}{x\text{-change}} = \frac{\delta y}{\delta x} = \frac{2\delta x \times x + (\delta x)^2}{\delta x} = 2x + \delta x$$

As the chord gets shorter, δx tends to 0. The gradient of the chord tends to $2x$. This is the gradient of the tangent at (x, y).

This process is **differentiation from first principles**.

The result is written as $\dfrac{dy}{dx}$.

$$\frac{dy}{dx} = 2x$$

The expression $\dfrac{dy}{dx}$ is the **derivative** of y, or the **derived function** of y.

Notes

1   For $x = 1$, the value of $2x$ is 2. This confirms the result above, that the gradient at $(1, 1)$ is 2.

2   The expression $\dfrac{dy}{dx}$ is *not* a fraction. It is the limit of the fraction $\dfrac{\delta y}{\delta x}$, as δx gets smaller.

EXAMPLE 23.1

Find the derivative of $y = 3x^2 + 7x$ from first principles.

Solution

Let δx be a small increase in x. The corresponding small increase in y is

$$\delta y = 3(x + \delta x)^2 + 7(x + \delta x) - (3x^2 + 7x)$$
$$= 3(x^2 + 2x\delta x + (\delta x)^2) + 7x + 7\delta x - 3x^2 - 7x$$
$$= 3x^2 + 6x\delta x + 3(\delta x)^2 + 7\delta x - 3x^2$$
$$= 6x\delta x + 7\delta x + 3(\delta x)^2$$

Divide through by δx.

$$\frac{\delta y}{\delta x} = \frac{6x\delta x + 7\delta x + 3(\delta x)^2}{\delta x} = 6x + 7 + 3\delta x$$

Now let δx tend to 0. Ignore the $3\delta x$ term. $\dfrac{\delta y}{\delta x}$ becomes $\dfrac{dy}{dx}$.

$$\frac{dy}{dx} = 6x + 7$$

The derivative is $6x + 7$

SELF TEST 23.1

Use differentiation from first principles to find $\dfrac{dy}{dx}$ for $y = 2x^2 - 8x$.

$$\frac{dy}{dx} = 4x - 8$$

23.2 Differentiation of powers

Usually there is no need to differentiate from first principles. Use the following formula

$$\text{If } y = x^n, \text{ then } \frac{dy}{dx} = nx^{n-1}.$$

Notes

1   For $n = 2$, the formula gives $2x^{2-1}$, i.e. $2x$. Above we found from first principles that the derivative of x^2 is $2x$.

2   For $n = 1$, the formula gives $1x^0$, i.e. 1. The gradient of the line $y = x$ is 1.

3   The number 1 can be regarded as x^0. Hence the derivative of 1 is $0x^{-1}$, i.e. 0. The derivative of any constant is 0.

EXAMPLE 23.2

Find the derivative of $y = x^5$.

Solution

Do not use first principles. Use the formula, putting $n = 5$.

$$\frac{dy}{dx} = nx^{n-1} = 5x^4$$

The derivative is $5x^4$

SELF TEST 23.2

Find the derivative of $y = x^4$.

$$\frac{dy}{dx} = 4x^3$$

Multiplying by a constant

When a function is multiplied by a constant, its derivative is multiplied by the constant.

$$\text{If } y = kx^n, \text{ then } \frac{dy}{dx} = knx^{n-1}.$$

Adding functions

When functions are added, their derivatives are added.

$$\text{If } y = x^n + x^m, \text{ then } \frac{dy}{dx} = nx^{n-1} + mx^{m-1}.$$

(Check that the formula works for the expression in Self Test 23.1.)

EXAMPLE 23.3

Find the derivative of $y = 8x^2 + 7x^3$.

Solution
The derivative of x^2 is $2x$, and the derivative of x^3 is $3x^2$. Multiply these by 8 and by 7, and then add.

$$\frac{dy}{dx} = 8 \times 2x + 7 \times 3x^2 = 16x + 21x^2$$

$$\frac{dy}{dx} = 16x + 21x^2$$

SELF TEST 23.3

Find the derivative of $y = 3x^5 - 2x^7$.

$$\frac{dy}{dx} = 15x^4 - 14x^6$$

EXAMPLE 23.4

Find the gradient of $y = 2x^2 + 3x - 5$ at the point $(2, 9)$.

Solution
Differentiation gives the gradient.

$$\frac{dy}{dx} = 2 \times 2x + 3$$

Hence the derivative at a general point is $4x + 3$. Put $x = 2$, obtaining 11.

The gradient at (2, 9) is 11

SELF TEST 23.4

Find the gradient of $y = x^3 - 2x^2$ at the point $(3, 9)$.

15

Negative and fractional powers

The rule for differentiating powers works for negative and fractional powers.

EXAMPLE 23.5

Differentiate $y = \frac{1}{x} + \sqrt{x}$.

Solution
Write $\frac{1}{x}$ as x^{-1}, and write $\sqrt{x}$ as $x^{\frac{1}{2}}$. Hence $y = x^{-1} + x^{\frac{1}{2}}$. Use the rule for differentiation.

$$\frac{dy}{dx} = -1 \times x^{-1-1} + \frac{1}{2} \times x^{\frac{1}{2}-1} = -x^{-2} + \frac{1}{2}x^{-\frac{1}{2}}$$

The derivative is $-x^{-2} + \frac{1}{2}x^{-\frac{1}{2}}$

SELF TEST 23.5

Find the derivative of $y = \frac{1}{x^2} + \sqrt[3]{x}$.

$$\frac{dy}{dx} = -2x^{-3} + \frac{1}{3}x^{-\frac{2}{3}}$$

EXAMPLE 23.6

Find the derivative of $y = (x + 3)(x - 4)$.

Solution
Expand the brackets. $(x + 3)(x - 4) = x^2 - x - 12$.
Now differentiate. The derivative of the constant 12 is 0.

The derivative is $2x - 1$

SELF TEST 23.6

Find the derivative of $y = (x^2 + 1)(x^3 + 2)$.

$$\frac{dy}{dx} = 5x^4 + 3x^2 + 4x$$

Distance and speed

Differentiation finds the gradient or rate of change of a quantity. The rate of change of distance is *speed*. So far we have always had x as the variable. In the following example we use t for time instead of x.

EXAMPLE 23.7

After t seconds, a particle has travelled $(2t^3 + 7t)$ m. Find the speed of the particle after 8 seconds.

Solution

Speed is the rate of change of distance. Let D m be the distance, so $D = 2t^3 + 7t$. Differentiate this expression for distance to find the speed.

$$\frac{dD}{dt} = 6t^2 + 7$$

Put $t = 8$ into this expression, obtaining 391.

The speed of the particle is 391 m s^{-1}

SELF TEST 23.7

After t seconds, the distance travelled by a particle is y m, where $y = 2t^2 - 3t$. Find the speed of the particle after 2 seconds.

speed = 5 m s^{-1}

23.3 Exponential and trigonometric functions

Table 23.1 shows what happens when you differentiate exponential and trigonometric functions. The number a is constant.

Table 23.1 Differentiation of exponential and trigonometric functions

Function	Derivative $\frac{dy}{dx}$
$y = e^{ax}$	ae^{ax}
$y = \sin ax$	$a \cos ax$
$y = \cos ax$	$-a \sin ax$

Notes

1 For the trigonometric functions, the angle is measured in radians.
2 Remember from Section 12.5 of Chapter 12 that if a quantity is increasing at a rate proportional to its value, then the quantity is of the form Ae^{kx}. This checks with the result above. The rate of increase of e^{ax} is a multiple of itself, i.e. is proportional to itself.

EXAMPLE 23.8

Differentiate
   a) $2 \sin 3x$ b) $4 \cos \frac{1}{2}\pi x$ c) $0.2e^{-1.5x}$.

Solution
a) Apply the rule above, with $a = 3$.
$$\text{derivative} = 3 \times 2 \cos 3x = 6 \cos 3x$$

The derivative is 6 cos 3x

b) Here $a = \frac{1}{2}\pi$.
$$\text{derivative} = -\tfrac{1}{2}\pi \times 4 \sin \tfrac{1}{2}\pi x = -2\pi \sin \tfrac{1}{2}\pi x$$

The derivative is $-2\pi \sin\frac{1}{2}\pi x$

c) Here $a = -1.5$. Do not ignore the minus sign.
$$\text{derivative} = -1.5 \times 0.2e^{-1.5x} = -0.3e^{-1.5x}$$

The derivative is $-0.3e^{-1.5x}$

SELF TEST 23.8

Differentiate a) $-3 \cos 7x$ b) $2e^{0.02x}$ c) $\sin \frac{1}{3}\pi x$.

a) 21 sin 7x   b) 0.04e$^{0.02x}$ c) $\frac{1}{3}\pi \cos \frac{1}{3}\pi x$

EXAMPLE 23.9

At time t seconds, the charge on a plate is Q coulombs, where $Q = 0.2(1 - e^{-0.3t})$. Find the rate of increase of charge after 2 seconds.

Solution
Find the rate of increase by differentiating Q. First expand, obtaining $0.2 - 0.2e^{-0.3t}$.

$$\frac{dQ}{dt} = -(-0.3)(0.2)e^{-0.3t}$$

Put $t = 2$, obtaining $0.06e^{-0.3 \times 2}$.
By a calculator or tables, evaluate this as 0.03293.

The rate of increase is 0.0329 coulombs per second

SELF TEST 23.9

The current, I amps, at time t seconds is given by $I = 15 \sin 12t$. Find the rate of change of the current at time 10 seconds.

147 amps sec^{-1}

Note   Remember the angle is in radians.

23.4 Maxima and minima

At a **maximum** a function reaches a high point. At a **minimum** a function reaches a low point. At either of these points the curve is flat, as shown in Figure 23.3. Hence at a maximum or minimum the derivative of the function (or the gradient) is zero.
   To decide whether it is a maximum or a minimum, consider the derivative on both sides of the stationary point.

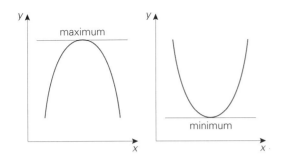

Figure 23.3

Positive on left, negative on right. A maximum.
Negative on left, positive on right. A minimum.

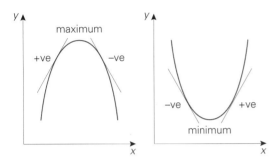

Figure 23.4

EXAMPLE 23.10

Find the maximum and minimum of the function
$y = x^3 + 6x^2 - 36x + 5$.

Solution
Differentiate, then equate the derivative to zero.

$$\frac{dy}{dx} = 3x^2 + 12x - 36$$

$$3x^2 + 12x - 36 = 0$$

$$3(x^2 + 4x - 12) = 0$$

$$3(x + 6)(x - 2) = 0$$

Hence there are stationary points at $x = -6$ and $x = 2$.
For $x = -6$,

$$y = (-6)^3 + 6(-6)^2 - 36(-6) + 5 = 221$$

For $x = 2$,

$$y = (2)^3 + 6(2)^2 - 36(2) + 5 = -35.$$

Hence there are stationary points at $(-6, 221)$ and at $(2, -35)$.
To decide which is a maximum and which is a minimum, find
the derivative on either side of $x = -6$ and on either side of
$x = 2$. For example find the derivative at $x = -7, x = -5, x = 1$
and $x = 3$.

$$\frac{dy}{dx} = 3(x + 6)(x - 2)$$

For $x = -7, \dfrac{dy}{dx} = 27 > 0$

For $x = -5, \dfrac{dy}{dx} = -21 < 0$

Hence $(-6, \ 221)$ is a maximum.

For $x = 1, \dfrac{dy}{dx} = -21 < 0$

For $x = 3, \dfrac{dy}{dx} = 27 > 0$

Hence $(2, -35)$ is a minimum.

$(-6, 221)$ is a maximum and $(2, -35)$ is a minimum

Notes

1   Figure 23.5 shows a sketch of the graph of the function.
2   The maximum is only a *local* high point. The function
    reaches higher values for large values of x. Similarly the
    minimum is only a local low point.

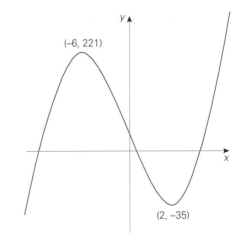

Figure 23.5 $y = x^3 + 6x^2 - 36x + 5$

SELF TEST 23.10

Find the maximum and minimum of $y = x^3 - 3x^2 - 105x + 1$.
$(-5, 326)$, max. $(7, -538)$, min.

Practical uses

At a maximum or minimum, a quantity reaches its greatest or
least value. This is often useful in practical cases. For example

● Business people want to maximise their profits.
● When planning a task, the time for it should be minimised.
● The energy loss in a machine should be minimised.

EXAMPLE 23.11

Trays are made from rectangular sheets of thin metal, by cutting out squares at each corner and folding. The rectangle is 30 cm by 40 cm. Find the greatest possible volume of the tray.

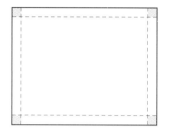

Figure 23.6

Solution

Suppose that squares of x cm are cut out. Then the tray has height x cm, and its base has sides $(30 - 2x)$ cm and $(40 - 2x)$ cm. Its volume, V cm^3, is given by

$$V = x(30 - 2x)(40 - 2x)$$

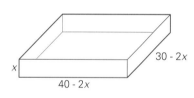

Figure 23.7

The maximum value of V occurs when $\dfrac{dV}{dx} = 0$. Expand V and differentiate.

$$V = 4x^3 - 140x^2 + 1200x$$

$$\frac{dV}{dx} = 12x^2 - 280x + 1200$$

Put $\dfrac{dV}{dx}$ equal to 0.

$$12x^2 - 280x + 1200 = 0$$

Hence $x = 17.7$ or $x = 5.66$

The first value of x gives a negative value of V. Test $\dfrac{dV}{dx}$ on either side of 5.66.

For $x = 5$, $\dfrac{dV}{dx} = 100 > 0$ (+ve)

For $x = 6$, $\dfrac{dV}{dx} = -48 < 0$ (−ve)

Hence the volume is a maximum. Finally put $x = 5.66$ into the formula for V, obtaining 3032.

The greatest volume is 3030 cm^3

SELF TEST 23.11

Soup cans are made out of thin metal in the shape of a cylinder. The can contains 1000 cm^3 of soup. Letting the radius of the base be r cm, show that the height of the can is $\dfrac{1000}{(\pi r^2)}$ cm and that the surface area is $\dfrac{2000}{r} + 2\pi r^2$ cm^2. Find the radius for which the can has least surface area.

5.4 cm

Figure 23.8

EXAMPLE 23.12

A particle is thrown upwards. After t seconds, its height h m is given by

$$h = 2000 - 2000e^{-0.1t} - 100t$$

Find the greatest height it reaches.

Solution

When h is a maximum, $\dfrac{dh}{dt} = 0$. (i.e. the *speed* is zero).

Differentiate the expression for h and equate to 0.

$$\frac{dh}{dt} = 200e^{-0.1t} - 100$$

If $200e^{-0.1t} = 100$, then $e^{-0.1t} = \frac{1}{2}$

Hence $-0.1t = \ln \frac{1}{2}$. Hence $t = 6.931$

Substitute this value into the expression for h.

$$h = 2000 - 2000e^{-0.1 \times 6.931} - 100 \times 6.931 = 306.9$$

The greatest height reached is 307 m

SELF TEST 23.12

At time t seconds, the current in a circuit is $(20 + 5t - 4\sin 2t)$ amps. Find the least value of the current.

19.1 amps

■ CHECK YOUR UNDERSTANDING

● The derivative of a function is its rate of change. The process of finding the derivative is called differentiation.
● The derivative of x^n is nx^{n-1}. When functions are added, their derivatives are added. When a function is multiplied by a constant, its derivative is multiplied by the constant.

● The derivative of e^{ax} is ae^{ax}. The derivative of $\sin ax$ is $a \cos ax$ and the derivative of $\cos ax$ is $-a \sin ax$. For these results the angle must be measured in radians.

● At a maximum or minimum point, $\dfrac{dy}{dx}$ is zero.
To find out whether the point is a maximum or a minimum, evaluate $\dfrac{dy}{dx}$ on both sides of the point.

● The technique of finding maxima and minima can be used to solve practical problems.

REVISION QUESTIONS AND EXERCISES

23.1 Differentiation from first principles

1 Differentiate the following from first principles.
   a) $4x^2 + 5x$ b) $3x - x^2$ c) $2x^3$

23.2 Differentiation of powers

2 Differentiate the following.
   a) x^6 b) $3x^5$ c) $2x^3 + 7$
   d) $3x^3 + 2x^4$ e) $1.5x^2 + 3x - 2$ f) $4x - 2x^3$
   g) $4\sqrt{x}$ h) $\dfrac{7}{x^2}$ i) $\dfrac{2}{\sqrt{x}} + \dfrac{3}{x}$
   j) $(x+1)(x+4)$ k) $(2-x^2)(3-x^3)$ l) $\sqrt{x}(2x+3)$
   m) $\dfrac{x+x^2}{x}$ n) $\dfrac{3x+4x^4}{x^2}$ o) $\dfrac{2x+3x^2}{\sqrt{x}}$

3 Find the gradient of the curve $y = x^2 - 3x + 1$ at the point $(2, -1)$.

4 Find the gradient of the curve $y = \sqrt{x} + \frac{1}{x}$ at the point $(4, 2\frac{1}{4})$.

5 After t seconds, a particle has travelled a distance of $(27t - 3t^2)$ m. Find its speed after 2 seconds.

23.3 Exponential and trigonometric functions

6 Differentiate the following.
   a) e^{6x} b) $3e^{0.1x}$ c) $3 - e^{-0.5x}$
   d) $\sin 3x$ e) $2 \sin 4x - 3 \cos 4x$ f) $2 \cos \frac{1}{3}\pi x$

7 Find the gradient of the curve $y = 3 \sin 2x$ at the point $(\frac{1}{8}\pi, 1\frac{1}{2}\sqrt{2})$.

8 Find the gradient of the curve $y = 5e^{0.3x}$ at the point $(0, 5)$.

9 A circuit is switched off. After t seconds, the current is $5e^{-4t}$ amps. Find the rate of change of the current after 0.2 seconds.

10 The electric charge on a plate at time t seconds is $5(1 - e^{-0.02t})\,\mu C$. Find the rate of increase of the charge at time $t = 5$.

11 At time t seconds, the current through a wire is $3 \sin 150t$ amps. Find the rate of change of the current at time $t = 0.1$.

23.4 Maxima and minima

12 Find the maxima and minima of the following functions.
   a) $y = x^2 + x - 3$ b) $y = x^3 - 12x$
   c) $y = 3 + 4x - 2x^2 - x^3$ d) $y = x + \dfrac{1}{x}$
   e) $y = t - e^t$ f) $y = 2t + \cos 3t$

13 A rectangular pen is to be built with 100 m of fencing. One side of the pen is a wall that is already built. (Figure 23.9). Find the maximum possible area of the pen.

Figure 23.9

14 A cylindrical can with an open top is to be made out of thin metal. If the volume of the can is 2000 cm³ find the least possible area of metal.

15 A tank with open top has a square base of side x m. (Figure 23.10). It is to hold 400 m³ of water. Find the height of the tank if the surface area of walls and base is to be a minimum.

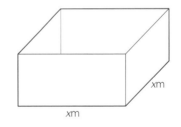

Figure 23.10

16 If an item is priced at $\#x$ each, the number sold is $10\,000 - 5x$. Show that the amount received is $\#(10\,000x - 5x^2)$. Find the value of x which will ensure that the amount received is a maximum.

17 A particle is thrown vertically upwards. After t seconds, its height is h m, where
$$h = 1000 - 1000e^{-0.2t} - 100t.$$
Find the greatest height reached by the particle.

Integration

Introduction

In the previous chapter we showed how differentiation finds the rate of change of a quantity. For example, we differentiate a formula for distance to give a formula for speed. Integration is the reverse of differentiation. We integrate a formula for speed to give a formula for distance.

Differentiation gives us the tangent of a curve. Integration calculates the area under a curve.

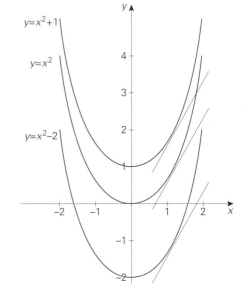

Figure 24.1

24.1 The opposite to differentiation

Differentiation goes from y to $\dfrac{\mathrm{d}y}{\mathrm{d}x}$. Integration goes from $\dfrac{\mathrm{d}y}{\mathrm{d}x}$ to y. For example:

Differentiation takes x^2 to $2x$. Integration takes $2x$ to x^2.

Constant of integration

When integrating $2x$, we look for a function with derivative $2x$. The derivative of x^2 is $2x$.

Remember that the derivative of a constant is 0. Hence the derivative of $x^2 + 3$ is also $2x$. In general, the derivative of $x^2 + c$ is $2x$, where c is any constant. Hence integration takes $2x$ to $x^2 + c$. The constant c is the **constant of integration**.

In Figure 24.1 all the curves are of the form $y = x^2 + c$. The tangents to the different curves are all parallel, i.e. they all have the same gradient.

The symbol for integration is $\displaystyle\int$. The result of integrating $2x$ is $x^2 + c$. It is written

$$\int 2x \, \mathrm{d}x = x^2 + c$$

Formula

The formula for integrating powers of x is

$$\int x^n \mathrm{d}x = \frac{1}{n+1} x^{n+1} + c \qquad \text{provided } n \neq -1$$

(Check this by differentiating $\dfrac{1}{n+1} x^{n+1} + c$.)

Notes

1 Be careful with the restriction that $n \neq -1$. The integral of x^{-1} is a different function.

2 The formula works even if n is negative or fractional.

3 If k is constant, $\displaystyle\int k \, \mathrm{d}x = kx + c$. (write k as kx^0)

EXAMPLE 24.1

Find $\int x^3 \, dx$.

Solution

Apply the formula, with $n = 3$.

$$\int x^3 \, dx = \frac{1}{3+1} x^{3+1} + c$$

$$\int x^3 \, dx = \tfrac{1}{4} x^4 + c$$

SELF TEST 24.1

Find $\int x^2 \, dx$.

$$\tfrac{1}{3} x^3 + c$$

Finding c

If we know a value of y and a value of x, then we can find the constant c.

EXAMPLE 24.2

The derivative of y is $2x$, and $y = 5$ when $x = 1$. Find y.

Solution

Integrating $2x$ gives $x^2 + c$. We say the integral of $2x$ is $x^2 + c$. Hence $y = x^2 + c$.

Put $x = 1$ and $y = 5$.

$$5 = 1^2 + c. \text{ Hence } c = 4.$$
$$y = x^2 + 4$$

SELF TEST 24.2

The derivative of y is x^2, and $y = 11$ when $x = 3$. Find y.

$$y = \tfrac{1}{3} x^3 + 2$$

Multiplying by a constant and adding

When we multiply a function by a constant, we multiply its integral by the constant.

$$\int kx^2 \, dx = k \int x^2 \, dx = \tfrac{1}{3} kx^3 + c$$

When we add functions, we add their integrals.

$$\int (x^2 + x^3) \, dx = \int x^2 \, dx + \int x^3 \, dx = \tfrac{1}{3} x^3 + \tfrac{1}{4} x^4 + c$$

Notes

1 For the first example, you do not need to multiply c by k.
2 For the second example, you only need one constant of integration.

EXAMPLE 24.3

Find $\int (2x^4 - 3x) \, dx$.

Solution

For the x^4 term, add 1 to the power and divide by 5. For the x term, add one to the power and divide by 2.

$$\int (2x^4 - 3x) \, dx = 2 \times \tfrac{1}{5} x^5 - 3 \times \tfrac{1}{2} x^2 + c$$

$$\int (2x^4 - 3x) \, dx = \tfrac{2}{5} x^5 - 1\tfrac{1}{2} x^2 + c$$

SELF TEST 24.3

Find $\int (3x^2 + 15x^4) \, dx$.

$$x^3 + 3x^5 + c$$

EXAMPLE 24.4

Find $\int \left(6\sqrt{x} + \dfrac{5}{x^2} \right) \, dx$.

Solution

Here the indices are fractional and negative. Rewrite and use the formula.

$$\int \left(6\sqrt{x} + \frac{5}{x^2} \right) dx = \int \left(6x^{\frac{1}{2}} + 5x^{-2} \right) dx$$

$$= \left(\frac{6}{1\frac{1}{2}} \right) x^{1\frac{1}{2}} + \left(\frac{5}{-1} \right) x^{-1} + c$$

$$= 4x^{1\frac{1}{2}} - 5x^{-1} + c$$

$$\int \left(6\sqrt{x} + \frac{5}{x^2} \right) dx = 4x^{1\frac{1}{2}} - 5x^{-1} + c$$

SELF TEST 24.4

Find $\int \left(\sqrt[3]{x} - \dfrac{6}{x^3} \right) \, dx$.

$$\tfrac{3}{4} x^{1\frac{1}{3}} + \frac{3}{x^2} + c$$

Integration of exponential and trigonometric functions

Table 24.1 shows the integration of the exponential and trigonometric functions. a is a non-zero constant.

Table 24.1 Integration of exponential and trigonometric functions

Function	Integral
e^{ax}	$\frac{1}{a}e^{ax} + c$
$\sin ax$	$-\frac{1}{a}\cos ax + c$
$\cos ax$	$\frac{1}{a}\sin ax + c$

Note The angles are measured in radians for the trigonometric integrals.

EXAMPLE 24.5

Find the integrals of a) $4\sin 3x$ b) $2e^{-0.1x}$.

Solution

a) Apply the formula, with $a = 3$.

$$\int 4\sin 3x \, dx = -\tfrac{4}{3}\cos 3x + c$$

b) Here $a = -0.1$ or $-\frac{1}{10}$. Do not forget the minus sign. The reciprocal of -0.1 is -10.

$$\int 2e^{-0.1x}\,dx = -20e^{-0.1x} + c$$

SELF TEST 24.5

Find the integrals of a) $5\cos 10x$ b) $3e^{4x}$.

a) $\tfrac{1}{2}\sin 10x + c$ b) $\tfrac{3}{4}e^{4x} + c$

EXAMPLE 24.6

A particle is moving away from a fixed point X. It starts 10 m away from X, and after t seconds its speed is $(15 - 3t^2)$ m s^{-1}. Find its distance from X after t seconds.

Solution

The distance is the integral of speed.

$$\text{distance} = \int (15 - 3t^2)\,dt = 15t - t^3 + c$$

When $t = 0$, the distance is 10.

$$10 = 15 \times 0 - 0^3 + c. \text{ Hence } c = 10.$$

After t seconds, the distance is $15t - t^3 + 10$ m

SELF TEST 24.6

A particle moves away from point A. It starts 5 m from A, and after t seconds its speed is $(4t + 3\sqrt{t})$ m s^{-1}. Find its distance from A after t seconds.

$$2t^2 + 2t^{1\frac{1}{2}} + 5 \text{ m}$$

EXAMPLE 24.7

Initally, the electrical charge on a plate is 60 coulombs. After t seconds, the charge is decreasing at a rate of $0.4e^{-0.01t}$ coulombs per second. Find the charge after 50 seconds.

Solution

The rate of change of the charge is $-0.4e^{-0.01t}$ (It is negative because the charge is decreasing). Integrate this to find the charge.

$$\int -0.4e^{-0.01t}\,dt = \frac{-0.4}{-0.01}e^{-0.01t} + c$$

$$\text{Charge} = 40e^{-0.01t} + c$$

When $t = 0$, the charge is 60.

$$60 = 40e^{-0.01 \times 0} + c = 40 + c. \text{ Hence } c = 20.$$

After t seconds, the charge is $40e^{-0.01t} + 20$ coulombs.

Finally, put $t = 50$. We obtain $40e^{-0.01 \times 50} + 20$, i.e. 44.26 coulombs.

After 50 seconds, the charge is 44.3 coulombs

Note As t increases, the expression $e^{-0.01t}$ tends to 0. Hence the charge tends to 20 coulombs.

SELF TEST 24.7

At time $t = 0$ seconds, the current through a wire is 0.05 amps. At time t, it is increasing at a rate of $0.2\sin 10t$ amps per second. Find the current at time $t = 2$.

current = 0.0618 amps

24.2 Definite integrals

An integral like $\int 2x\,dx$ gives a function of x. It is an **indefinite integral**.

The **definite** integral is found by evaluating the indefinite integral at two values, called **limits**, and subtracting. To find the definite integral of $2x$ between 2 and 5 first find the indefinite integral, $x^2 + c$. The value of this function at $x = 5$ is $5^2 + c$, i.e. $25 + c$. The value at $x = 2$ is $2^2 + c$, i.e. $4 + c$. The difference is $25 - 4$, i.e. 21.

We write out the definite integral as follows. The two limits are written at the top and bottom of the integral sign.

$$\int_2^5 2x\,\mathrm{d}x = [x^2]_2^5 = 5^2 - 2^2 = 21$$

Note that you do not need to put in the constant of integration, as it cancels.

$$[x^2 + c]_2^5 = (5^2 + c) - (2^2 + c) = 25 + c - 4 - c = 21$$

EXAMPLE 24.8

Evaluate $\displaystyle\int_0^2 \sin\tfrac{1}{4}\pi x\,\mathrm{d}x$.

Solution
The indefinite integral is $\dfrac{-4}{\pi}\cos\tfrac{1}{4}\pi x + c$. Hence

$$\int_0^2 \sin\tfrac{1}{4}\pi x\,\mathrm{d}x = [-\tfrac{4}{\pi}\cos\tfrac{1}{4}\pi x]_0^2$$

$$= (-\tfrac{4}{\pi}\cos\tfrac{1}{2}\pi) - (-\tfrac{4}{\pi}\cos 0)$$

$\cos\tfrac{1}{2}\pi = 0$ and $\cos 0 = 1$. (See figure 20.20.)
Hence the integral is

$$(-\frac{4}{\pi} \times 0) - (-\frac{4}{\pi} \times 1) = \frac{4}{\pi}$$

$$\int_0^2 \sin\tfrac{1}{4}\pi x\,\mathbf{d}x = \frac{4}{\pi}$$

SELF TEST 24.8

Evaluate $\displaystyle\int_0^3 \mathrm{e}^{0.1x}\,\mathrm{d}x$.

3.50

Finding change by definite integrals

The definite integral finds the change of a quantity between two values.

EXAMPLE 24.9

At time t seconds, the speed of a particle is $(12 - 3t)$ m s^{-1}. Find the distance travelled between $t = 2$ and $t = 4$.

Solution
The distance is the integral of the speed. The integral of $12 - 3t$ is $12t - \tfrac{3}{2}t^2 + c$. Use the definite integral between $t = 2$ and $t = 4$.

$$\int_2^4 (12 - 3t)\,\mathrm{d}t = \left[12t - \frac{3}{2}t^2\right]_2^4$$

$$= (12 \times 4 - \frac{3}{2} \times 4^2) - (12 \times 2 - \frac{3}{2} \times 2^2)$$

$$= (48 - 24) - (24 - 6) = 6$$

The distance travelled is 6 m

SELF TEST 24.9

At time t seconds, the speed of a particle is $(4t + \tfrac{1}{4}t^3)$ m s^{-1}. Find the distance travelled between $t = 1$ and $t = 3$.

distance = 21 m

24.3 Integration to find area

Integration is also used to find area.

In Figure 24.2 the area shaded is under the curve $y = \mathrm{f}(x)$, between $x = a$ and $x = b$. It is given by the definite integral of the function between those values.

$$\text{area} = \int_a^b \mathrm{f}(x)\,\mathrm{d}x$$

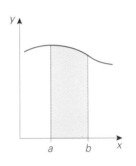

Figure 24.2

EXAMPLE 24.10

Find the area under the curve $y = 2x^3$, from $x = 1$ to $x = 2$.

Solution
Figure 24.3 shows the region. We want the definite integral of $2x^3$, between $x = 1$ and $x = 2$. The *indefinite* integral is $\tfrac{1}{2}x^4 + c$.

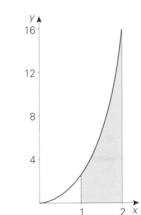

Figure 24.3 $y = 2x^3$

Hence

$$\int_1^2 2x^3 \, dx = \left[\tfrac{1}{2}x^4\right]_1^2 = \tfrac{1}{2} \times 2^4 - \tfrac{1}{2} \times 1^4 = 8 - \tfrac{1}{2} = 7\tfrac{1}{2}$$

The area is $7\frac{1}{2}$ square units

Find the area under the curve $y = 7x^5$, between $x = 2$ and $x = 3$.

$775\frac{5}{6}$ square units

EXAMPLE 24.11

Figure 24.4 shows the graph of $y = \sin x$, where x is measured in radians. Find the area of the first arch of the curve.

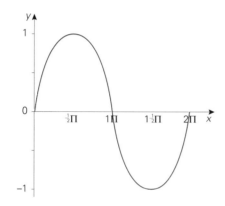

Figure 24.4 $y = \sin x$

Solution
The arch goes from $x = 0$ to $x = \pi$. The indefinite integral is $-\cos x$. Note that $\cos 0 = 1$ and $\cos \pi = -1$. Hence

$$\int_0^\pi \sin x \, dx = \left[-\cos x\right]_0^\pi = (-\cos \pi) - (-\cos 0) = 1 + 1 = 2$$

The area is 2 square units

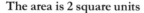

Figure 24.5 shows the graph of $y = 2 - e^{2x}$. Find where the curve cuts the x-axis. Hence find the shaded area, under the curve above the x-axis and to the right of the y-axis.

0.3466. 0.1931 square units

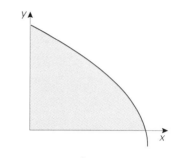

Figure 24.5 $y = 2 - e^{2x}$

■ CHECK YOUR UNDERSTANDING

● Integration is the opposite to differentiation. The integrals of standard functions are as follows.

$$\int x^n \, dx = \frac{1}{n+1}x^{n+1} + c \ (n \neq -1) \qquad \int e^{ax} \, dx = \frac{1}{a}e^{ax} + c$$

$$\int \sin ax \, dx = -\frac{1}{a}\cos ax + c \qquad \int \cos ax \, dx = \frac{1}{a}\sin ax + c$$

Do not forget the constant of integration. For the trigonometric integrals, the angle is measured in radians.
● The definite integral of a function is the difference between the indefinite integral, evaluated at two values.
● The area under a curve is the definite integral of the function between two values.

REVISION EXERCISES AND QUESTIONS

24.1 The opposite to differentiation

1   Find the integrals of the following.

  a) x^5 b) x^7 c) $\dfrac{1}{x^3}$

  d) $\sqrt[3]{x}$ e) $6x$ f) $5x^3$

  g) $3x^5 - 2x^6$ h) $3\sqrt{x} + 2x^{-3}$ i) e^{2x}

  j) $3\sin 4x$ k) $0.2\cos 5x$ l) $e^{3x} - e^{2x}$

2   In each of the following, find y from the information given.

  a) $\dfrac{dy}{dx} = 6x$ $(y = 2$ for $x = 1)$

  b) $\dfrac{dy}{dx} = 3\sqrt{x}$ $(y = 20$ for $x = 4)$

  c) $\dfrac{dy}{dx} = 2e^{4x}$ $(y = 6$ for $x = 0)$

d) $\dfrac{dy}{dx} = e^{-0.01x}$ ($y = 0$ for $x = 0$)

e) $\dfrac{dy}{dx} = 6\cos 3x$ ($y = 8$ for $x = 0$)

f) $\dfrac{dy}{dx} = 2\sin \frac{1}{2}x$ ($y = 7$ for $x = 2\pi$)

3 A particle is thrown upwards from a point 2 m above the ground. After t seconds, its speed upwards is $(40 - 10t)$ m s^{-1}. Find its height above the ground after 1.5 seconds.

4 A circuit is switched on. After t seconds, the rate of increase of the current is $4e^{-0.1t}$ amps per second. Find the current after t seconds.

24.2 Definite integrals

5 Evaluate the following definite integrals.

a) $\displaystyle\int_0^2 2x^3\,dx$

b) $\displaystyle\int_1^4 \dfrac{8}{x^3}\,dx$

c) $\displaystyle\int_0^\pi 3\cos \frac{1}{2}x\,dx$

d) $\displaystyle\int_1^3 (1+x)^2\,dx$

e) $\displaystyle\int_0^2 e^{-0.1x}\,dx$

f) $\displaystyle\int_0^{\frac{1}{8}} 2\sin 2\pi x\,dx$

6 A particle is moving so that after t seconds its speed is $(2 - 2e^{-0.1t})$ ms^{-1}. Find the distance travelled between $t = 1$ and $t = 3$.

24.3 Integration to find area

7 In each of the following, find the area under the curve between the given values of x.

a) $y = x^2 + 1$, between $x = 0$ and $x = 2$

b) $y = (1-x)^2$, between $x = 2$ and $x = 3$

c) $y = \dfrac{1}{x^2}$, between $x = 1$ and $x = 10$

d) $y = 8 - e^{2x}$, between $x = 0$ and $x = 1$

e) $y = 2\cos \frac{1}{3}\pi x$, between $x = 0$ and $x = \frac{1}{2}$

8 Let $y = 4 - x^2$. Find where the curve crosses the x-axis, i.e. where $y = 0$. Find the area between the curve and the x-axis.

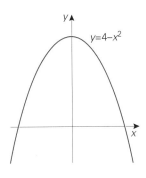

Figure 24.6

9 Find the area between the curve $y = -x^2 + 5x - 6$ and the x-axis.

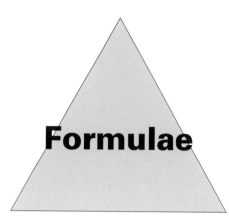

Formulae

Units

The basic SI units are:

Length	metre	(m)
Mass	kilogram	(kg)
Time	second	(s)

Larger or smaller units are obtained by adding prefixes to the basic units.

tera	T	1 000 000 000 000	
giga	G	1 000 000 000	billion
mega	M	1 000 000	million
kilo	k	1 000	thousand
milli	m	0.001	thousandth
micro	μ	0.000 001	millionth
nano	n	0.000 000 001	billionth
pico	p	0.000 000 000 001	
femto	f	0.000 000 000 000 001	

Square units

There are 1000^2, i.e. 1 000 000 mm^2 in 1 m^2.
There are 1000^2, i.e. 1 000 000 m^2 in 1 km^2.

Conversion between the SI system and the Imperial system

Length		Mass	
1 m	= 39.37 in	1 kg	= 2.205 pounds
	= 3.281 ft	1 g	= 0.035 27 ounce
1 km	= 0.621 mile		
1 in	= 25.40 mm	1 ounce	= 28.35 g
1 ft	= 0.3048 m	1 pound	= 0.4536 kg
1 mile	= 1.609 km		

Scientific rules

$$\text{force} = \text{stress} \times \text{area}$$

$$\text{power} = \frac{\text{work done}}{\text{time taken}}$$

$$\text{efficiency} = \frac{\text{output power}}{\text{input power}} \times 100\,\%$$

$$\text{power of circuit} = \text{resistance} \times \text{current}^2$$

Ohm's Law   potential difference = current × resistance

Combining resistance

$$R = R_1 + R_2 \quad \text{(in series)}$$

$$\frac{1}{R} = \frac{1}{R_1} + \frac{1}{R_2} \quad \text{(in parallel)}$$

Hooke's Law   extension = constant × tension

Boyle's Law   pressure × volume = constant

Algebraic rules

Laws of powers

$$a^n \times a^m = a^{n+m} \qquad a^n \div a^m = a^{n-m} \qquad (a^n)^m = a^{nm}$$

$$a^0 = 1 \qquad a^{-n} = \frac{1}{a^n} \qquad a^{\frac{1}{n}} = \sqrt[n]{a}$$

Laws of logarithms

$$\log ab = \log a + \log b \qquad \log(a \div b) = \log a - \log b$$

$$\log a^x = x \log a$$

$$\log \frac{1}{x} = -\log x \qquad \qquad \log 1 = 0$$

Quadratic equation

If $ax^2 + bx + c = 0$, then $x = \dfrac{-b \pm \sqrt{(b^2 - 4ac)}}{2a}$

Pythagoras' theorem

Figure A.1 shows a triangle right-angled at A.
Then $AB^2 + AC^2 = BC^2$

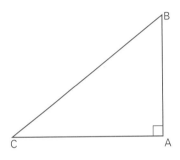

Figure A.1

Trigonometry

Figure A.2 shows a right-angled triangle. The six trigonometric functions are

$$\sin\theta = \frac{OPP}{HYP} \quad \cos\theta = \frac{ADJ}{HYP} \quad \tan\theta = \frac{OPP}{ADJ}$$

$$\csc\theta = \frac{HYP}{OPP} \quad \sec\theta = \frac{HYP}{ADJ} \quad \cot\theta = \frac{ADJ}{OPP}$$

cosec, sec and cot are the reciprocals of sin, cos and tan respectively.

$$\csc\theta = \frac{1}{\sin\theta} \quad \sec\theta = \frac{1}{\cos\theta} \quad \cot\theta = \frac{1}{\tan\theta}$$

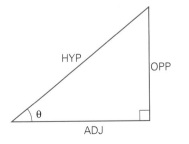

Figure A.2

In the triangle of Figure A.3, side a is opposite angle $\hat{A}$ etc.

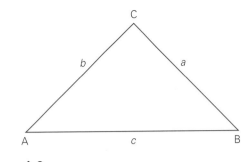

Figure A.3

Sine rule

$$\frac{a}{\sin\hat{A}} = \frac{b}{\sin\hat{B}} = \frac{c}{\sin\hat{C}}$$

The sine rule may be ambiguous when finding angles. If θ is one solution, $180° - \theta$ may be another solution.

Cosine rule

$$a^2 = b^2 + c^2 - 2bc\cos\hat{A} \quad \text{(to find an unknown side)}$$

rearranging gives

$$\cos\hat{A} = \frac{b^2 + c^2 - a^2}{2bc} \quad \text{(to find an unknown angle)}$$

sin, cos, tan for angles greater than 90°

- For $90° < \theta < 180°$, subtract θ from $180°$.
  sin is +ve, cos and tan −ve
- For $180° < \theta < 270°$, subtract $180°$ from θ.
  tan is +ve, sin and cos −ve
- For $270° < \theta < 360°$, subtract θ from $360°$.
  cos is +ve, sin and tan −ve
- For $360° < \theta$, subtract $360°$ from θ.

Length

Shape	Perimeter
Rectangle with breadth b and height h	$2b + 2h$
Circle with radius r	$2\pi r$ (also called circumference)
Ellipse, axes $2a$ and $2b$	$\simeq \pi(a + b)$

Area

Shape	Area
Rectangle with breadth b and height h	bh
Square with side x	x^2
Triangle with breadth b and height h	$\frac{1}{2}bh$
Parallelogram with breadth b and height h	bh
Trapezium with parallel sides a and b, height h	$\frac{1}{2}(a+b)h$
Circle with radius r	πr^2
Triangle, sides a and b enclosing angle $\hat{C}$	$\frac{1}{2}ab\sin\hat{C}$
Triangle, sides a, b and c Let $s = \frac{1}{2}(a+b+c)$	$\sqrt{(s(s-a)(s-b)(s-c))}$
Sector of angle θ from a circle, radius r	$\pi r^2 \dfrac{\theta}{360}$
Segment of angle θ from circle, radius r	$\frac{1}{2}r^2(\pi\dfrac{\theta}{180} - \sin\theta)$
Ellipse, axes $2a$ and $2b$	πab
Surface of sphere, radius r	$4\pi r^2$
Curved surface of cylinder, radius r and height h	$2\pi rh$
Curved surface of cone with radius r and height h, $l = \sqrt{(r^2+h^2)}$	πrl
Curved surface of frustum of cone, height h, radii r and R, $l = \sqrt{(h^2 + (R-r)^2)}$	$\pi l(R+r)$

Volume

Shape	Volume
Cuboid with sides a, b and c	abc
Cube with side x	x^3
Prism with cross-sectional area A and height h	Ah
Pyramid with base area A and height h	$\frac{1}{3}Ah$
Sphere with radius r	$\frac{4}{3}\pi r^3$
Cylinder with base radius r, height h	$\pi r^2 h$
Cone with base radius r, height h	$\frac{1}{3}\pi r^2 h$
Frustum, height h, areas a and A	$\frac{1}{3}h(A + \sqrt{(Aa)} + a)$
Frustum of cone, height h radii R and r	$\frac{1}{3}\pi h(R^2 + Rr + r^2)$

Graphs

Approximate areas

Mid-ordinate rule
$$d(h_1 + h_2 + \ldots + h_n)$$
Trapezium rule
$$\tfrac{1}{2}d[y_0 + y_n + 2(y_1 + y_2 + \ldots + y_{n-1})]$$
Simpson's rule
$$\tfrac{1}{3}d[y_0 + y_n + 4(y_1 + y_3 + \ldots) + 2(y_2 + y_4 + \ldots)]$$

Statistics

Mean of x
$$\bar{x} = \tfrac{1}{n}\Sigma x_i$$
Variance of x
$$\tfrac{1}{n}\Sigma(x_i - \bar{x})^2 \quad \text{or} \quad \tfrac{1}{n}\Sigma x_i^2 - \bar{x}^2$$
Linear equation for y in terms of x
$$y = ax + b, \quad \text{where} \quad a = \frac{\tfrac{1}{n}\Sigma x_i y_i - \bar{x}\bar{y}}{\tfrac{1}{n}\Sigma x_i^2 - \bar{x}^2} \quad \text{and} \quad b = \bar{y} - a\bar{x}$$

Differentiation

Function	Derivative $\dfrac{dy}{dx}$
$y = x^n$	nx^{n-1}
$y = e^{ax}$	ae^{ax}
$y = \sin ax$	$a\cos ax$
$y = \cos ax$	$-a\sin ax$

Integration

Function	Integral
x^n	$\dfrac{1}{n+1}x^{n+1} + c$
e^{ax}	$\dfrac{1}{a}e^{ax} + c$
$\sin ax$	$-\dfrac{1}{a}\cos ax + c$
$\cos ax$	$\dfrac{1}{a}\sin ax + c$

Extra questions

Chapter 1 Arithmetical operations

1 Find the following.

   a) the sum of 18 and 11 b) the product of 5 and 7
   c) the total of 3, 5 and 8 d) the difference
      between 20 and 9
   e) 21 divided by 3 f) 10 times 12
   g) the quotient and remainder when 22 is divided by 5
   h) 17 less 5 i) 5 into 60

2 Evaluate the following.

   a) $5 + 3 \times 2$ b) $(5 + 3) \times 2$ c) $20 \div 4 + 1$
   d) $20 \div (4 + 1)$ e) $30 - 12 \div 3$ f) $(30 - 12) \div 3$
   g) $18 - 3 + 5$ h) $18 - (3 + 5)$

3 Evaluate the following.

   a) -7×-2 b) $-9 \times -8 \div -6$ c) -3^2
   d) $(-3)^2$ e) $(1 - 6) \times (2 - 12)$

4 Factorise the following.

   a) 48 b) 90 c) 112

5 Find the HCF and LCM of the following sets of numbers.

   a) 30 and 24 b) 35 and 49 c) 39 and 20
   d) 40 and 10 e) 30, 42 and 33 f) 15, 21 and 28

6 In a house, the following are switched on. Five 60 W bulbs, two 100 W bulbs and a 1200 W heater. Find the total power in use.

7 8000 m of fibre weighs 440 g. Find the tex of the fibre.

8 A fibre has tex 150. Find the weight of 500 m.

9 When a battery is charged, the charging current is the difference between the incoming voltage and the battery voltage, divided by the internal resistance of the battery. Calculate the current when a 12 V battery of internal resistance 2 Ω is charged by a voltage of 16 V.

10 The storage of a battery is 120 ampere-hours. For how long can it deliver a current of 8 amps?

Chapter 2 Fractions and decimals

1 Simplify the following.

   a) $\frac{3}{21}$ b) $\frac{4}{6}$ c) $\frac{33}{99}$

2 Convert the following to mixed numbers.

   a) $\frac{17}{5}$ b) $\frac{23}{21}$ c) $\frac{57}{10}$

3 Convert the following to improper fractions.

   a) $3\frac{1}{2}$ b) $5\frac{2}{3}$ c) $6\frac{3}{5}$

4 Evaluate the following, simplifying your answers where possible.

   a) $\frac{1}{2} \times \frac{5}{11}$ b) $1\frac{1}{4} \times 1\frac{1}{3}$ c) $2\frac{4}{7} \times 3\frac{3}{10}$
   d) $\frac{3}{4} \div \frac{4}{5}$ e) $1\frac{2}{3} \div 1\frac{3}{4}$ f) $2\frac{3}{11} \div 4\frac{1}{5}$
   g) $2\frac{1}{2} + 3\frac{3}{4}$ h) $\frac{8}{13} - \frac{2}{5}$ i) $2\frac{5}{6} + 1\frac{4}{9}$

5 Evaluate the following, giving your answers correct to 3 significant figures.

   a) $0.142 + 0.734$ b) $87.3 - 71.36$ c) 12.5×0.8
   d) 4.02×2.5 e) $13 \div 0.3$ f) $12.3 \div 80$

6 a) Convert $1\frac{3}{16}$ and $2\frac{4}{11}$ to decimals.
   b) Convert 0.3 and 0.375 to fractions.

7 A drain pipe is bent through an eighth of a right-angle (90°). Through what angle is it bent? Give your answer as a mixed number of degrees.

8 The current at which a fuse will blow is 1.8 times its nominal value. Find the current which will blow a fuse of nominal value 13 amps.

9 Current I, voltage V and resistance R are connected by the equation $V = IR$. Complete the following table.

V (V)	200	100		10 000
I (A)	50		0.1	
R (Ω)		20	500	200 000

10 Energy of 4187 joules is needed to raise the temperature of 1 kg of water by 1°C. Find the energy needed to raise 0.043 kg of water from 22°C to 100°C.

11 Energy of 50 000 joules is supplied to 4 kg of water at 10°C. What is the final temperature of the water?

12 When fitting a pipe the following expression gives its length. Evaluate this expression. The measurements are in inches.

$$10 - (2 \times 2\tfrac{3}{8} - 2 \times \tfrac{1}{2})$$

13 A pipe is $2\tfrac{5}{16}$ inches in diameter. Express this as a decimal. Convert to mm, given that 1 inch is 25.4 mm.

Chapter 3 Percentages and ratio

1 Out of a workforce of 800, 350 are women. Express the proportion of women as a percentage.

2 Find 23% of 480.

3 A fabric contains 30% cotton, 70% polyester. Find the mass of cotton in 7 kg of the cloth.

4 The water content of a cloth is 35%. Find the mass of 40 kg of the cloth once it has been dried.

5 The estimated cost of a job increases from #40 500 to #47 000. Find the percentage increase.

6 In a clothing sale, all prices are reduced by 30%. A suit costs #1400 in the sale. What was its price before the reduction?

7 After drying, the mass of a quantity of wood is reduced by 10%. If it had mass 540 kg after drying, what was its mass before drying?

8 An alloy contains 24 kg of tin and 39 kg of copper. Find the ratio of tin to copper, in its simplest form.

9 The ratio of cotton to polyester in a fibre is 3:5. How much cotton will be mixed with 80 kg of polyester?

10 An alloy contains zinc and copper in the ratio 2:9. How much zinc is there in 900 kg of the alloy?

11 A concrete mix contains cement, sand and aggregate in the ratio 2:7:11. How much cement will 380 kg of concrete contain?

12 The input power of a generator is 2000 W, and its output is 1800 W. Find the percentage efficiency of the generator.

13 A current of 60 amps is delivered at 220 volts through cables of resistance 0.2 Ω. Calculate the percentage voltage drop.

Chapter 4 Indices and logarithms

1 Evaluate the following.

a) 11^2 b) 3^4 c) $\left(\tfrac{1}{3}\right)^2$

d) 5×2^2 e) $(5 \times 2)^2$ f) $2^3 + 3^2$

g) $\sqrt{64}$ h) $\sqrt{(16 + 9)}$ i) $\sqrt{16} + \sqrt{9}$

j) 20^0 k) $81^{\frac{1}{2}}$ l) $100^{1\frac{1}{2}}$

m) 2^{-3} n) $\tfrac{1}{3}^{-2}$ o) $0.25^{-\frac{1}{2}}$

2 Simplify the following.

a) $2^3 \times 2^4 \times 2^5$ b) $9^2 \times 27^3$ c) $(5^3)^{\frac{2}{3}}$

3 Convert

a) 254 millicoulombs to coulombs   b) 0.35 megawatts to watts

c) 132 000 V to kV   d) 9800 μA to mA.

4 Write the following in standard form.

a) 24 500 000   b) 0.000 0034   c) 571×10^{12}

d) 0.634×10^6 e) 72.4×10^{-8} f) 0.0243×10^{-4}

5 Evaluate the following, giving your answers in standard form.

a) $4.3 \times 10^5 \times 2 \times 10^6$ b) $6.3 \times 10^8 \times 3 \times 10^5$

c) $8.4 \times 10^6 \div 2 \times 10^3$ d) $1.2 \times 10^{15} \div 4 \times 10^3$

e) $4 \times 10^{-6} \times 2.1 \times 10^{-5}$ f) $2 \times 10^{-5} \div 5 \times 10^{-8}$

g) $4.7 \times 10^9 + 3.2 \times 10^9$ h) $8.2 \times 10^6 - 9.1 \times 10^5$

i) $6.7 \times 10^{-8} + 5.34 \times 10^{-7}$

6 a) Convert 7×10^{-4} mF to μF.

b) Convert 5×10^7 N to MN.

7 Calculate the current that flows when a voltage of 4×10^8 V is across a resistance of 8×10^{12} Ω. ($I = V \div R$)

8 The following resistances are in series. Find the total resistance, in kΩ.

$$450\ \Omega,\ 1.3\ \text{k}\Omega,\ 0.000\,61\ \text{M}\Omega$$

9 When a current of I A flows through a resistance of R Ω, the power generated is $I^2 R$ W.

a) Find the power when 23 amps flows through 20 Ω.

b) Find the current needed through 15 Ω to generate power of 400 W.

c) A current of 45 A gives a power of 5×10^8 W. Find the resistance.

d) Find the current needed through 20 Ω to generate a power of 7.2×10^{12} W.

10 A bottle of mineral water contains 280 mg of solids per kg of water. Find the percentage of solids in the water.

11 Evaluate the following.

a) $\log 1000$ b) $\log 0.000\,01$ c) $\log_2 32$

12 Simplify the following.

a) $\log 125 + \log 0.8$ b) $\log_3 1\frac{1}{2} + \log_3 18$

c) $2 \log_2 36 - 4 \log_2 6$

13 In alternating current, the r.m.s. (root mean square) current is equal to $\dfrac{1}{\sqrt{2}}$ times the maximum current.

a) If the maximum current is 4.9 A, find the r.m.s. current.

b) If the r.m.s. current is 2.46 A, find the maximum current.

Chapter 5 Techniques of calculation

1 Evaluate the following. Give your answers correct to three significant figures.

a) 6.493×43.28 b) 0.4563×0.01523

c) $1684 + 54.78$ d) $0.3089 + 0.00352$

e) $3.2734 \times (563 + 841)$ f) $6.552 + (478 \times 0.934)$

g) $(45.54 + 23.19)(2.653 + 9.012)$

h) $(1045 + 2036)(2.786 - 1.956)$ i) $2^{2.34}$ j) $5^{0.673}$

k) $3^{-1.76}$ l) $10^{(2.356 + 4.289)}$ m) $2^{\frac{-43.2}{20.97}}$

n) $(23.65 + 47.77)^{1.254}$ o) $\sqrt{(7645 - 2674)}$

p) $(\sqrt{0.01671} + \sqrt{0.06715})^{5.123}$ q) $2.3^{\sqrt{(2.112 - 1.003)}}$

r) $\pi\, 1.275^2$ s) $\frac{4}{3}\pi 2.345^3$

t) $2\pi 43.65\,(43.65 + 68.19)$

u) $1.027 + 4.55 \times 1.027^2 - 1.288 \times 1.027^3$

v) $1 + 2 \times 65.79 + 3 \times 65.79^2 + 4 \times 65.79^3$

w) $\log(1.249 - 0.986)$

x) $\dfrac{5.987 + 4.983}{1.238 + 2.078}$ y) $\sqrt{\left(\dfrac{1.23^2 - 1.17^2}{6.96 + 2.39}\right)}$

z) $\log\left(\dfrac{63.98}{21.09}\right)$

Chapter 6 Accuracy and error

1 A distance of 97 m is measured as 95 m. Find the error, the relative error and the percentage error.

2 An object of 1.24 kg is weighed. The result is too low, with a relative error of 0.03. Find the result.

3 Find the ranges within which the following lie.

a) 96.3 ± 0.1 b) 0.0043 ± 0.0002 c) $6.98 \pm 5\%$

d) 4.76, given correct to 2 decimal places

e) 54 100, given correct to 3 significant figures

f) $11.0^{+0.3}_{-0.2}$ g) $0.17^{+0.03}_{+0.01}$ h) $460^{+20\%}_{-10\%}$

4 A job is broken into three tasks, which take 35 hours, 46 hours and 51 hours. All times are given correct to the nearest hour. What is the total time for the job? What is the maximum error in your answer?

5 Liquid with volume 4.5 m^3 (correct to one decimal place) has density 0.956 kg/m^3 (correct to three decimal places). Find the mass of the liquid, and give the maximum error in your answer.

6 A large factory employs 2500 workers (correct to the nearest 100) and its monthly wage bill is #3 640 000 (correct to the nearest #10 000). What is the average monthly wage? Give the maximum error in your answer.

7 The time for an aeroplane flight is 53 minutes. The departure time may be delayed by about 50 minutes. What is the maximum total time for the waiting time and flight?

8 The temperature of a substance was measured as 41.6°C. After an hour, its temperature had fallen by about 20°C. What was the new temperature?

9 Evaluate the following. Check your results by approximation.

a) $0.2561 + 0.1887$ b) $1674 - 988$ c) 23.8×0.0532

d) $19.33 \div 2.001$ e) $(6.374 + 4.287) \times (12.06 + 7.99)$

f) $\pi 2.335^2$ g) $10^{4.113 - 2.098}$ h) $\sqrt{(44.32 + 51.65)}$

Chapter 7 Arithmetic in other bases

1 Convert the following to degrees, minutes and seconds.

a) $25.60°$ b) $103.75°$ c) $42.984°$

2 Convert the following to decimals.

a) $55° 15'$ b) $64° 12' 45''$ c) $12° 34' 29''$

3 Evaluate the following, giving your answers in degrees, minutes and seconds.

a) $75° 30' + 16° 45'$

b) $33° 19' - 15° 44'$

c) $20° 12' 50'' + 18° 41' 27''$

d) $40° 16' 17'' - 18° 32' 29''$

4 a) Convert the denary number 68 to binary.

b) Convert the binary number 110011011 to denary.

c) Convert the denary number 3849 to hex.

d) Convert the hex number E53 to denary.

e) Convert the hex number 3AC to binary.

f) Convert the binary number 11001011010011 to hex.

g) Convert the denary number 731 to bcd.

h) Convert the bcd number 001110010101 to denary.

5 Evaluate the following binary arithmetic expressions.

a) $1101 + 11101$ b) 10001×1101

6 Arthmetic to base 8 is **octal** arithmetic.

a) Convert 734 in octal to denary.

b) Convert 982 in denary to octal.

c) Convert 110011011010 in binary to octal.

Chapter 8 Algebra

1   Simplify the following.

   a) $7x - 3x$ b) $5\frac{1}{4}x + 2\frac{3}{4}x$ c) $4a + 3b + 8a - b$

   d) $a^2 + ab - 2ba + b^2$ e) $xyz + 3yzx + 2zyx$

   f) $6 \times 5a$ g) $3x \times 4x$ h) $7x \times 3y$

   i) $-2m \times \frac{1}{4}n$ j) $-8a \times -9a$ k) $5x^2 \div x$

   l) $2xyz \div xz$ m) $x^3 \times x^4$ n) $a^8 \div a^3$

   o) $(n^4)^3$ p) $(x^2 \times x^4)^5$

   q) $(m^4 \div m^8)^{-3}$ r) $(2x^2y^3)^4$

   s) $\dfrac{1}{y^{-3}}$ t) $(a^{\frac{1}{2}})^4$

   u) $\sqrt{(x^3 \times x^5)}$ v) $m^3 \times m^2 \times m^7$

   w) $x^6 \div (x^2 \times x^3)$ x) $x^6 \div x^2 \times x^3$

   y) $\left(\dfrac{x^2}{y^3}\right)^{-4}$ z) $\sqrt{\left(\dfrac{x^5}{x^3}\right)}$

2   Find the value of $3x + 8$ when x is
    a) 2,   b) $\frac{2}{3}$,   c) $-2\frac{1}{2}$.

3   Find the value of $z^2 - 3z - 7$ when z is
    a) 2,   b) -3,   c) $-1\frac{1}{2}$.

4   Find the value of $\sqrt{(a^2 + b^2)}$ when $a = 7$ and $b = 24$.

5   Expand the following and simplify where possible.

   a) $8(x - y)$ b) $5(2a + 3b)$ c) $x(y + z)$

   d) $3x(y + 3z)$ e) $a(a + a^2)$ f) $-7m(m - 1)$

   g) $3(a + b) + 4(a - b)$ h) $2(x + 2y) - 3(x - y)$

   i) $m(m + 2n) + n(m + 3n)$ j) $3x(2x + 5y) - 4y(3x - 7y)$

   k) $(x + 2)(x + 5)$ l) $(y - 4)(y + 12)$

   m) $(z - 1)(z - 9)$ n) $(2a + 3)(3a + 2)$

   o) $(7x + 2y)(x + 3y)$ p) $(5m - 2n)(m - 3n)$

   q) $(3a + b)^2$ r) $(x - 2y)^2$

   s) $(3x + 7)^2$ t) $(m + n)(m - n)$

   u) $(\frac{1}{3} - a)(\frac{1}{3} + a)$ v) $8(y + \frac{1}{2})(y - \frac{1}{2})$

6   Factorise the following.

   a) $2x + 4y$ b) $25 - 30m$ c) $x^2 + 3x$

   d) $9q + 6q^2$ e) $a^2b + 2ab^2$ f) $\pi a^2 + \pi ab + \pi b^2$

7   Electrical impedance is given by

$$Z = \sqrt{(X_R^2 + (X_L - X_C)^2)}$$

   where $X_C = \dfrac{1}{2\pi fC}$ and $X_L = 2\pi fL$.

   Find an expression for Z in terms of X_R, f, C and L.

Chapter 9 Coordinates and graphs

1   Copy the graph in Figure E.1, give the coordinates of point A. Place B at $(2.4, 1.7)$.

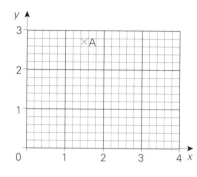

Figure E.1

2   Copy the graph in Figure E.2, give the coordinates of point C. Place D at $(-1.3, 1.9)$.

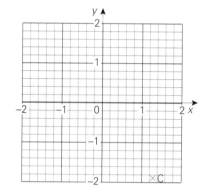

Figure E.2

3   Figure E.3 shows the temperature of a liquid over a period of 4 hours.

   a) What is the temperature at $t = 2.7$?
   b) When is the temperature $40°C$?

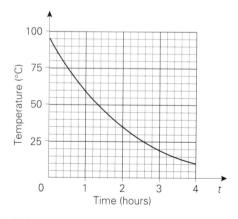

Figure E.3

4 The table below gives the air resistance, R N, on a vehicle when it is moving at v m/s. Plot a graph of R against v.

v (m s)	0	5	10	15	20	25	30
R (N)	0	23	58	82	121	162	209

5 Tyre pressure can be measured in lb/in^2, or in kg/cm^2. A pressure of 30 lb/in^2 is equivalent to 2.1 kg/cm^2. Construct a chart converting between lb/in^2 and kg/cm^2.

6 Plot the following graphs, for the range of values given.

a) $y = 1\frac{1}{2}x - 2$, for x between -1 and 4

b) $y = -2\frac{1}{2}x + 3$, for x between -2 and 3

c) $y = x^2 + 3x - 1$, for x between -3 and 2

d) $y = 4 - \dfrac{2}{x}$, for x between $\dfrac{1}{4}$ and 8

7 Find the equations of the following straight lines.

a) with gradient -2, through $(1,7)$

b) through $(2, 1)$ and $(5,7)$

c) through $(-2, 5)$ and $(2, -1)$

8 The mass of a yarn can be measured by its *cotton count*, which is the number of 840 yard lengths to have a mass of 1 pound. Cotton count c and tex t are related by

$$c = \frac{590.5}{t}$$

Prepare a graph to convert between cotton count and tex.

Chapter 10 Equations

1 Solve the following equations.

a) $7x - 3 = 25$ b) $2x + 3 = 31$ c) $19 - x = 5$

d) $17 - 2x = 3$ e) $5x + 1 = 2x + 19$

f) $3 - x = 17 - 3x$ g) $\frac{1}{2}x = \frac{1}{3}x + 7$

h) $3(x - 8) = 4(x - 27)$ i) $\frac{2}{7}(x - 3) = \frac{4}{13}(x - 1)$

j) $\dfrac{24}{x} = 6$ k) $\dfrac{3}{x - 7} = 8$ l) $\dfrac{1}{x + 1} = \dfrac{2}{x + 7}$

m) $3^{x-1} = 3^{2x-8}$ n) $9^{2x-5} = 3^{x+7}$

o) $(3x - 1)^2 = 64$ p) $(3x + 1)^3 = 1000$

q) $\sqrt{(2x - 3)} = 5$ r) $\sqrt[4]{(2x + 1)} = 3$

2 Solve the following pairs of simultaneous equations.

a) $2x + y = 7$ b) $3x + 2y = 7$ c) $5x + 3y = 31$

$\quad 3x + y = 15$ $\quad 5x - 2y = 17$ $\quad 2x + y = 11$

d) $7x - 5y = 20$ e) $\frac{1}{5}x + \frac{3}{4}y = 16$ f) $0.2x + 0.7y = 35$

$\quad 5x - 4y = 13$ $\quad \frac{3}{5}x - \frac{3}{8}y = 6$ $\quad 0.1x - 0.3y = 11$

3 Draw the graph of $y = 2x^2 - 5x - 4$, for values of x between -1 and 4. Hence solve the equation

$$2x^2 - 5x - 4 = 0$$

4 A type of fuel has 5% oil. How much oil must be added to 240 litres of this fuel to make it 10% oil?

5 The formula connecting Fahrenheit and Celsius temperatures is $C = \frac{5}{9}(F - 32)$. What temperature is the same on both scales?

6 A tank can be filled in 3 hours from tap A. It can be filled in 5 hours from tap B. If both taps are turned on, how long will it take to fill the tank?

7 A type of solder has 30% tin and 70% lead. Another type has 60% tin and 40% lead. How much of each should be taken to make 300 kg of a solder with equal quantities of tin and lead?

8 A company has #8 000 000 invested, some at 8% interest, some at 7% interest. If the interest is #610 000, how much is invested at each rate of interest?

Chapter 11 Further algebra

1 Simplify the following.

a) $\dfrac{3a}{9b}$ b) $\dfrac{x^2}{2x}$ c) $\dfrac{3x + x^2}{3x}$

d) $\dfrac{p^2 + pq}{p}$ e) $\dfrac{xy}{x^2 + xy}$ f) $\dfrac{1}{\frac{1}{a} - \frac{1}{b}}$

2 Write the following as single fractions, simplifying your answers if possible.

a) $\dfrac{p}{2} \times \dfrac{m}{3}$ b) $\dfrac{2x}{y} \times \dfrac{y}{3x}$ c) $\dfrac{a}{b} \div \dfrac{x}{y}$

d) $\dfrac{p}{2} \div \dfrac{p}{3}$ e) $\dfrac{x}{2} + \dfrac{x}{3}$ f) $\dfrac{3}{x} - \dfrac{2}{y}$

3 Express the following as single fractions.

a) $\dfrac{1}{x^2y} + \dfrac{2}{xy^2}$ b) $\dfrac{a}{6x^2y^2} + \dfrac{b}{9xy^3} + \dfrac{c}{15x^3y}$

4 Evaluate the following.

a) $e^{4.121}$ b) $e^{2(1.34+2.07)}$

c) $\ln 65.33$ d) $\ln\left(\dfrac{62.35}{22.07}\right)$

5 Solve the following equations.

a) $e^x = 3.165$ b) $\ln x = -1.376$ c) $e^{3x} = 51.59$

d) $e^{3x+7} = 9874$ e) $\ln(2x^2 - 7) = 2.65$

f) $e^{-2.7x/4.76} = 0.0123$ g) $3^x = 7$

h) $5^{x-3} = 100$ i) $2^{x+1} = 3^x$

6 At time t seconds, the charge on a metal plate is $6e^{\frac{-t}{63}}$ μC.

a) Find the charge after 20 seconds.

b) When will the charge be 2 μC?

7 The value of a machine is decreasing at 5% each year. When new, it was worth #12 000.

a) What is its value after 6 years?
b) When will it be worth #5000?

8 For each of the following, change the subject to the letter in brackets.

a) $y = 8x + 3$ (x) b) $2a = 3b - 4$ (b)

c) $\frac{1}{2}m = \frac{1}{3}n - 2$ (n) d) $y = ax$ (x)

e) $p = \frac{b}{q}$ (q) f) $P = \pi(a + b)$ (a)

g) $at = bt + c$ (t) h) $0 = 2x + kx - 7$ (x)

i) $\frac{2}{x - 4} = z$ (x) j) $y = \frac{5 + 3t}{2x}$ (x)

k) $k = \frac{x + 1}{x - 1}$ (x) l) $y = \frac{t}{\frac{1}{2}t + 3}$ (t)

m) $V = \pi ab^2$ (b) n) $l = \sqrt{(r^2 + b^2)}$ (b)

o) $y = \sqrt{(2x - 3)}$ (x) p) $E = Ae^t$ (t)

q) $I = Ae^{-\frac{t}{8}}$ (t) r) $I = A(1 - e^{-\frac{t}{4}})$ (t)

s) $y = \ln(3x - 2)$ (x) t) $y = \ln\left(\frac{z}{x}\right)$ (x)

Chapter 12 Proportion and linear laws

1 Two quantities x and y are proportional. When $x = 3$, then $y = 0.21$. Find an equation giving y in terms of x. Find x when $y = 0.28$.

2 Two quantities p and q are inversely proportional to each other. When $p = 5$, then $q = 40$. Find an equation giving q in terms of p. Find p when $q = 50$.

3 The wavelength of a radio wave is inversely proportional to its frequency. A wave of length 2000 m has frequency 125 000 Hz. Find the frequency of a wave with length 500 m.

4 The resistance of a length of wire is proportional to its length. A wire 2.4 m long has a resistance of 0.6 Ω. Find the resistance of a wire which is 10 m long.

5 The quantity T is proportional to the square of the quantity r. When $r = 0.8$, then $T = 32$. Find an equation giving T in terms of r. Find r when $T = 1024$.

6 Soup cans are made to contain a fixed volume. The height of the can is inversely proportional to the square of the radius. A can of radius 5.4 cm has height 11.3 cm. Find the height of a can with radius 3.8 cm.

7 The deflection of the end of a beam is proportional to the cube of the length of the beam. A beam of length 3.2 m is

deflected by 0.08 m. Find the deflection of a beam of length 4.2 m.

8 The energy of a circuit is proportional to the square of the voltage across it. Find the percentage loss of energy if the voltage falls by 10%.

9 The flow rate through a pipe of diameter d is approximately proportional to $d^{2\frac{1}{2}}$.

a) Four pipes of diameter 15 mm are to be replaced with a single pipe. What is the diameter of the single pipe, if it has the same flow rate as the original four pipes?
b) How many pipes of diameter 20 mm would have approximately the same flow as a single pipe of diameter 40 mm?

10 The cost of a job, #C, is related to the time it takes, t days, by $C = at + b$. If it takes 10 days it will cost #35 000, and if it takes 12 days it will cost #40 000. Find a and b.

11 A room has window area w m^2. The hourly heat loss, H MJ, is given by $H = aw + b$. If the window area is 4 m^2, the heat loss is 6 MJ per hour. If the area is 6 m^2, the loss is 6.7 MJ per hour. Find a and b.

12 The rate of growth of y is equal to 3.5 times y. At time $t = 0$, $y = 4.7$. Find an equation giving y in terms of t. Find the value of t for which $y = 8.3$.

13 The rate of decrease of T is proportional to T. At time $t = 0$, $T = 73$. At time $t = 10$, $T = 24$. Find an equation giving T in terms of t. Find the value of T when $t = 25$.

14 A rope is sliding round a cylinder. One end of the rope is at tension T_0. The other end is at T N. T increases exponentially with the angle, θ, subtended by the rope in contact with the cylinder. If $\theta = 0°$, then $T = T_0 = 150$ N. If $\theta = 30°$, then $T = 380$ N. Find T in terms of θ. Find the value of θ for which $T = 430$ N.

15 A current of 10 A flows in a circuit. When it is switched off, the current decreases exponentially with time. After 0.5 s the current is 0.6 A. Find an equation giving the current, I A, in terms, of time, t s. Find the time when the current has been reduced to 0.1 A.

Chapter 13 Laws from experimental data

1 The quantities x and y obey a law of the form $y = ax + b$. A table of approximate values is given below. Plot the values, draw a line of best fit, and find the law.

x	10	20	30	40	50	60
y	63	81	105	122	131	155

2 The quantities x and y obey a law of the form $y = ax + b$. A table of approximate values is given below, but one value of y is inaccurate. Plot the values and find the correct value of y.

x	1	2	3	4	5	6
y	0.094	0.148	0.202	0.276	0.310	0.364

3 From your results of Question 1, predict the value of y when $x = 35$.

4 From your results of Question 1, predict the value of y when $x = 100$.

5 The quantities x and y obey a law of the form $y = ax^2 + b$. A table of approximate values is given below. Make a suitable change of variables, plot the points and find the law.

x	1	2	3	4	5
y	2.4	3.3	4.6	6.4	8.8

6 The quantities x and y obey a law of the form $y = \dfrac{a}{x} + bx$.
A table of approximate values is given below. Make a suitable change of variables, plot the points and find the law.

x	0.2	0.3	0.4	0.5	0.6	0.7
y	0.096	0.091	0.098	0.108	0.121	0.134

7 Liquid flows through a pipe. When the pipe has diameter d mm, the flow is F millilitres per second, where F is approximately proportional to a power of d. The table below gives experimental values of d and F. Use logs to reduce the equation to linear form. Hence find F in terms of d.

d (mm)	20	25	30	35	40
F (ml/s)	98	182	293	417	573

8 The quantities x and y obey a law of the form $y = ab^x$. A table of approximate values is given below. Use logs to reduce the equation to linear form. Hence find y in terms of x.

x	1.1	1.2	1.3	1.4	1.5
y	37.8	39.4	41.3	43.2	45.4

Chapter 14 Quadratics

1 Factorise the following.
a) $x^2 + 13x + 30$ b) $x^2 - 8x + 12$ c) $x^2 + 3x - 40$
d) $x^2 - 5x - 50$ e) $x^2 + 8x + 16$ f) $2x^2 + 7x + 3$
g) $6x^2 - 7x + 2$ h) $3x^2 + x - 10$ i) $5x^2 - 80$

2 Complete the square of the following expressions.
a) $x^2 + 6x + 11$ b) $x^2 - 14x + 40$ c) $x^2 + 3x^2 - 2$
d) $12x + 3$ e) $13 - 2x - x^2$ f) $14 + 6x - 3x^2$

3 For each of the expressions in Question 2, find the minimum or maximum value of the expression, and the value of x which gives this minimum or maximum. Sketch the graph of the expression.

4 Solve the following equations, giving your answers correct to 3 significant figures.
a) $2x^2 + 8x + 3 = 0$ b) $x^2 - 11x - 29 = 0$

c) $0.12x^2 + 0.563x - 0.24 = 0$

d) $x^2 = 4x - 3$ e) $\dfrac{1}{x} + 4 = 2x$

f) $\dfrac{1}{x+3} + \dfrac{1}{x-4} = 7$

5 Solve the following pairs of simultaneous equations.
a) $y = 4x + 1$, $y = 2x^2 - 8x - 13$
b) $2y + 5x = 8$, $y = 23 - x - x^2$

6 A closed tank is in the shape of a cuboid with a square base. The height of the tank is 0.8 m. The total surface area of the tank is 7.32 m^2. Find the side of the base.

7 A strip of thin metal, 400 mm wide, is bent into an open trough as shown in Figure E.4. Let the width of the trough be x mm. Find, in terms of x, expressions for the height of the trough and its cross-sectional area. If the area is 14 500 mm^2, find x.

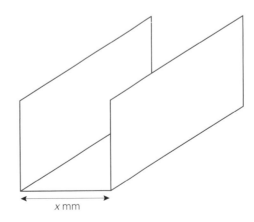

Figure E.4

Chapter 15 Geometry

1 Find the angles in the diagrams of Figure E.5.

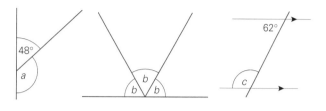

Figure E.5

2 A gear wheel has 40 teeth. A and B are points of teeth next to each other. Find the angle subtended by AB at the centre of the wheel.

3 Find the angles which are a) complementary to 68°, b) supplementary to 68°.

4 A wheel is rotating at 1500 revolutions per minute. How many degrees does it pass through in one second?

5 Figure E.6 shows two parallel beams, joined by struts which bisect each other. Find a pair of congruent triangles.

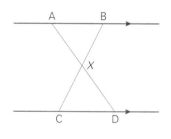

Figure E.6

6 Find the unknown angles in the triangles and quadrilaterals of Figure E.7.

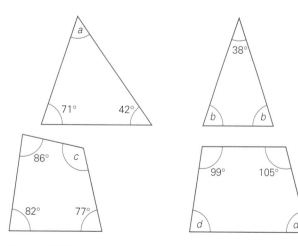

Figure E.7

7 Find the sum of the interior angles of a 15 sided figure.

8 The interior angle of a regular polygon is 8 times the exterior angle. Find the number of sides of the polygon.

9 The radius of a circle is 44 m. Find its diameter and its circumference.

10 Figure E.8 is a diagram of a desk. What are the names of the following shapes.
a) ABCDEFGH   b) the region above EFGH

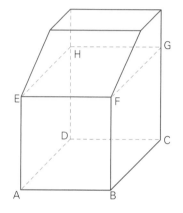

Figure E.8

11 A wire is coiled 200 times round a circle of diameter 80 mm. What is the length of wire?

12 Figure E.9 shows a cold chisel with ends at an angle of 60°. Find the obtuse angle x between the end and the side of the chisel.

Figure E.9 Cold chisel

13 A thin pipe is bent round 90° of a circle of radius 250 mm. Find the length of the curved part of the pipe.

Chapter 16 Area and volume

1 Find the areas of the following.

a) a rectangle, 34 mm by 50 mm
b) a square of side 4.2 m
c) a circle with radius 24 mm
d) a right-angled triangle with sides 4 m, 3 m and 5 m
e) a rectangle, 58 mm by 1.05 m

2 Find the areas of the shapes shown in Figure E.10. Lengths are in m.

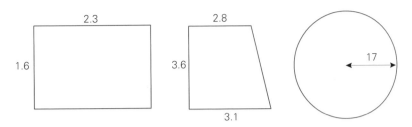

Figure E.10

3 The area of a rectangular field is 12 000 m². One side is 0.08 km long. What is the other side?

4 Find the volumes of the following.

a) a cube of side 2.7 m

b) a cuboid, 14 mm by 20 mm by 32 mm

c) a pyramid with a square base of side 8 m and height 12 m

d) a cylinder of diameter 0.4 m and height 0.6 m

e) a cone of height 140 mm and base diameter 48 mm

f) a sphere of diameter 94 mm

e) a cylinder of radius 84 mm and height 0.12 m

5 A water tank is a cuboid with square base of side 0.8 m. A sphere of diameter 0.1 m is immersed into the tank. Assuming that water does not overflow, how much does the water level rise?

6 A tank is a cylinder with base radius 0.6 m. A cube of side 0.1 m is immersed in the tank. Assuming that the water does not overflow, how much does the water level rise?

7 A tall cylinder of diameter 0.1 m is placed vertically in the tank of Question 5. The cylinder is not immersed, and water does not overflow. By what percentage does the water level rise?

8 Figure E.11 shows a desk. Lengths are in cm. What is the volume of the desk?

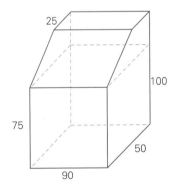

Figure E.11

9 A sphere is made from 0.32 m³ of plastic. Find the radius of the sphere.

10 Find the masses of the following.

a) a solid cube of side 0.1 m, of metal with density 7600 kg/m³

b) a circular disc of diameter 2.7 m, of metal with density 2.98 kg/m²

c) 1.65 km of wire, of metal with density 5.6 g per metre

11 A formula used in metal work is:

Punch force = Maximum shear strength × Area.

A region consisting of a circle of radius 2.2 mm is to be punched out. Find the force needed, if the maximum shear strength is 450 N/mm².

Chapter 17 Applications of geometry

1 A model of a car is in the scale 1:20.

a) The length of the car is 4.2 m. What is the length of the model?

b) The width of the model is 110 mm. What is the width of the car, in m?

c) The area of the car's roof is 3.8 m². What is the area of the roof of the model?

d) The volume of the model is 0.03 m³. What is the volume of the car?

2 A building plot is 120 m long.

a) A plan of the plot is 60 mm long. What is the scale of the plan?

b) The area of the plan is 2300 mm². What is the area of the plot, in m²?

3 In Figure E.12, the triangles ABC and LMN are similar. They are not drawn to scale.

a) If AC = 8, AB = 6 and LM = 24, find LN.

b) If AB = $\frac{2}{3}$, LM = $\frac{4}{5}$ and the area of ABC is 1000, find the area of LMN.

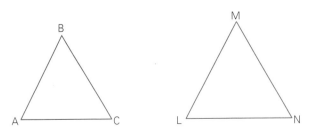

Figure E.12

4 In triangle ABC, Â = 90°.

    a) If AB = 12 and AC = 17, find BC.

    b) If BC = 120 and AB = 96, find AC.

5 Figure E.11 on page 251 shows a desk. Find the length of the sloping edge. Find the total surface area of the desk.

6 A pipe of length 0.85 m is at 45° to the vertical. Find the vertical distance between the ends of the pipe.

7 The horizontal distance between the ends of a pipe is 2.7 m, and the vertical distance is 0.34 m. Find the length of the pipe.

8 An isosceles triangle has sides 4.2 m, 4.2 m and 2.8 m. Find the area of the triangle.

9 Two pulleys each have radius 58 mm. Their centres are 160 mm apart. A belt passes tightly over the pulleys, crossing half way between them, as shown in Figure E.13. Find the length of a straight section of the belt.

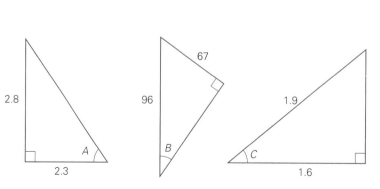

Figure E.13

10 An arc subtends 102° at the centre of a circle of radius 350 mm. Find the length of the arc.

11 An arc of length 1.3 m subtends 56° at the centre of a circle. Find the radius of the circle.

12 With ruler and compasses, construct angles of a) $22\frac{1}{2}°$, b) 105°.

13 In the following, construct the triangle and measure the angle or side.

    a) AB = 41 mm, B̂ = 49°, BC = 51 mm. Find AC.

    b) P̂ = 90°, QR = 63 mm, PQ = 38 mm. Find R̂.

    c) LM = 71 mm, MN = 66 mm, NL = 56 mm. Find M̂.

    d) X̂ = 68°, Ŷ = 73°, XZ = 50 mm. Find XY.

Chapter 18 Trigonometry

1 Find the lengths *a*, *b* and *c* in the triangles shown in Figure E.14.

2 Find the angles *A*, *B* and *C* in the triangles shown in Figure E.15.

3 In triangle PQR, Q̂ = 90°, PQ = 7.3 m and QR = 4.7 m. Find P̂.

4 In triangle ABC, Â = 90°, AB = 63 m and Ĉ = 27°. Find BC.

5 A terrace of seats at a football ground slopes at 12° to the horizontal. The terrace is 30 m deep. What is the difference in height between the back and the front of the terrace?

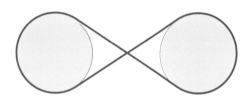

Figure E.14

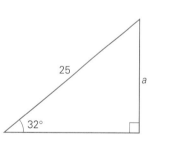

Figure E.15

6   A pipe slopes at $22\frac{1}{2}°$ to the horizontal. If the length of the pipe is 1.8 m, find the vertical and horizontal distances between its ends.

7   A pipe slopes at $11\frac{1}{4}°$ to the horizontal. If it falls a distance of 0.15 m, find the length of the pipe and the horizontal distance between its ends.

8   A sine bar has length 300 mm.
   a) The difference in height between the ends is 23.5 mm. What angle is measured?
   b) To measure an angle of 12.06°, what is the required difference in height between the ends?

9   A lamp of luminosity 3000 candelas is 2.7 m above point X on a floor. At point A on the floor, the illuminance is 400 lux. Find the distance of A from X.

10 A circuit has impedance 250 Ω and phase angle 21°. Find the resistance.

11 Find the lengths a and b in the triangles shown in Figure E.16.

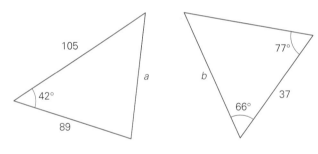

Figure E.16

12 Find the angles A and B in the triangles shown in Figure E.17.

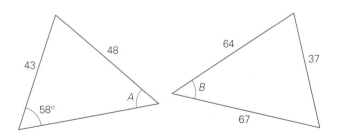

Figure E.17

13 Figure E.18 shows four bars linked together. Distances are in mm. Find BD, AD̂B and hence find AD̂C.

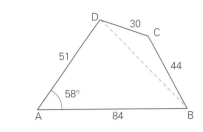

Figure E.18

Chapter 19 Further areas and volumes

1   Find the areas of the triangles shown in Figure E.19. Lengths are in mm.

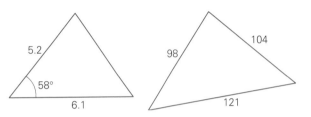

Figure E.19

2   Find the areas of the sector and segment in Figure E.20. Lengths are in m.

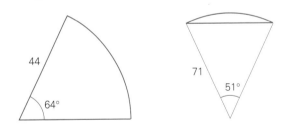

Figure E.20

3   A cylinder of length 430 mm and diameter 28 mm is fixed horizontal, and the top 4 mm is planed off. Calculate the volume removed.

4   Find the curved surface area of the following.
   a) a sphere with diameter 52 mm
   b) a sphere with volume 2.1 m^3
   c) a cylinder with height 230 mm and diameter 173 mm
   d) a cone with height 3.1 m and base diameter 4.8 m

5   A rubber ball of diameter 38 mm is made from thin rubber which has a mass of 2.1 kg/m^2. Find the mass of the ball.

6   A frustum of a cone has height 1.3 m, top radius 0.056 m and base radius 0.044 m. Find its volume and its curved surface area.

7 A building is in the shape of a frustum of a pyramid. The base is a rectangle 24 m by 30 m, and the top is a rectangle 20 m by 25 m. The volume is 6000 m³. Find the height of the building.

8 An irregular sheet of metal is 1.2 m wide. Its length is measured at intervals of 0.2 m, as below. Estimate its area by the trapezium rule and by Simpson's rule.

Distance (m)	0	0.2	0.4	0.6	0.8	1.0	1.2
Length (m)	2.3	2.5	2.7	3.0	3.1	2.8	2.5

9 A wall is 40 m long. Its height is measured at distances from the left-hand end, as shown below. Estimate the area of the wall by the mid-ordinate rule.

Distance (m)	5	15	25	35
Height (m)	2.2	1.9	1.6	1.3

10 A spindle, 80 mm long, has circular cross-section. Its radius at 10 mm intervals is given below. Estimate its volume, using the trapezium rule and Simpson's rule.

Distance (mm)	0	10	20	30	40	50	60	70	80
Radius (mm)	5.2	5.6	6.3	7.8	8.5	9.4	9.9	9.8	9.6

11 The cross-section of a metal trough, shown in Figure E.21, is a segment of a circle of diameter 200 mm. The width of the trough is 150 mm. The length of the trough is 950 mm. Calculate the volume of the trough and the area of metal.

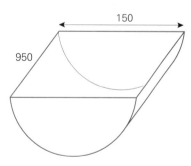

Figure E.21

12 A formula for the approximate area of the segment shown in Figure E.22 is

$$\text{Area} \simeq \frac{4h^2}{3} \sqrt{\left(\frac{d}{h} - 0.608\right)}$$

Use this formula to approximate the area when $h = 17$ mm and $d = 56$ mm.

Find the exact area. Find the percentage error in the approximation.

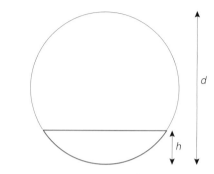

Figure E.22

13 Figure E.23 shows the hexagonal top of a bolt. The distance from side to side is 18.4 mm. What is the distance from corner to corner?

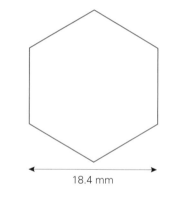

18.4 mm

Figure E.23

14 An ellipse has greatest diameter 58 mm and least diameter 36 mm.
   a) Calculate its area and the approximate value of its perimeter.
   b) A solid is formed by rotating the ellipse, so that its centre moves round a circle of radius 107 mm. Calculate the volume of the solid. Estimate the surface area of the solid.

15 A pyramid has a square base ABCD of side 2.7 m. Its vertex V is 0.6 m above the centre of ABCD. Find
   a) VA   b) the area of VAB
   c) the angle between VA and ABCD
   d) the angle between VAB and ABCD.

16 A terrace of seats at football ground consists of a square ABCD of side 40 m. AB is horizontal and AD is sloping. ABCD is at 23° to the horizontal. Calculate the height of CD above AB. Find the angle between AC and the horizontal.

17 For the desk of Figure E.11 (page 251), find the angle to the horizontal of the sloping section.

Chapter 20 Further trigonometry

1 Evaluate the following.

a) cot 82°   b) sec 54°   c) cosec 25°
d) $cosec^{-1}2.65$ e) $cot^{-1}0.76$ f) $sec^{-1}1.05$

2 Convert the following from degrees to radians. Where appropriate, leave your answer as a multiple of π.

a) 30°   b) 47°   c) 61.43°   d) 23° 24′

3 Convert the following from radians to degrees.

a) 0.478   b) 1.231   c) $1\frac{3}{4}\pi$

4 Find the following. The angle is measured in radians.

a) sin 1.2   b) cos 0.47   c) $\tan\frac{1}{3}\pi$
d) cot 0.34   e) sec 1.24   f) $cosec\frac{1}{4}\pi$

5 Find the following, giving your answers in radians.

a) $sin^{-1}0.567$ b) $cos^{-1}0.53$ c) $cot^{-1}2.76$

6 An arc AB subtends 0.24 radians at the centre C of a circle of radius 0.58 m.

a) Find the length of the arc.
b) Find the area of the sector ABC.
c) Find the length of the chord AB
d) Find the area of the segment cut off by the chord AB.

7 Find the following.

a) sin 296°   b) cos 104°
c) tan 205°   d) sec 332°

8 For each of the following equations, find two solutions between 0° and 360°.

a) cos x = −0.43   b) sin x = 0.12   c) tan x = 1.34

9 Sketch the graphs of the following.

a) $y = 4 \sin x$ b) $y = -\cos x$ c) $y = \sin 2\frac{1}{2}x$
d) $y = \sin(x + 40°)$ e) $y = 3\sin(x - 20°)$

10 Sketch the graphs of the following.

a) $y = \frac{1}{2}\cos^2 x$ b) $y = 2\sin x + 3\cos x$

11 State

a) the amplitude of $3\frac{1}{2}\sin x$,
b) the period of $\sin\frac{1}{3}x$,
c) the phase angle of $\sin(x + 23°)$.

Chapter 21 Statistics

1 The mains voltage was measured 30 times, with the results as below. Arrange the data in a frequency table, taking intervals 230–234, 235–239, 240–244 and 245–249.

241	242	243	239	238	240	234	233	243	248
242	236	235	240	241	249	244	236	247	240
232	232	236	241	231	247	237	238	237	239

2 The pictogram of Figure E.24 shows the volumes of cement, sand and aggregate needed for a type of concrete. Express the information in terms of the ratio of cement:sand:aggregate.

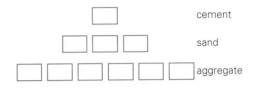

Figure E.24

Draw a pictogram for concrete which is composed of cement, sand and aggregate in the ratio 2:5:7.

3 The soil type of an area is classified as below. Illustrate the data using a bar chart and using a pie chart.

Type of ground	rock	compact sand		
Area (hectares)	23	43		
Type of ground	stiff clay	soft clay	loose sand
Area (hectares)	21	13	20

4 A bottling machine should deliver 1000 ml of liquid into bottles. The table below gives the volumes of 100 deliveries. Construct a histogram to show the data.

Volume (ml)	996–998	998–1000	1000–1002
Frequency	7	13	39
Volume (ml)	1002–1004	1004–1006	
Frequency	33	8	

5 The amount of lead in 180 samples of water was found. The results, in parts per million, are below. Construct a histogram to illustrate the data.

Amount (ppm)	20–30	30–35	35–40
Frequency	21	34	45
Amount (ppm)	40–42.5	42.5–45	45–50
Frequency	31	28	21

6 Find the mean and median of the following sets of data.

a) 23 24 28 31 37 37 40 43 45 48 53 59
b) 0.08 0.09 0.10 0.12 0.17 0.19 0.20 0.22 0.23

7 From the data of Question 4, estimate the mean volume delivered by the machine.

8 From your histogram for Question 4, estimate the mode volume delivered.

9 For each of the data sets of Question 6, find
  a) the range
  b) the variance.

10 For the data of Question 4, construct a cumulative frequency graph. From the graph estimate the median and the interquartile range.

11 The table below gives the length, l mm, of a wire under tension of T N. Assuming that length and T are connected by a law of the form $l = aT + b$, calculate the values of a and b.

T (N)	10	20	30	40	50
l (mm)	63	65	68	72	75

Chapter 22 Matrices and vectors

1 Let $\mathbf{A} = \begin{pmatrix} 8 & 5 \\ 2 & -1 \end{pmatrix}$ and $\mathbf{B} = \begin{pmatrix} 7 & -3 \\ 0 & 1 \end{pmatrix}$. Find $\mathbf{A} + \mathbf{B}$, $\mathbf{AB}$ and $\mathbf{BA}$.

2 Let $\mathbf{C} = \begin{pmatrix} 4 & 9 \\ 1 & 3 \\ 2 & -1 \end{pmatrix}$. With $\mathbf{A}$ as in Question 1, find $\mathbf{CA}$. Explain why $\mathbf{A} + \mathbf{C}$ and $\mathbf{AC}$ cannot be found.

3 Find the inverses of the matrices $\mathbf{A}$ and $\mathbf{B}$ of Question 1.

4 Solve the simultaneous equations below by inverse matrices or by determinants.
  a) $1.23x + 0.94y = 24$ b) $0.023x - 0.092y = 2.17$
      $0.65x + 1.34y = 33$ $0.456x - 0.734y = 15.3$

5 Vector $\mathbf{a}$ has magnitude 23 and acts north east. Vector $\mathbf{b}$ has magnitude 17 and acts on a bearing of $116°$. Find the magnitude and bearing of the following.
  a) $\mathbf{a} + \mathbf{b}$ b) $\mathbf{a} - \mathbf{b}$ c) $2\mathbf{a} + 3\mathbf{b}$

6 A vector has magnitude 120 and makes $49°$ with the x-axis. Express the vector in terms of components and as a column vector.

7 Use phasors to write the following in the form $A \sin(x + a)$.
  a) $\sin(x + 30°) + 2 \sin(x - 30)$
  b) $2 \sin(x + 20°) + 3 \sin(x - 50°)$

8 Solve the following equations.
  a) $x^2 = -100$ b) $x^2 + \frac{1}{4} = 0$
  c) $x^2 - 6x + 34 = 0$ d) $x^2 + x + 3 = 0$

9 Let $z = 3 - 2j$ and $w = 4 + 5j$. Evaluate the following.
  a) $z + w$ b) zw c) $\bar{z}$ d) $z \div w$

10 Let Z_1 and Z_2 be impedances represented by $Z_1 = 2 + 3j$ and $Z_2 = 1 + 2j$. Find the total impedance if Z_1 and Z_2 are connected
  a) in series   b) in parallel.

Chapter 23 Differentiation

1 Differentiate from first principles: $y = 3x^2 - 2x - 8$.

2 Differentiate the following.
  a) x^7 b) $7x^3 - 2x^2 + 4x$ c) $5\sqrt{x} - \dfrac{8}{x^3}$
  d) $(2x - 3)(x + 8)$ e) $7e^{3x}$ f) $3 \cos 1.5x$

3 Find the gradient of the curve $y = 4 \sin \frac{1}{2}\pi x$ at $(0, 0)$.

4 Find the maxima and minima of the following.
  a) $y = 4 - 3x - x^2$ b) $y = 2x + \dfrac{1}{x^2}$

5 If a certain cutting machine is operated at speed V, then the cost of cutting a unit volume of metal is
$$\frac{12k}{V} + \frac{3kV^3}{150^4}$$
where k is constant. Find the value of V which will give the least cost.

Chapter 24 Integration

1 Find the integrals of the following.
  a) $x^{3.1}$ b) $(x - 1)(x + 7)$ c) $\sqrt{x}(2x - 3)$
  d) $3e^{-2x}$ e) $5 \cos \frac{1}{4}\pi x$ f) $3 - 3 \sin \frac{1}{2}x$

2 Find y from the information given.
  a) $\dfrac{dy}{dx} = 3x - 7$, $y = 4$ for $x = 1$
  b) $\dfrac{dy}{dx} = 1 - e^{2x}$, $y = 4$ for $x = 0$

3 A particle is fired upwards from the ground. After t seconds, its speed upwards is v m s^{-1}, where
$$v = 80e^{-0.1t} - 40$$
Find the height of the particle after 3 seconds.

4 Evaluate the following definite integrals.
  a) $\int_1^2 3x^8 \, dx$ b) $\int_1^5 2e^{-0.4x} \, dx$ c) $\int_0^{\frac{1}{4}\pi} \sin 2x \, dx$

5 Find the following areas.
  a) under $y = 2 + x^3$, between $x = 1$ and $x = 2$
  b) under $y = \sin 2x + \cos 2x$, between $x = 0$ and $x = \frac{1}{4}\pi$

Solutions

Chapter 1   Page 1

1 a) 66   b) 231   c) 230   d) 35   e) 81
   f) 84   g) 108   h) 2200   i) 1212   j) 3
   k) 30   l) 8

2 a) 45   b) 96   c) 16   d) 8   e) 4, 5

3 a) 180 kg   b) 45 hours   c) 76 mm   d) 40 m
   e) 195 g   f) 56 mm   g) 15

4 200 N/mm^2 **5** 15

6 a) 16   b) 88   c) 20   d) 11   e) 1   f) 31

7 #98   **8** 415 mm   **9** #475

10 a) 18   b) 54   c) 2   d) 5   e) 7   f) 17

11 #256   **12** 900 kg

13 #32   **14** 4%

15 a) 18   b) 112   c) -36 d) 3   e) -4
   f) 6   g) 12   h) 2   i) -14

16 a) 5°C   b) -13°C

17 a) $2 \times 2 \times 2 \times 3 \times 3$ b) $2 \times 3 \times 5 \times 5$
   c) $3 \times 3 \times 11$ d) $7 \times 11 \times 13$

18 a) 8   b) 5   c) 15   d) 2

19 a) 48   b) 140   c) 60   d) 154

20 a) 2,840   b) 2,120

21 #30   **22** 60 seconds

Chapter 2   Page 10

1 a) $\frac{1}{3}$ b) $\frac{3}{4}$ c) $\frac{4}{9}$

2 a) $1\frac{7}{16}$ b) $3\frac{7}{15}$ c) $15\frac{2}{3}$

3 a) $\frac{31}{8}$ b) $\frac{18}{7}$ c) $\frac{67}{12}$

4 a) $\frac{35}{108}$ b) $\frac{2}{7}$ c) $2\frac{11}{12}$ d) $\frac{21}{32}$ e) $\frac{2}{3}$ f) $\frac{72}{145}$
   g) $\frac{2}{3}$ h) $1\frac{2}{7}$ i) $8\frac{1}{2}$ j) $1\frac{7}{15}$ k) $\frac{59}{72}$ l) $1\frac{3}{8}$
   m) $\frac{1}{5}$ n) $\frac{19}{56}$ o) $\frac{7}{12}$

5 $\frac{1}{5}$ hour   **6** 105   **7** $\frac{23}{360}°$,

8 $\frac{3}{20}$ kg   **9** $1\frac{1}{2}$ km/hr

10 a) 4.08   b) 4.34   .c) 11.30   d) 0.00

11 a) 6.96   b) 6.959   c) 6.9590

12 a) 2.46   b) 987 000   c) 0.0180   d) 50.5

13 a) 0.73   b) 0.625   c) 0.52   d) 0.4375

14 a) 0.83   b) 0.43   c) 0.73   d) 0.37

15 a) $\frac{7}{10}$ b) $\frac{231}{1000}$ c) $\frac{1}{20}$ d) $\frac{13}{125}$

16 a) 15.79   b) 120.5   c) 0.1248   d) 5.5
   e) 0.44   f) 0.000 74   g) 11.2   h) 0.3053
   i) 0.0624   j) 18   k) 0.0025   l) 9

17 6.35 mm   **18** 10.6 mm   **19** 14.2 mm

20 5100   **21** 3360 g   **22** $3\frac{1}{3}$ kg/m

23 550   **24** 6560   **25** 2.725 Ω

Chapter 3   Page 19

1 45%   **2** 56%   **3** 120

4 5.75 or $5\frac{3}{4}$ **5** 17 kg   **6** 41 kg

7 #1344   **8** #5184   **9** 276 kg

10 a) 27.5 mm^3 b) 40 mm^3 **11** 0.792 m

12 #7820   **13** 239.2 mm   **14** 29 340

15 7000 W, 3000 W   **16** 5%   **17** 3:1

18 5:3   **19** 100:137   **20** 147 g

21 1:10, 70   **22** 0.014 mm   **23** 4.8 kg

24 240 g   **25** 100 kg, 250 kg, 50 kg

26 1350 m^2, 1200 m^2, 1050 m^2

27 #1000, #1250, #1250, #1500

28 90 kg   **29** a) 50 rpm   b) 160 rpm

30 a) 25   b) 50

Chapter 4   Page 25

1 a) 64   b) 64   c) 125   d) −1

2 a) 11   b) $\frac{1}{2}$ c) 3   d) $\frac{1}{2}$

3 a) 10   b) 1   c) 2   d) $\frac{1}{36}$

4 a) 3^{13} b) 7^8 c) 2^{35} d) 3^{16} e) 2^6 f) 3^{13}

5 a) 20 000 N   b) 30 kF
   c) 0.000 23 mg   d) 120 mm

6 a) 3.6×10^6 J   b) 3.6 MJ

7 a) 2 GN   b) 1.39 g   c) 300 μm
   d) 700 μA   e) 3.1 mV   f) 2.14 MP

8 a) 6.3×10^{10} b) 1.2×10^{-7}
   c) 9.1×10^{10} d) 4.2×10^{11}

9 a) 4 540 000   b) 0.000 102

10 a) 600 MN   b) 0.054 mg   c) 4.1 mΩ d) 10.3 MF

11 a) 6.9×10^{20} b) 1.11×10^{12} c) 1.2×10^6
   d) 2×10^{-7} e) 6.1×10^8 f) 2×10^8
   g) 2.72×10^{12} h) 8.16×10^{21}

12 a) 5×10^4 b) 9.9×10^{-17} c) 1.2×10^{-15}
   d) 2.2×10^{-8} e) 1.03×10^{-5} f) 2.64×10^{-6}

13 a) 500×10^6 b) 58×10^{18} c) 230×10^{-15}

14 a) 2×10^{11} N m^{-2} b) 200 000 N m^{-2}

15 a) −3   b) 5   c) −2   d) $\frac{1}{4}$

16 a) 3   b) 3   c) 1   d) 0

17 a) 1.4   b) 0.3   c) 2.7   d) −0.3   e) −0.9

Chapter 5   Page 36

1 a) 6.969   b) 2.623   c) 80.05   d) 10.95
   e) 54.60   f) 58 850   g) 0.2799   h) 16.45
   i) 0.004 209   j) 9.073   k) 88.10   l) 0.7380
   m) 0.1830   n) 4.918   o) 40 510

2 a) $\frac{13}{20}$ b) $\frac{5}{36}$ c) $\frac{36}{91}$ d) $4\frac{1}{8}$
   e) $2\frac{3}{10}$ f) $4\frac{1}{2}$ g) $14\frac{23}{35}$ h) $4\frac{5}{16}$ i) $\frac{153}{203}$

3 a) 29.73   b) 0.027 25   c) 3 269 000   d) 19 020
   e) 3.123   f) 1.023×10^{-6} g) 4.661   h) 4077
   i) 0.006 481   j) 1.605   k) 49.66   l) 0.7489

4 a) 1.567   b) 10.19   c) 0.5383   d) 4.569   e) 106.8
   f) 1.976   g) 0.3128   h) 3.276   i) 113.4   j) 893.3
   k) 2.090   l) 2.567   m) 0.2928   n) 8.458
   o) 0.5363   p) −0.8332   q) 1.530

5 a) 4.498×10^{18} b) 2.883×10^{19} c) 8.203×10^8
   d) 7.991×10^{11} e) 3.448×10^{16} f) 8.933×10^{-31}
   g) 6.837×10^{10} h) 9.8×10^{13} i) 5.245×10^{-28}
   j) 1.300×10^{-12}

Chapter 6   Page 45

1 0.004, 0.0009, 0.09%

2 0.000 03, 0.09, 9%

3 a) 5.3 − 5.9   b) 985 − 989   c) 0.000 22 − 0.000 24
   d) 22.7 − 25.1   e) 0.0172 − 0.0174   f) 10 800 − 13 200

4 a) 0.63 − 0.66   b) 12.5 − 13.2   c) 135 − 225

5 11.7 mm − 12.9 mm   **6** 57s − 69s   **7** 0.04%

8 2375 Ω − 2625 Ω **9** 28V − 87.5 V   **10** 230 ± 10 V

11 0.0005 s, 0.0002   **12** 5 m s^{-1}, 1.4%

13 54 mm, 0.15 mm

14 32.84 kg, 0.01 kg   **15** 36.7, 0.06   **16** 0.360, 0.0015

17 510 kg   **18** 453 Ω **19** 70 mm

20 a) 94.87 (40 + 50 = 90)
   b) 0.0047 (0.007 − 0.002 = 0.005)
   c) 22 534.2 (200 × 100 = 20 000)
   d) 20.70 (600 ÷ 30 = 20)
   e) 27.2448 (5 × (2 + 3) = 25)
   f) 17.25 (0.1 × 20 + 0.2 × 70 = 16)
   g) 60.98 (350 ÷ 5 = 70)
   h) 0.02968 (60 ÷ 2000 = 0.03)
   i) 0.001 927 (0.08 ÷ 40 = 0.002)
   j) 3.274 ($\sqrt{10} \simeq 3$)
   k) 8.167 ($\sqrt{(49 + 16)} = \sqrt{65} \simeq 8$)
   l) 37.08 ($6^2 = 36$)

21 122.1 kg (20 + 100 = 120)

22 61.32 kg (0.07 × 1000 = 70)

23 535°C (700 − 200 = 500)

24 3399 m^2 (60 × 60 = 3600)

Chapter 7   Page 51

1 a) 8° 15′   b) 28° 12′   c) 17° 48′
   d) 60° 22′ 48″   e) 27° 21′ 4″   f) 83° 54′ 18″

2 a) $7.5°$ b) $61.2°$ c) $29.67°$
     d) $12.35°$ e) $20.52°$ f) $82.01°$

3 a) $53°\,10'$ b) $58°\,2'$
     c) $41°\,46'\,7''$ d) $61°\,0'\,7''$
     e) $25°\,20'$ f) $17°\,37'$
     g) $27°\,10'\,50''$ h) $26°\,57'\,46''$

4 a) $9° + 3° + 9' - 1'$ b) $27° + 3° + 1° - 3' + 1'$
     c) $27° + 3° + 1° - 27' + 9' + 9'' + 3''$
     d) $90° + 9° - 1° + 27' - 9' + 3' - 1' - 9'' - 3''$

5 a) 11011   b) 111010   c) 1011101

6 a) 147   b) 59   c) 34

7 a) 101110   b) 1011101   c) 1101001   d) 1101100

8 a) 4E   b) ACE   c) BABE

9 a) 1050   b) 1001   c) 666

10 a) 116   b) 101000111111

11 a) 01000101   b) 4935

Chapter 8   Page 58

1 a) $12x$ b) $6y$ c) $5\frac{1}{2}z$ d) $4x + 9y$ e) $11a - 11b$
     f) $x^2 - x$ g) $8y^2 + 11\frac{1}{2}y$ h) $11xy$
     i) $9abc$ j) $7ab + a + 3b$ k) $11xy + 5x - 3y$
     l) $4xy + 4yz$ m) $1.1x^2 + 7.3x^3$ n) $15x^2$
     o) $2y^2$ p) $28ab$ q) $24n$
     r) $-4xy$ s) $8ab$ t) $24z^2$
     u) $6pqr$ v) $-xyz$ w) $6x^2$
     x) y^4 y) $3a$ z) 7
     aa) $4b$ bb) $3p$ cc) $4x$
     dd) $2ab$ ee) $3xy$ ff) $3n$
     gg) $-2a$ hh) $7y^2$

2 a) x^{11} b) a^{16} c) p^{30}
     d) y^5 e) z^{11} f) q^8
     g) x^{12} h) y^{15} i) a^{10}
     j) x^{20} k) q^{14} l) x^{18}

3 a) $p^{\frac{1}{2}}$ b) x^{-3} c) $y^{-\frac{1}{2}}$
     d) $a^{1\frac{1}{2}}$ e) $x^{-3\frac{1}{2}}$ f) $x^{1\frac{1}{2}}$
     g) $y^{\frac{2}{3}}$ h) $x^{\frac{2}{3}}$ i) $x^{-\frac{1}{4}}$
     j) $x^{\frac{5}{6}}$ k) y^{-4} l) b^{-14}
     m) $x^{4\frac{1}{2}}$ n) $x^{\frac{3}{4}}$ o) y^{15}

4 a) 16   b) $-2\frac{3}{8}$ c) -54

5 a) 9   b) $-1\frac{1}{9}$ c) 27

6 a) 3   b) 2.236   c) $\frac{1}{2}$

7 13 m   **8** 838.4 J   **9** 353.2 J

10 2.646 s   **11** 15 990 W   **12** 2.878 m^2

13 $2l + 2w$ **14** $2v_1 + 2\frac{1}{2}v_2$, $\frac{(2v_1 + 2\frac{1}{2}v_2)}{4\frac{1}{2}}$

15 a) $1.5d$ kg   b) $\dfrac{850}{d}$ m^3

16 $(0.3d_1 + 0.2d_2)$ kg   **17** $\#32b$ **18** $\#(44m + 12)$

19 $\dfrac{Gm_1m_2}{d^2}$

20 a) $5a + 5b$ b) $7x - 7y$ c) $3p + 6q$
     d) $8x + 12y$ e) $ab + ac$ f) $6xy + 2xz$
     g) $3x^2 + 7x$ h) $2r^2 - rt$ i) $-a - 7$
     j) $-x + y$ k) $-3n + 9m$ l) $-12x + 2x^2$

21 a) $5x + 14y$ b) $37a + 38b$ c) $-10p + 3q$
     d) $-n + 11m$ e) $2x + 41$ f) $18v - 25u$
     g) $3x^2 - x$ h) $26a^2 - 2ab$ i) $2x^2 + 6xy + 9y^2$
     j) $2a^2 - ab + 3b^2$

22 a) $x^2 + 10x + 21$ b) $x^2 + 10x + 16$
     c) $y^2 - 3y - 10$ d) $y^2 - 12y + 32$
     e) $p^2 + 8p - 9$ f) $2x^2 + 11x + 5$
     g) $3y^2 + 22y - 16$ h) $6x^2 - 13x + 6$
     i) $ab + 4a + 3b + 12$ j) $xy - 7x + 3y - 21$
     k) $8mn + 18m + 12n + 27$ l) $14kj - 2k - 21j + 3$

23 a) $p^2 + 2pq + q^2$ b) $m^2 - 2mn + n^2$
     c) $4a^2 + 4ab + b^2$ d) $9r^2 + 12rt + 4t^2$
     e) $25x^2 - 30xy + 9y^2$ f) $1 - 14x + 49x^2$
     g) $p^2 - q^2$ h) $4x^2 - 9y^2$
     i) $8x^2 - 2y^2$ j) $\frac{1}{4} - x^2$

24 a) $3(x + 2y)$ b) $4(a + 2)$ c) $5(z + 1)$
     d) $7(a - 3b)$ e) $x(x + 4)$ f) $3y(1 - 2y)$
     g) $x(a + b)$ h) $x(x + y)$ i) $2a(2a + 3b)$
     j) $5xy(3y + 2x)$ k) $a(a^2 + a + 1)$
     l) $a(b + c + a)$ m) $xy(x^2 + xy + y^2)$

Chapter 9   Page 66

1 A(2.2, 1.2)   B(3.2, 0.4)   C(0.8, 2.2)

2 D(5, 10.5)   E(14, 13)   F(21, 6.5)

3 G(−1, 1.4)   H(−1.2, −1.4)   I(0.8, −1)

7 a) 13   b) 3.8

14 a) (iii)   b) (i)   c) (ii)

15 a) $y = 2x - 1$ b) $y = 2x + 2$ c) $y = -3x + 17$

16 a) $y = x$ b) $y = -\frac{1}{2}x + 2$ c) $y = 0.6x - 1.4$

18 a) (iii)   b) (i)   c) (ii)   d) (iv)

Chapter 10   Page 77

1 a) 17   b) 11   c) 9
     d) 8   e) 7   f) 13
     g) 14   h) 10   i) 1
     j) 18   k) 84   l) 1
     m) 45   n) $3\frac{1}{2}$ o) 3
     p) $-\frac{3}{5}$ q) 13

2 a) $x = 11, y = 6$ b) $x = 4, y = -3$ c) $x = 2, y = 0$
   d) $x = 7, y = 1$ e) $x = 3, y = 1$ f) $x = 4, y = -1$
   g) $x = 2, y = 3$ h) $x = 8, y = -1$ i) $x = -3, y = 2$
   j) $x = 12, y = 6$ k) $x = 10, y = 20$ l) $x = 48, y = 24$

3 a) 4   b) 7   c) 9
   d) 10   e) $2\frac{1}{2}$ f) $-\frac{2}{3}$
   g) $3\frac{2}{3}$ h) $2\frac{1}{2}$ i) -208

4 $x = -0.8, y = 4.6$

5 $x = -1.2$ or $x = 4.2$

6 153 mg   **7** #27   **8** 40

9 80 m   **10** $26\frac{2}{3}$ kg   **11** 50 litres, 140 litres

12 29   **13** 80 litres, 20 litres   **14** $k = 0.005, c = 2.6$

15 $k = 0.2, c = 138$ **16** $k_0 = 1.233, a = 6.307 \times 10^{-5}$

Chapter 11   Page 85

1 a) $\dfrac{x}{2y}$ b) $\dfrac{3}{8}$ c) $3x$

   d) $\dfrac{b}{a}$ e) $1 + x$ f) xy

2 a) $\dfrac{ax}{by}$ b) $\dfrac{6x^2}{yz}$ c) $\dfrac{2}{3}$

   d) $\dfrac{pt}{qr}$ e) $\dfrac{35x^2}{6y^2}$ f) $\dfrac{2x^3}{y^3}$

   g) $\dfrac{xb + ya}{yb}$ h) $\dfrac{7x}{12}$ i) $\dfrac{2y - 3x}{xy}$

3 a) abc b) $18xy$ c) a^2b
   d) m^2n^2 e) $300x^2y^2$

4 a) $\dfrac{c + b}{abc}$ b) $\dfrac{3ay - 2bx}{18xy}$ c) $\dfrac{ab + a + b}{a^2b}$

   d) $\dfrac{2mn + 3n + 4m}{m^2n^2}$ e) $\dfrac{20y^3 + 15xy + 12x^3}{300x^2y^2}$

5 a) 12.58   b) 0.8047   c) 3.543

6 a) 2.135   b) -1.044 c) 8.837   d) 0.06891

7 a) 0.06081   b) 30.53   c) 0.9396   d) 2.164

8 a) 0.9336   b) -11.52 c) 7.023
   d) 0.01731   e) 3.190   f) 2.232
   g) 0.2280   h) 2.307   i) 3.322
   j) 1.138   k) 0.2925   l) 6.213

9 0.3812 s   **10** 0.8881 s

11 a) 0.01736   b) 3039

12 a) 1.432   b) 5.046   c) 2.146

13 37.2 years   **14** 13.5 years

15 a) $\frac{1}{3}y + 3\frac{1}{3}$ b) $3\frac{1}{2} - \frac{1}{2}y$ c) $3a - 15$

   d) $2p + 1\frac{1}{2}$ e) $a - b + c$ f) $\dfrac{y}{z}$

   g) $\dfrac{C}{\pi b}$ h) yz i) $4ac$

   j) $\dfrac{x}{y}$ k) $\dfrac{2}{a}$ l) $\dfrac{PE}{R}$

   m) $\dfrac{k}{\pi a^2}$ n) $\dfrac{7t}{y}$ o) $\dfrac{5}{y} - 1$

   p) $\dfrac{14}{y} + 10$ q) $\dfrac{3V}{\pi r^2}$ r) $\dfrac{kL^2}{4S}$

   s) $\dfrac{y}{a + b}$ t) $\dfrac{10}{a - b}$ u) $\dfrac{2}{y - 1}$

   v) $\dfrac{T}{1 - T}$ w) $\dfrac{fv}{v - f}$ x) $\dfrac{tP + t}{1 - P}$

   y) $\sqrt{\left(\dfrac{A}{\pi}\right)}$ z) $\sqrt{(8y + 56)}$ aa) $\sqrt{\left(\dfrac{b^2}{a^2} + 1\right)}$

   bb) $\sqrt{\left(\dfrac{2E}{m}\right)}$ cc) $\sqrt{(c^2 - a^2)}$ dd) $\sqrt[3]{\left(\dfrac{\frac{3}{4}V}{\pi}\right)}$

   ee) $\sqrt{\left(\dfrac{2E - 2mgd}{m}\right)}$ ff) $\sqrt{\left(\dfrac{k}{F}\right)}$ gg) $\frac{1}{2}y^2$

   hh) $a^2 - c$ ii) $\sqrt{(4Q^2 - b^2)}$ jj) $\frac{1}{4}(y - 5\sqrt{z})^2$

   kk) $g\left(\dfrac{T}{2\pi}\right)^2$ ll) $l\left(\dfrac{2\pi}{T}\right)^2$ mm) $\dfrac{3S^2}{d} + d$

   nn) $\sqrt{\left[12\left(R^2 - \frac{1}{4}r^2\right)\right]}$ oo) $\frac{1}{2}\log y$ pp) $\ln \frac{1}{5}p$

   qq) $\frac{1}{2}\ln\left(\frac{1}{8}I - 1\right)$ rr) $-3\ln\left(\dfrac{V}{0.9}\right)$ ss) $\frac{1}{5}(\ln A + 3)$

   tt) $-L\ln\left(1 - \dfrac{I}{I_0}\right)$ uu) $10^y - 1$ vv) $\sqrt{\left(\frac{1}{5}e^k\right)}$

   ww) $B_0 e^{\frac{1}{2}E}$ xx) $B_1 e^{-\frac{1}{2}E}$

Chapter 12   Page 94

1 $y = 2.6x, 39, 20$ **2** $T = 40R, 60$

3 $R = \frac{7}{12}l, 0.175\ \Omega, 4.8$ m

4 $T = 1666\frac{2}{3}e, 666\frac{2}{3}$ N   **5** $y = \dfrac{1210}{x}, 110, 27.5$

6 19.5 m³   **7** $R = \dfrac{0.0002}{A}, 1\frac{1}{3}$ mm²

8 $I = \dfrac{700}{R}, 175$ A   **9** $y = 2x^2, 4.5$

10 $q = \dfrac{5.16}{p^2}, 57\frac{1}{3}, 0.275$

11 $R = \dfrac{16}{r^2}, 0.1789$ mm   **12** 0.2479 m

13 $L = 0.000\,167T + 1.647$ a) 1.663 m   b) 80°C

14 $u = 4$, $a = 8$, After 3.25 seconds.

15 $R = \frac{4}{9}F - 14\frac{2}{9}$ **16** $R_0 = 27.6875$, $a = 0.002\,257$

17 $y = 45e^{0.025\,38t}$ a) 52.40   b) 32.24

18 $m = 7e^{-0.2824t}$ a) 5.744   b) 11.15

19 $Q = 0.4e^{-0.4332t}$ a) 0.019\,28 coulombs   b) 4.8 seconds

20 $a = 4.999\,75 \times 10^{-6}$ **21** $7.3e^{0.0284t}$, After 17.5 years

22 $£20\,000e^{-0.144t}$, After 4.82 years

Chapter 13   Page 101

1 a) $y = 0.45x + 5.5$ b) $y = 0.041x - 1.73$
   c) $y = -15.7x + 29.5$

2 a) $x = 40$, $y = 12.4$ b) $x = -1$, $y = 4.9$
   c) $x = 0.1$, $y = 100$

3 a) 7.1   b) 1.55   c) 35.8

4 $L = 0.027T + 1.05$ **5** $E = 0.26W + 0.38$

6 $y = 0.19T + 33$, 50 grams per litre

7 a) $y = 7.4\sqrt{x} + 3.6$ b) $y = 0.14x^2 + 2.2x$
   c) $\dfrac{1}{y} = \dfrac{0.388}{x - 4.6}$

8 $W = -2.7I^2 + 7.6$

9 a) $y = 2.4x^{1.3}$ b) $y = 1.75x^{4.3}$ c) $y = 13.2x^{1.3}$

10 a) $y = 3.6 \times 1.06^x$ b) $y = 0.046 \times 1.02^x$
   c) $y = 63 \times 0.96^x$

11 $V = 102d^{0.73}$ **12** $F = 1.2t^{-2.1}$

13 $V = 12.6 \times 0.97^t$

14 $i = 0.058 \times 0.0018^t$ **15** $I = 22.4V^{0.79}$

Chapter 14   Page 111

1 a) $(x + 3)(x + 4)$ b) $(x + 3)(x + 6)$
   c) $(x + 5)(x + 12)$ d) $(x - 2)(x - 3)$
   e) $(x - 3)(x - 5)$ f) $(x - 2)^2$
   g) $(x + 6)(x - 2)$ h) $(x - 11)(x + 3)$
   i) $(x + 6)(x - 12)$ j) $(2x + 1)(x + 2)$
   k) $(3x - 4)(x - 1)$ l) $(5x + 1)(x + 2)$
   m) $(2x - 1)(x + 3)$ n) $(5x + 2)(x - 2)$
   o) $(3x + 2)(x - 3)$ p) $(x - 4)(x + 4)$
   q) $2(x - 5)(x + 5)$ r) $\frac{1}{2}(x - 6)(x + 6)$

2 a) $(x + 2)^2 + 2$ b) $(x - 3)^2 - 15$
   c) $(x + 1\frac{1}{2})^2 - 1\frac{1}{4}$ d) $2(x + 2)^2 - 7$
   e) $3(x + \frac{2}{3})^2 - 6\frac{1}{3}$ f) $9 - (x + 2)^2$

3 a) 2, −2   b) −15, 3   c) $-1\frac{1}{4}$, $-1\frac{1}{2}$
   d) −7, −2   e) $-6\frac{1}{3}$, $-\frac{2}{3}$ f) 9, −2

5 a) −2, −5   b) 2, 4   c) −10.84, 1.844
   d) −7.317, −0.6834   e) 0.5209, 4.479
   f) −2.777, −0.2661   g) −5.140, 2.140
   h) −6.854, −0.1459   i) −4.887, 3.887
   j) −1.303, 2.303   k) −4.877, 3.837
   l) −24.80, −0.2016

6 a) $(0.7321, -1.536)$ or $(-2.732, -8.464)$
   b) $(-2.266, 6.398)$ or $(1.766, 0.3517)$
   c) $(0.1802, -3.459)$ or $(2.220, 2.659)$
   d) $(1, 1)$ or $(-1.483, -0.6552)$

7 2.3 N, 60.4 m s^{-1} **8** 23.1 mm   **9** 0.0891 m

10 0.688 m   **11** a) 118 mm   b) 109 mm

12 1.49 m   **13** 2.27 mm   **14** 199 m (or 0.857 m)

Chapter 15   Page 119

1 a) 124°   b) 37°   c) 75°

2 a) 113°   b) 76°   c) 86°

3 30°   **4** 39°   **5** 112°, 48°

6 19.8°

7 AXB isosceles, ABD right-angled

8 a) 79°   b) 71°   c) 74°

9 ADB, ADC   **11** ACGI trapezium, JAXH trapezium

12 a) 94°   b) 76°   c) 145°

13 a) AHED   b) AHGB   c) AHGD (many others)

14 1800°   **15** 156°   **16** 9

17 a) chord   b) arc   c) sector   d) segment

18 100 m, 314.2 m   **19** 81.5 mm, 40.7 mm

20 cuboid, cone, triangular-based pyramid

21 a) triangular prism   b) cuboid

Chapter 16   Page 134

1 a) 2.11 km   b) 3354 mm   c) 48\,300 m^2
   d) 2.204 m^2 e) 1350 m^2 f) 9.770 m^2

2 0.336 m^2 **3** 0.19 m^3

4 a) 3224 mm^2 b) 4950 mm^2
   c) 1092 mm^2 d) 4536 mm^2

5 12.5 m   **6** 21.44 mm   **7** 40 mm

8 a) 2124 mm^2 b) 2.011 m^2 c) 58.01 km^2

9 1.178 m   **10** 60.89 mm

11 a) 486 m²   b) 4.44 m²   c) 1743 m²

12 27 300 mm²   **13** 169 m²   **14** 472 mm²

15 77.4 m²   **16** 4495 mm²

17 a) 480 m³   b) 42 m³   c) 4976 m³

18 a) 4.096 m³   b) 57 906 mm³   c) 124 600 mm³
        d) 2.808 m³   e) 1.366×10^8 mm³

19 14.26 m³   **20** 1.432×10^6 mm³, 126 000

21 662.4 m³   **22** 5.6×10^7 mm³

23 18.39 m³   **24** 0.2464 m³   **25** 0.0986 m

26 1.17×10^7 mm³   **27** 5.03×10^6 mm³   **28** 3255 mm

29 0.2429 m³   **30** 1.65 mm   **31** 249 600 mm³

32 6786 mm³, 1131 mm³   **33** 0.204 m   **34** 34 kg

35 0.2022 m³, 202.2 kg   **36** 8.38 kg   **37** 23.7 mm

38 0.874 kg   **39** 1.144 km

Chapter 17   Page 147

1 a) 7 m   b) 150 mm

2 a) 1250 m   b) 140 mm

3 1:2 000 000

4 a) 13.5 cm   b) $13\frac{1}{3}$ cm

5 a) 8 m   b) 5 m

6 36 m²

7 a) 19.6 m²   b) 12 m

8 a) 160 m²   b) 0.1 m²

9 11.85 g   **10** 17 m   **11** 12 mm

12 100 m   **13** 35.5 m

14 20.6 inches   **15** 0.396 m   **16** 383 mm

17 1.77 m   **18** 94.3 km   **19** 34.3 m

20 100.7 m²   **21** 4.75 m   **22** 26.6 mm

23 55.4 mm   **24** 29.9 mm   **25** 43.7 m

26 37.3°   **27** 25.3°   **28** 0.283 m

29 7.21 mm   **30** 148.1 mm

32 a) 83°   b) 30 mm, 105°   c) 58 mm   d) 55°

Chapter 18   Page 159

1 $x = 7.64$ $y = 36.7$ $z = 292$

2 $P = 38.4°$ $Q = 56.9°$ $R = 38.5°$

3 10.2 m, 13.6 m   **4** 857 mm   **5** 31.2°

6 39.9°

7 $x = 87.5$ $y = 31.4$ $z = 36.9$

8 88.8 mm   **9** 70.8 mm   **10** 3.06 m

11 10.7 mm   **12** 11.3°   **13** 14.1 m

14 a) 92.1 mm   b) 9.94°

15 a) 2.70°   b) 37.8 mm

16 192 lux

17 a) 36.9°   b) 93.3 Ω

18 $a = 28.2$ $b = 65.0$

19 $A = 94.1°$ $B = 47.6°$

20 28.0 mm   **21** 81.4°   **22** 84.7° or 9.3°

23 67.5°   **24** 140 mm   **25** 61.9°, 69.0°, 49.0°

26 4.58 m, 5.70 m, 1.19 m   **27** 29.1 m, 23.6 m

28 45.2 km

Chapter 19   Page 172

1 226.5 mm²   46.72 mm²   1118 mm²   748.9 mm²

2 781.3 m²   14 230 m²   2745 m²

3 84.58 mm²   9274 mm²   1177 mm²

4 38.7°, 39.42 m²   **5** 385.5 mm²

6 39 420 mm², 714.7 mm   **7** 3.153 m

8 a) 66.48 m²   b) 6648 mm²   c) 9495 mm²
        d) 10 980 mm²   e) 1.131 m²   f) 0.1527 m²
        g) 1853 mm²

9 0.04172 kg   **10** 0.000 643 4 kg   **11** 164.2 litres

12 1.759 m²   **13** 38 850 mm²

14 a) 12.73 m³, 25.26 m²   b) 1 194 000 mm³, 49 820 mm²

15 4.163 m³   **16** 1.286×10^8 mm³, 1 068 000 mm²

17 0.1009 m²   **18** 1.302 m³   **19** 657 500 mm³, 0.1121 kg

20 63:64. 15:16   **21** 24 m², 24.27 m²   **22** 188 m²

23 1370 m²   **24** 2.252 m³

25 7.76 m³ (trap), 7.84 (Simp)

26 36 240 m³   **27** 11.16 m³   **28** 76 750 mm³

29 0.006 317 m³   **30** 116.2 m²   **31** 12 790 mm²

32 8.706 m³, 175.9 m²

33   a) $3.158\,\text{m}$ b) $46.8°$ c) $38.0°$

34   a) $15.10\,\text{m}$ b) $41.5°$ c) $51.3°$

35   a) $2.19\,\text{m}$ b) $6.58\,\text{m}$ c) $27.6°$ d) $19.5°$

36 $21.5\,\text{m}^2,\ 23.2\,\text{m}^2$ **37** $142\,000\,\text{mm}^3$ **38** $361.8\,\text{m}^2$

Chapter 20   *Page 190*

1   a) 3.420 b) 2.203 c) 1.150
    d) 1.012 e) 3.271 f) 1.390

2   a) $65.4°$ b) $19.7°$ c) $11.5°$
    d) $68.2°$ e) $57.9°$ f) $25.8°$

3 $30.14\,\text{mm}$

4   a) 0.471 b) 0.838 c) 0.513

5   a) $\frac{2}{3}\pi$ b) $\frac{1}{12}\pi$ c) 4π

6   a) $67.8°$ b) $38.4°$ c) $3.2°$
    d) $120°$ e) $135°$ f) $540°$

7   a) 0.8462 b) 0.8447 c) 0.1024
    d) 1.732 e) 0.3827 f) 0.7071

8   a) 0.9508 b) 1.273 c) 1.217

9 0.7105 radians   **10** $3.485\,\text{m},\ 7.144\,\text{m}^2$

11 $1.131\,\text{m},\ 0.046\,10\text{m}^2$ **12** $1230\,\text{mm}$

13   a) 0.7071 b) -0.9925 c) -4.331
    d) -0.3584 e) -0.2588 f) 1
    g) -0.9659 h) 0.5 i) -0.0875

14   a) $26.7°,\ 153.3°$ b) $242.9°,\ 297.1°$
    c) $48.7°,\ 311.3°$ d) $116.1°,\ 243.9°$
    e) $69.7°,\ 249.7°$ f) $142.0°,\ 322.0°$

16   a) $5,\ 360°,\ 0°$ b) $1\frac{1}{2},\ 360°,\ 180°$ c) $1,\ 120°,\ 0°$
    d) $1,\ 1080°,\ 0°$ e) $1,\ 360°,\ 10°$ f) $1,\ 360°,\ -50°$
    g) $2,\ 360°,\ 120°$ h) $2\frac{1}{2},\ 360°,\ -40°$

Chapter 21   *Page 203*

4 550

11   a) $23.4,\ 24$ b) $11.3,\ 11.2$ c) $0.475,\ 0.45$

12 $1.25,\ 1,\ 0$ **13** $14.98\,\text{cm}$ **14** 392.5 tonnes

15 $101.3\,\Omega$ **16** $30.7\,\text{mm}$

17   a) 32 b) 12 c) 0.08

18   a) $80.31,\ 8.962$ b) $14,\ 3.742$ c) $0.000\,544,\ 0.023\,32$

19   A: $5.361,\ 0.013$ B: $5.336,\ 0.0600$

20 $101.5\,\Omega,\ 99.8\,\Omega,\ 103.3\,\Omega$ **21** $1.25\,\text{mm},\ 30.4\,\text{mm}$

22   a) $y = 24.5x + 98$ b) $y = 0.065x - 0.439$
    c) $y = -3.72x + 48$

23 $R = 0.0579T + 29.9$ **24** $P = 5.6T + 1507,\ -270°\text{C}$

Chapter 22   *Page 216*

1 $\begin{pmatrix} 6 & 11 \\ 5 & 1 \end{pmatrix}$, $\begin{pmatrix} 17 & 15 \\ 7 & 12 \end{pmatrix}$ **2** $\begin{pmatrix} -2 & 13 & 3 \\ 5 & -1 & 6 \end{pmatrix}$

3 $\begin{pmatrix} \frac{1}{9} & \frac{4}{9} \\ \frac{2}{9} & -\frac{1}{9} \end{pmatrix}$, $\begin{pmatrix} -\frac{2}{11} & \frac{7}{11} \\ \frac{3}{11} & -\frac{5}{11} \end{pmatrix}$

4   a) $x = 32,\ y = -38$ b) $x = \frac{91}{19},\ y = \frac{29}{19}$
    c) $x = 19.71,\ y = -2.210$

5 $13.86,\ 65.9°$ **6** 16.97

7   a) $5,\ 53.1°$ b) $3.606,\ 123.7°$ c) $\frac{5}{6},\ 53.1°$

8 $11.28\mathbf{i} + 4.10\mathbf{j},\ \begin{pmatrix} 11.28 \\ 4.10 \end{pmatrix}$

9 $7.071,\ 55.6°$

10   a) $1.732 \sin(x + 30°)$ b) $6.766 \sin(x + 22.8°)$
    c) $0.7585 \sin(x - 19.7°)$ d) $4.359 \sin(x + 3.4°)$

11   a) $10\mathbf{j}$ b) $\frac{1}{2}\mathbf{j}$ c) $9\mathbf{j}$

12   a) $7\mathbf{j},\ -7\mathbf{j}$ b) $3 + 4\mathbf{j},\ 3 - 4\mathbf{j}$
    c) $-0.5 + 0.866\mathbf{j},\ -0.5 - 0.866\mathbf{j}$

13   a) $9 + \mathbf{j}$ b) $-5 + 9\mathbf{j}$ c) $34 + 27\mathbf{j}$
    d) $7 + 4\mathbf{j}$ e) $-6 + 43\mathbf{j}$ f) $-\frac{6}{65} + \frac{43}{65}\mathbf{j}$

14   a) $13 + 7\mathbf{j}$ b) $4.587 + 1.376\mathbf{j}$

Chapter 23   *Page 227*

1   a) $8x + 5$ b) $3 - 2x$ c) $6x^2$

2   a) $6x^5$ b) $15x^4$ c) $6x^2$
    d) $9x^2 + 8x^3$ e) $3x + 3$ f) $4 - 6x^2$
    g) $\dfrac{2}{\sqrt{x}}$ h) $\dfrac{-14}{x^3}$ i) $-\dfrac{1}{\sqrt{x^3}} - \dfrac{3}{x^2}$
    j) $2x + 5$ k) $5x^4 - 6x^2 - 6x$
    l) $3\sqrt{x} + \dfrac{1.5}{\sqrt{x}}$ m) 1 n) $\dfrac{-3}{x^2} + 8x$
    o) $\dfrac{1}{\sqrt{x}} + 4.5\sqrt{x}$

3 1 **4** $\frac{3}{16}$ **5** $15\,\text{m s}^{-1}$

6   a) $6e^{6x}$ b) $0.3e^{0.1x}$ c) $0.5e^{-0.5x}$
    d) $3\cos 3x$ e) $8\cos 4x + 12\sin 4x$
    f) $-\frac{2}{3}\pi \sin \frac{1}{3}\pi x$

7 $3\sqrt{2}$ **8** 1.5 **9** -8.99 amps per sec

10 $0.0905\,\mu\text{C}$ per sec   **11** -342 amps per sec

12 a) $(-\frac{1}{2}, -3\frac{1}{4})$ min   b) $(-2, 16)$ max, $(2, -16)$ min
   c) $(-2, -5)$ min, $(\frac{2}{3}, 4.48)$ max
   d) $(-1, -2)$ max, $(1, 2)$ min
   e) $(0, -1)$ max   f) $(0.243, 1.232)$ min

13 1250 m^2 **14** 697 cm^2 **15** 4.64 m

16 1000   **17** 153 m

Chapter 24 Page 234

1 a) $\frac{1}{6}x^6 + c$ b) $\frac{1}{8}x^8 + c$ c) $-\frac{1}{2x^2} + c$
   d) $\frac{3}{4}x^{1\frac{1}{3}} + c$ e) $3x^2 + c$ f) $1\frac{1}{4}x^4 + c$
   g) $\frac{1}{2}x^6 - \frac{2}{7}x^7 + c$ h) $2x^{1\frac{1}{2}} - x^{-2} + c$ i) $\frac{1}{2}e^{2x} + c$
   j) $-\frac{3}{4}\cos 4x + c$ k) $0.04\sin 5x + c$ l) $\frac{1}{3}e^{3x} - \frac{1}{2}e^{2x} + c$

2 a) $3x^2 - 1$ b) $2x^{1\frac{1}{2}} + 4$ c) $\frac{1}{2}e^{4x} + 5\frac{1}{2}$
   d) $100 - 100e^{-0.01x}$ e) $2\sin 3x + 8$ f) $-4\cos\frac{1}{2}x + 3$

3 $50\frac{3}{4} \text{ m}$ **4** $40 - 40e^{-0.1t}$ amps

5 a) 8   b) $3\frac{3}{4}$ c) 6
   d) $18\frac{2}{3}$ e) 1.813   f) 0.093 23

6 0.7196 m

7 a) $4\frac{2}{3}$ b) $2\frac{1}{3}$ c) 0.9
   d) 4.805   e) 0.9549

8 -2 and 2, $10\frac{2}{3}$ **9** $\frac{1}{6}$

Solutions to extra questions

Chapter 1 Page 243

1 a) 29   b) 35   c) 16
   d) 11   e) 7   f) 120
   g) 4,2   h) 12   i) 12

2 a) 11   b) 16   c) 6
   d) 4   e) 26   f) 6
   g) 20   h) 10

3 a) 14   b) -12 c) -9
   d) 9   e) 50

4 a) $2 \times 2 \times 2 \times 2 \times 3$ b) $2 \times 3 \times 3 \times 5$
   c) $2 \times 2 \times 2 \times 2 \times 7$

5 a) 6, 120   b) 7, 245   c) 1, 780
   d) 10, 40   e) 3, 2310   f) 1, 420

6 1700 W   **7** 55   **8** 75 g

9 2 A   15 hours

Chapter 2 Page 243

1 a) $\frac{1}{7}$ b) $\frac{2}{3}$ c) $\frac{1}{3}$

2 a) $3\frac{2}{5}$ b) $1\frac{2}{21}$ c) $5\frac{7}{10}$

3 a) $\frac{7}{2}$ b) $\frac{17}{3}$ c) $\frac{33}{5}$

4 a) $\frac{5}{22}$ b) $1\frac{2}{3}$ c) $8\frac{17}{35}$
   d) $\frac{15}{16}$ e) $\frac{20}{21}$ f) $\frac{125}{231}$
   g) $6\frac{1}{4}$ h) $\frac{14}{65}$ i) $4\frac{5}{18}$

5 a) 0.876   b) 15.94   c) 10
   d) 10.1   e) 43.3   f) 0.154

6 a) 1.1875 2.364   b) $\frac{3}{10}$, $\frac{3}{8}$

7 $11\frac{1}{4}°$ **8** 23.4 A

9 missing values: 50, 5, 0.05, 4

10 14 043 J   **11** $13°$ **12** $6\frac{1}{4}$ in.

13 2.3125 in, 58.74 mm

Chapter 3 Page 244

1 43.75%   **2** 110.4   **3** 2.1 kg

4 26 kg   **5** 16%   **6** #2000

7 600 kg   **8** 8:13   **9** 48 kg

10 164 kg   **11** 38 kg   **12** 90%

13 5.5%

Chapter 4 Page 244

1 a) 121   b) 81   c) $\frac{1}{9}$
   d) 20   e) 100   f) 17
   g) 8   h) 5   i) 7
   j) 1   k) 9   l) 1000
   m) $\frac{1}{8}$ n) 9   o) 2

2 a) 2^{12} b) 3^{13} c) 5^2

3 a) 0.254 C   b) 350 000 W
   c) 132 kV   d) 9.8 mA

4 a) 2.45×10^7 b) 3.4×10^{-6} c) 5.71×10^{14}
   d) 6.34×10^5 e) 7.24×10^{-7} f) 2.43×10^{-6}

5 a) 8.6×10^{11} b) 1.89×10^{14} c) 4.2×10^3
   d) 3×10^{11} e) 8.4×10^{-11} f) 4×10^2
   g) 7.9×10^9 h) 7.29×10^6 i) 6.01×10^{-7}

6 a) $0.7 \, \mu\text{F}$ b) 50 MN

7 5×10^{-5} A   **8** $2.36 \text{ k}\Omega$

9 a) 10 580 W   b) 5.16 A
   c) $2.47 \times 10^5 \, \Omega$ d) 6×10^5 A

10   0.028%

11   a) 3   b) -5 c) 5

12   a) 2   b) 3   c) 0

13   a) 3.465 A   b) 3.479 A

Chapter 5   Page 245

1
a) 281	b) 0.006 95	c) 1740
d) 0.312	e) 4600	f) 453
g) 802	h) 2560	i) 5.06
j) 2.95	k) 0.145	l) 4 420 000
m) 0.240	n) 211	o) 70.5
p) 0.007 87	q) 2.40	r) 5.11
s) 54.0	t) 30 700	u) 4.43
v) 1 150 000	w) -0.580	x) 3.31
y) 0.124	z) 0.482	

Chapter 6   Page 245

1   2 m, 0.021, 2.1%   **2**   1.203

3
a) $96.2 - 96.4$ b) $0.0041 - 0.0045$
c) $6.63 - 7.33$ d) $4.755 - 4.765$
e) $54\,050 - 54\,150$ f) $10.8 - 11.3$
g) $0.18 - 0.20$ h) $414 - 552$

4   132 hours, 1.5 hours   **5**   4.302 kg, 0.05 kg

6   #1456, #32   **7**   100 minutes   **8** $20°$

9
a) 0.4448 $(0.2 + 0.2 = 0.4)$
b) 686 $(1700 - 1000 = 700)$
c) 1.266 $(20 \times 0.05 = 1)$ d) 9.66 $(20 \div 2 = 10)$
e) 213.8 $(10 \times 20 = 200)$ f) 17.13 $(3 \times 2^2 = 12)$
g) 103.5 $(10^2 = 100)$ h) 9.796 $(\sqrt{100} = 10)$

Chapter 7   Page 245

1   a) $25° 36'$ b) $103° 45'$ c) $42° 59' 2''$

2   a) $55.25°$ b $64.2125°$ c) $12.575°$

3   a) $92° 15'$ b) $17° 35'$
c) $38° 54' 17''$ d) $21° 43' 48''$

4
a) 1000100   b) 411   c) F09
d) 3667   e) 1110101100   f) 32D3
g) 11100110001   h) 395

5   a) 101010   b) 11011101

6   a) 476   b) 1726   c) 6332

Chapter 8   Page 246

1
a) $4x$	b) $8x$	c) $12a + 2b$
d) $a^2 - ab + b^2$	e) $6xyz$	f) $30a$
g) $12x^2$	h) $21xy$	i) $-\frac{1}{2}mn$
j) $72a^2$	k) $5x$	l) $2y$
m) x^7	n) a^5	o) n^{12}
p) x^{30}	q) m^{12}	r) $16x^8y^{12}$
s) y^3	t) a^2	u) x^4
v) m^{12}	w) x	x) x^7
y) $y^{12}x^{-8}$	z) x	

2   a) 14   b) 10   c) $\frac{1}{2}$

3   a) -9 b) 11   c) $-\frac{1}{4}$

4   25

5
a) $8x - 8y$ b) $10a + 15b$ c) $xy + xz$
d) $3xy + 9xz$ e) $a^2 + a^3$ f) $-7m^2 + 7m$
g) $7a - b$ h) $-x + 7y$ i) $m^2 + 3mn + 3n^2$
j) $6x^2 + 3xy + 28y^2$ k) $x^2 + 7x + 10$
l) $y^2 + 8y - 48$ m) $z^2 - 10z + 9$
n) $6a^2 + 13a + 6$ o) $7x^2 + 23xy + 6y^2$
p) $5m^2 - 17mn + 6n^2$ q) $9a^2 + 6ab + b^2$
r) $x^2 - 4xy + 4y^2$ s) $9x^2 + 42x + 49$
t) $m^2 - n^2$ u) $\frac{1}{9} - a^2$ v) $8y^2 - 2$

6
a) $2(x + 2y)$ b) $5(5 - 6m)$ c) $x(x + 3)$
d) $3q(3 + 2q)$ e) $ab(a + 2b)$ f) $\pi(a^2 + ab + b^2)$

7 $Z = \sqrt{\left[X_R^2 + \left(2\pi fL - \frac{1}{(2\pi fC)}\right)^2\right]}$

Chapter 9   Page 246

1 $(1.5, 2.7)$ **2** $(1.3, -1.9)$

3   a) $23°C$ b) 1.75 hours

7   a) $y = -2x + 9$ b) $y = 2x - 3$
c) $y = -1\frac{1}{2}x + 2$

Chapter 10   Page 247

1
a) 4	b) 14	c) 14
d) 7	e) 6	f) 7
g) 42	h) 84	i) -25
j) 4	k) $7\frac{3}{8}$	l) 5
m) 7	n) $5\frac{2}{3}$	o) 3
p) 3	q) 14	r) 40

2
a) $x = 8, y = -9$ b) $x = 3, y = -1$ c) $x = 2, y = 7$
d) $x = 5, y = 3$ e) $x = 20, y = 16$ f) $x = 140, y = 10$

3 $-0.6, 3.1$ **4** $13\frac{1}{3}$ litres   **5** $-40°$

6 $1\frac{7}{8}$ hours   **7**   100 kg, 200 kg

8   #5 000 000 and # 3 000 000

Chapter 11   Page 247

1 a) $\dfrac{\frac{1}{3}a}{b}$ b) $\frac{1}{2}x$ c) $1+\frac{1}{3}x$

d) $p+q$ e) $\dfrac{y}{x+y}$ f) $\dfrac{ab}{b-a}$

2 a) $\frac{1}{6}pm$ b) $\frac{2}{3}$ c) $\dfrac{ay}{bx}$

d) $1\frac{1}{2}$ e) $\frac{5}{6}x$ f) $\dfrac{3y-2x}{xy}$

3 a) $\dfrac{y+2x}{x^2y^2}$ b) $\dfrac{15axy+10bx^2+6cy^2}{90x^3y^3}$

4 a) 61.62   b) 916.0   c) 4.179   d) 1.039

5 a) 1.152   b) 0.2526   c) 1.314
d) 0.7326   e) 3.252   f) 7.754
g) 1.771   h) 5.861   i) 1.710

6 a) 4.368 μC   b) 69.21 s

7 a) $\#8821$ b) after 17.1 years

8 a) $x=\frac{1}{8}y-\frac{3}{8}$ b) $b=\frac{2}{3}a+1\frac{1}{3}$ c) $n=1\frac{1}{2}m+6$

d) $x=\dfrac{y}{a}$ e) $q=\dfrac{b}{p}$ f) $a=\dfrac{P}{\pi}-b$

g) $t=\dfrac{c}{a-b}$ h) $x=\dfrac{7}{2+k}$ i) $x=\dfrac{2}{z}+4$

j) $x=\dfrac{5+3t}{2y}$ k) $x=\dfrac{k+1}{k-1}$

l) $t=\dfrac{6y}{2-y}$ m) $b=\sqrt{\left(\dfrac{V}{\pi a}\right)}$ n) $b=\sqrt{(l^2-r^2)}$

o) $x=\frac{1}{2}y^2+1\frac{1}{2}$ p) $t=\ln\dfrac{E}{A}$ q) $t=-8\ln\dfrac{I}{A}$

r) $t=-4\ln\left(1-\dfrac{I}{A}\right)$ s) $x=\frac{1}{3}(e^y+2)$ t) $x=\dfrac{z}{e^y}$

Chapter 12   Page 248

1 $y=0.07x,\ 4$ **2** $q=\dfrac{200}{p},\ 4$ **3** 500 000 Hz

4 2.5 Ω **5** $T=50r^2,\ 4.525$ **6** 22.82 cm

7 0.181 m   **8** 19%

9 a) 26.1 mm   b) 6

10 $a=2500,\ b=10\,000$ **11** $a=0.35,\ b=4.6$

12 $y=4.7e^{3.5t},\ 0.1625$ **13** $T=73e^{-0.1112t},\ 4.524$

14 $T=150e^{0.030\,98t},\ 34°$ **15** $I=10e^{-5.627t},\ 0.8184$ s

Chapter 13   Page 248

1 $y=1.8x+47$ **2** For $x=4,y=0.256$

3 110   **4** 227   **5** $y=0.26x^2+2.2$

6 $y=\dfrac{0.0125}{x}+0.17x$ **7** $F=0.05d^{2.54}$

8 $y=23\times1.58^x$

Chapter 14   Page 249

1 a) $(x+10)(x+3)$ b) $(x-6)(x-2)$
c) $(x+8)(x-5)$ d) $(x-10)(x+5)$
e) $(x+4)^2$ f) $(x+3)(2x+1)$
g) $(2x-1)(3x-2)$ h) $(x+2)(3x-5)$
i) $5(x-4)(x+4)$

2 a) $(x+3)^2+2$ b) $(x-7)^2-9$
c) $(x+1\frac{1}{2})^2-4\frac{1}{4}$ d) $2(x-3)^2-15$
e) $14-(x+1)^2$ f) $17-3(x-1)^2$

3 a) $2,-3$ b) $-9,7$ c) $-4\frac{1}{4},-1\frac{1}{2}$
d) $-15,3$ e) $14,-1$ f) $17,1$

4 a) $-3.58,-0.419$ b) $-2.20,13.2$ c) $-5.08,0.393$
d) $1,3$ e) $-0.225,2.22$ f) $-2.86,4.15$

5 a) $(-1,-3)$ or $(7,29)$ b) $(-3.67,13.2)$ or $(5.17,-8.93)$

6 1.27 m   **7** $200-\frac{1}{2}x,\ x(200-\frac{1}{2}x),\ 95.1$ mm or 305 mm

Chapter 15   Page 250

1 a) 132°   b) 60°   c) 118°

2 9°   **3** a) 22°   b) 112°

4 9000°   **5** AXB and DXC

6 a) 67°   b) 71°   c) 115°   d) 78°

7 2340°   **8** 18   **9** 88 m, 276.5 m

10 a) cuboid   b) prism

11 50 270 mm   **12** 150°   **13** 392.7 mm

Chapter 16   Page 250

1 a) 1700 mm^2 b) 17.64 m^2 c) 1810 mm^2
d) 6 m^2 e) 0.0609 m^2

2 3.68 m^2, 10.62 m^2, 907.9 m^2 **3** 150 m

4 a) 19.68 m^3 b) 8960 mm^3 c) 256 m^3
d) 0.0754 m^3 e) 84 450 mm^3 f) 434 900 mm^3
g) 0.002 66 m^3

5 0.006 54 m   **6** 0.000 884 m   **7** 1.24%

8 422 000 cm^3 **9** 0.424 m

10 a) 7.6 kg   b) 17.1 kg   c) 9.24 kg

11 6842 N

Chapter 17 Page 251

1 a) 210 mm   b) 2.2 m
   c) 0.0095 m^2 d) 240 m^3

2 a) 1:2000   b) 9200 m^2

3 a) 18   b) 1440

4 a) 20.81   b) 72

5 35.4 cm, 35 060 cm^2 **6** 0.601 m   **7** 2.721 m

8 5.544 m^2 **9** 110.2 mm   **10** 623.1 mm

11 1.33 m

13 a) 39 mm   b) 37°   c) 48°   d) 33 mm

Chapter 18 Page 252

1 a) 13.2   b) 48.6   c) 0.204

2 a) 50.6°   b) 44.3°   c) 32.6°

3 32.8°   **4** 138.8 m   **5** 6.24 m

6 0.689 m, 1.663 m   **7** 0.7689 m, 0.7541 m

8 a) 4.49°   b) 62.68 mm

9 0.373 m   **10** 233.4 Ω

11 a) 71.1   b) 59.9

12 a) 49.4°   b) 32.7°

13 71.5 mm, 84.8°, 102.8°

Chapter 19 Page 253

1 13.45 mm^2, 4887 mm^2 **2** 1081 m^2, 284.7 m^2

3 23 200 mm^3

4 a) 8495 mm^2 b) 7.93 m^2
   c) 125 000 mm^2 d) 29.56 m^2

5 9.53 g   **6** 0.010 26 m^3, 0.4084 m^2 **7** 9.89 m

8 3.3 m^2, 3.307 m^2 **9** 70 m^2

10 17 160 mm^3, 17 230 mm^3

11 3 344 000 mm^3, 168 200 mm^2

12 631.5 mm^2. 631.7 mm^2. 0.03%

13 21.2 mm

14 a) 1640 mm^2, 148 mm   b) 1 103 000 mm^3, 99 300 mm^2

15 a) 2.001 m   b) 1.994 m^2 c) 17.4°   d) 24.0°

16 15.6 m, 16.0°   **17** 45°

Chapter 20 Page 255

1 a) 0.141   b) 1.701   c) 2.366
   d) 22.2°   e) 52.8°   f) 17.8°

2 a) $\frac{\pi}{6}$ b) 0.820   c) 1.072   d) 0.408

3 a) 27.4°   b) 70.5°   c) 315°

4 a) 0.932   b) 0.892   c) 1.732
   d) 2.827   e) 3.079   f) 1.414

5 a) 0.603   b) 1.012   c) 0.348

6 a) 0.1392 m   b) 0.040 37 m^2
   c) 0.1389 m   d) 0.000 386 4 m^2

7 a) -0.8988 b) -0.2419 c) 0.4663   d) 1.133

8 a) 115.5°, 244.5°   b) 6.9°, 173.1°   c) 53.3°, 233.3°

11 a) $3\frac{1}{2}$ b) 1080°   c) 23°

Chapter 21 Page 255

2 1:3:6

6 a) 39, 38.5   b) 0.1555, 0.17

7 1001.4   **8** 34

9 a) 36, 0.15   b) 117, 0.003 047

10 1001.5, 2.7   **11** $a = 0.31, b = 59.3$

Chapter 22 Page 256

1 $\begin{pmatrix} 15 & 2 \\ 2 & 0 \end{pmatrix}$, $\begin{pmatrix} 56 & -19 \\ 14 & -7 \end{pmatrix}$, $\begin{pmatrix} 50 & 38 \\ 2 & -1 \end{pmatrix}$ **2** $\begin{pmatrix} 50 & 11 \\ 14 & 2 \\ 14 & 11 \end{pmatrix}$

3 $\begin{pmatrix} \frac{1}{18} & \frac{5}{18} \\ \frac{1}{9} & -\frac{4}{9} \end{pmatrix}$, $\begin{pmatrix} \frac{1}{7} & \frac{3}{7} \\ 0 & 1 \end{pmatrix}$

4 a) $x = 1.099, y = 24.09$ b) $x = -7.387, y = -25.43$

5 a) 32.75, 74.4°   b) 23.74, 2.4°   c) 79.02, 82.6°

6 $78.73\mathbf{i} + 90.57\mathbf{j}$, $\begin{pmatrix} 78.73 \\ 90.57 \end{pmatrix}$

7 a) $2.646 \sin (x - 10.9°)$ b) $4.136 \sin (x - 23°)$

8 a) $\pm 10\mathbf{j}$ b) $\pm\frac{1}{2}\mathbf{j}$ c) $3 \pm 5\mathbf{j}$ d) $-0.5 \pm 1.658\mathbf{j}$

9 a) $7 + 3\mathbf{j}$ b) $22 + 7\mathbf{j}$ c) $3 + 2\mathbf{j}$ d) $\frac{2}{41} - \frac{23}{41}\mathbf{j}$

10 a) $3 + 5\mathbf{j}$ b) $\frac{23}{34} + \frac{41}{34}\mathbf{j}$

Chapter 23   Page 256

1 $6x - 2$

2   a) $7x^6$ b) $21x^2 - 4x + 4$
      c) $2\frac{1}{2}x^{-\frac{1}{2}} + 24x^{-4}$ d) $4x + 13$
      e) $21e^{3x}$ f) $-4.5 \sin 1.5x$

3 2π

4   a) 6.25 (max)   b) 3 (min)

5   161

c) $0.8x^{2.5} - 2x^{1.5} + c$ d) $-1\frac{1}{2}e^{-2x} + c$

e) $\dfrac{20}{\pi} \sin \frac{1}{4}\pi x + c$ f) $3x + 6 \cos \frac{1}{2}x + c$

2   a) $y = 1\frac{1}{2}x^2 - 7x + 9\frac{1}{2}$ b) $y = x - \frac{1}{2}e^{2x} + 4\frac{1}{2}$

3   87.3 m

4   a) $170\frac{1}{3}$ b) 2.675   c) $\frac{1}{2}$

5   a) $5\frac{3}{4}$ b) 1

Chapter 24   Page 256

1   a) $\dfrac{1}{4.1}x^{4.1} + c$ b) $\frac{1}{3}x^3 + 3x^2 - 7x + c$

Index